ALTERNATIVE TRAVEL DIRECTORY

The Complete Guide to Traveling, Studying & Living Overseas

GENERAL EDITOR

Clayton A. Hubbs

CONTRIBUTING EDITORS

Cynthia Harriman (Family Travel, Home and Hospitality Exchanges), Clay Hubbs (Language Schools, Study Abroad, Teen Study and Travel), Ron Mader, Deborah McLaren (Responsible Travel), William Nolting (Study Abroad, Volunteering and Internships), Victor Poetzl (Living Abroad), Kent St. John (Internet Travel Resources), Susan Sygall (Disability Travel), Kathy Widing (Independent Travel), Ann Waigand (Special Interest Travel, Educational Travel), Arline K. Wills (Senior Travel)

Transitions Abroad Publishing
Amherst, Massachusetts
http://www.TransitionsAbroad.com/

©2002 by Transitions Abroad Publishing, Inc.
All Rights Reserved
Published by Transitions Abroad Publishing, Inc.
P.O. Box 1300, Amherst, Massachusetts 01004-1300

www.TransitionsAbroad.com

Manufactured in the United States of America

ISBN 1-886732-10-8
Library of Congress Control Number
2001 126982
Seventh Edition

Cover Design: RICK SCHNEIDER

Cover Photo: INGRID MARN WOOD

Typesetting: JANIS SOKOL

Production: JANET LOWRY

INDEPENDENT TRAVEL

STUDY ABROAD

LIVING ABROAD

PREFACE TO THE SEVENTH EDITION

The *Alternative Travel Directory*, produced annually by the editors of *Transitions Abroad* magazine since 1993, is a one-volume selection of the most essential information on overseas alternatives to mass tourism: independent travel, educational travel and study, ecotravel, and living overseas. Opportunities for working overseas are collected separately in *Work Abroad: The Complete Guide to Finding a Job Overseas* [www.WorkingTraveler.com]. Ordering information for all Transitions Abroad publications is on page 261.

Over the past 25 years, thousands of *Transitions Abroad* readers have sent us firsthand reports on their own transitions abroad. A selection of their contributions comprises one part of this book. The second and much larger part comes from the magazine's team of travel-wise contributing editors:

Rick Steves (Budget Travel) is host of the PBS series Rick Steves' Europe and author of 20 European travel guides, including *Europe Through the Back Door* (Avalon).

Kathy Widing (Independent Travel), co-owner of the country's first travel book store, Wide World Books in Seattle, selects the best travel planning guides and single country guides based on her own travel and guidebook writing for Lonely Planet and others.

Kent St. John (Internet Travel Resources) is owner of the Palms Travel Service, a company specializing in educational group travel and a contributor to many publications and web sites.

Ann Waigand (Special Interest Travel and **Educational Travel)** used *Transitions Abroad's* listings to select a study abroad program 25 years ago. Years later, Ann introduced a column called "The Educated Traveler" and a highly successful newsletter of the same title.

Arnie Wills (Senior Travel) made her first solo trip (to Cuba) in 1958. Since then she has raised a traveling family and continues go abroad at least twice yearly.

Cynthia Harriman (Family Travel and **Home and Hospitality Exchanges)**, Arnie's daughter, learned the great rewards of travel at an early age. Now Cynthia teaches other families how to travel with children. Her popular *Take Your Kids to Europe* (Globe Pequot), just out in a fourth edition, is not simply a list of places to go but an intercultural guide to why and how to travel.

Susan Sygall (Disability Travel) heads up Mobility International USA, the country's leading nonprofit disability travel organization, dedicated to expanding equal opportunities in educational travel.

Clay Hubbs (Language Schools, Teen Study and Travel, Study Abroad), the founder and editor of *Transitions Abroad*, taught modern European literature and directed international studies at Hampshire College in Amherst, MA until his retirement in 1998.

Dianne Brause, a former Peace Corps volunteer and lifetime leader of socially responsible group trips abroad (currently Lisle Fellowship groups to Costa Rica and India), was our first **Responsible Travel** editor and remains a regular contributor. **Deborah McLaren**, founder of the Rethinking Tourism Project and author of *Rethinking Tourism and Ecotravel* (Kamarian Press), joined Dianne to compile our first list of Responsible Travel Resources and Programs over 10 years ago. She and Dianne have since been joined by **Ron Mader**, host of the award-winning web site, www.planeta.com, and author of *Mexico: Adventures in Nature* (Avalon Travel Publishing).

William Nolting (Work Abroad and International Education), Director of International Opportunities at the Univ. of Michigan, selected and compiled the resources for the chapters on Volunteering and Internships and Study Abroad. For even more comprehensive education and work abroad bibliographies go to Bill's web site: [www.umich.edu/~icenter/overseas]. Bill is co-editor, with Susan Griffith, of *Work Abroad* (Transitions Abroad Publishing).

Volker Poelzl (Living Abroad) has written about living in a number of countries. His latest work is *Culture Shock! Brazil* (Culture Shock! Guides).

In 1977 I launched *Transitions Abroad*, a magazine of practical information for independent travelers who go abroad to live, work, or study. The title suggests the changes that occur when travelers leave home behind and truly immerse themselves in a new place, as engaged "travelers" and not detached "tourists."

Gary Langer drew the distinction in the first issue when he described staying at the Jerusalem guesthouse of an elderly Armenian called Mr. A. Those who sought out Mr. A, wrote Langer, were travelers, not tourists:

> The distinction is simple: Tourists are those who bring their homes with them wherever they go, and apply them to whatever they see. . . . Travelers left home at home, bringing only themselves and a desire to see and hear and feel and take in and grow and learn. Tourists do not go to Mr. A's. They would not appreciate him, nor he them. And the main reason travelers go to Mr. A's is for Mr. A.

Langer's contrast may sound a bit exaggerated—after all, we are all tourists when we travel to another country. But he was not the first to distinguish between those who travel to confirm what they already know and those who travel to gain new understanding of themselves and others. One thinks of Mark Twain's 1860s satirical novel, *Innocents Abroad*. Twain's American travelers brought along so much cultural baggage that they were only "*In-a-Sense*" *Abroad*.

The tourist of cartoons—whether in Twain's time or ours—doesn't abandon his own familiar environment for the sake of engaging with the new. He views unfamiliar people, places, and cultures through the windows of the familiar and pretends that he is still at home. If he must speak to the natives he does so loudly, thereby giving them every opportunity to understand!

The modern traveler, on the other hand, is interested in encountering new people, places, and cultures on their own terms and precisely because they are unfamiliar. The transition is not simply a passage from one place to another; it is a change in perspective and perception.

(Adam Gopnik in *Paris to the Moon* [Random House, 2001], makes a different distinction: "There are two kinds of travelers. There is the kind who goes to see what there is to see and sees it, and the kind who has an image in his head and goes out to accomplish it. The first visitor has an easier time, but I think the second visitor sees more. He is constantly comparing what he sees to what he wants, so he sees with his mind, and maybe even with his heart, or tries to." If we follow Gopnik's division, I see myself and *Transitions Abroad* readers as representing yet a third kind of visitor: one who has an image in his head and goes out to dispel it.)

Detailing the ways to meet and learn from people of other cultures has been the purpose of *Transitions Abroad* since its beginning 25 years ago. In each issue of the magazine we select and publish the most important sources of information on the alternatives to mass tourism—immersion travel, volunteer and paid work, study, and living—along with a selection of programs and other opportunities for the curious and independent-minded.

We revise and update this information continuously, then bring it all together in one annual volume: the *Alternative Travel Directory*. (A volume on *Work Abroad* is published separately.)

Of all the forms of alternative travel, the fastest growing is ecotourism. As contributing editors Deborah McLaren and Ron Mader write in the introduction to Responsible Travel Resources (Chapter 6), "As people around the planet become more concerned about their environment, more curious about people of different cultures, and more willing to think differently, travel is changing."

The editors are proud that for more than two and a half decades *Transitions Abroad* has provided readers with the best and most comprehensive information on ways to travel responsibly; that is, on ways to obey the Golden Rule of travel.

Independent ("Life-Seeing") Travel Abroad. The travel resources and programs in the first seven chapters are grouped under the heading of independent or "life-seeing travel." The term, which comes from the concept of Scandinavian adult continuing education described in the first issue of *Transitions Abroad*, involves travel as learning. For more and more travelers, including our readers, life seeing has replaced sight seeing.

Study Abroad. The programs and resources for people of all ages described in this section are structured learning experiences. Adult nonstudents are welcome to take part in most academic programs for no credit, usually at a reduced cost. More commonly, *Transitions Abroad* readers pursue personal interests, like the special interest travel programs described in Chapter 2, or take a language-learning vacation (Chapter 12).

Living Abroad. The final chapter is a comprehensive list of places to find almost anything you need to know about living abroad. As in the earlier chapters, we provide full contact information, including up-to-date email addresses and web sites. Should you have trouble finding one the thousands of listed organizations or resources listed here or elsewhere in the book, go to our own continuously updated web site, [www.TransitionsAbroad.com], for current details.

Clay Hubbs
Amherst, MA
December 2001

INDEPENDENT TRAVEL

ONE

INDEPENDENT TRAVEL
BEST RESOURCES

Independent travel takes good planning. And good planning requires two kinds of guides: Planning Guides (below), which cover the practicalities like tickets and accommodations, and Country Guides (18), which provide an in-depth introduction to your destination. The editors' collective selection of the Best Travel Web Sites starts on page 13. Kent St. John's personal Web picks are on page 21.

Best Planning Guides

Active Woman Vacation Guide by Evelyn Kaye (Blue Panda Publications). True stories by women travelers and complete information on adventure vacations worldwide.

Adventures in Nature Series (Avalon Travel Publishing). Titles include: Belize, Caribbean, Costa Rica, Guatemala, Mexico.

Air Courier Bargains: How to Travel Worldwide for Next to Nothing by Kelly Monaghan (Intrepid Traveler). Complete guide to courier travel in U.S. and around the world.

Air Travel's Bargain Basement by Kelly Monaghan (Intrepid Traveler). A 124-page list of U.S., Canadian, and international companies that buy blocks of seats from the airlines at discounts and pass savings on to the consumer (new version of Consolidators).

Amateur's Guide to the Planet by Jeannette Belliveau (Beau Monde Press). Reports on 12 adventure journeys reflect author's responses to diverse cultures and how people live. Good background reading for responsible travelers.

Archaeology Abroad, 31-34 Gordon Sq., London WC1H 0PY, England. Two bulletins per year list worldwide archaeological digs with

details of staffing needs and costs; fax 011-44-020-7383-2572; arch.abroad@ucl.ac.uk, [www.britarch.ac.uk/archabroad].

The Art of Pilgrimage: The Seeker's Guide to Making Travel Sacred by Phil Cousineau (Conari Press). Travel for personal meaningfulness.

Auto Europe Wallet Card. Toll-free telephone access codes to reach AT&T, MCI, and Sprint in 20 countries; 800-223-5555; [www.autoeurope.com]. Also the Auto Europe free CD Rom Travel Planner, an interactive guide to planning your trip to Europe.

Big Book of Adventure Travel by James Simmons (Avalon Travel Publishing). A source book of worldwide guided adventure tours.

Bugs, Bites and Bowels by Dr. J. Howarth (Cadogan). A guide on healthy travel covering prevention, diagnosis, and cure.

Create Your Own European Adventure: Leave the Guidebooks at Home by Clive Shearer (Newjoy Press). Remarkably detailed planning and preparation guide.

Damron Men's Travel Guide edited by Ian Philips (Damron Company, annual). The original gay travel guide lists over 10,000 gay-friendly B and Bs, bars, cafes, and more in North America and major European cities.

Do's and Taboos Around the World: A Guide to International Behavior by Roger Axtell (John Wiley & Sons). Advice for the business and pleasure traveler on what to do and not to do in other cultures.

Europe Through the Back Door, Europe 101, Mona Winks by Rick Steves (Avalon Travel Publishing). Rick is the expert on independent travel in Europe.

Fly Cheap! by Kelly Monaghan (Intrepid Traveler). All you need to know to save on airfares, including strategies, contacts, and Internet sites.

Foiling Pickpockets and Bag Snatchers and Other Travel Related Crimes or Scams. Order Jens Jurgen's 24-page booklet from: Travel Companion Exchange, Inc., P.O. Box 833, Amityville, NY 11701-0833; tce@whytravelalone.com, [www.foilingpickpockets.com]. One copy $4.70, two copies $6.70 ppd.

Ford's Freighter Travel Guide (Ford's Travel Guides). Very informative. Updated semi-annually.

Freighter Travel News. Monthly newsletter by Leland J. Pledger (Freighter Travel Club of America, 3524 Harts Lake, Roy, WA 98580; www.webup.com/ftn). $20 per year.

Going Abroad? Superintendent of Documents, U.S. Government Printing Office, Washington, DC 20420; 202-512-1800. Free pamphlet with safety tips; includes order form for other U.S. government publications on foreign travel and residency.

Going Solo Travel Tools edited by Diane Redfern. Tips, advice, tales, and contacts for planning going solo adventures. Connecting, P.O. Box 29088, Delamont RPO, Vancouver, BC V6J 5C2, Canada; 800-557-1757; [www.cstn.org].

Hostelling International, 733 15th St., Suite 840, NW, Washington, DC 20005; 202-783-6161, fax 202-783-6171; hiayhserv@hiayh.org, [www.hiayh.org]. Detailed information for nearly 4,500 hostels in over 70 countries for all ages. Two annual volumes: *Europe* and *Africa/Americas/Asia/Pacific.*

Jewish Travel Guide by Betsy Sheldon (Hunter). Lists Jewish organizations throughout the world.

The Latin American Travel Advisor, P.O. Box 17-17-908, Quito, Ecuador; fax 011-593-2-562-566; LATA@pi.pro.ec, [www.amerispan.com/lata/]. Newsletter with sound advice for safe travel in 17 South and Central American countries.

More Women Travel (Penguin). From Rough Guide series.

Ordnance Survey Maps, Atlases and Guides Catalogue. Ordnance Survey Customer Information: 011-44-1703-792755, fax 011-44-1703-792602; psharp@ordsvy.gov.uk, [www.ordsvy.gov.uk]. Detailed maps and atlases for U.K. and Commonwealth countries as well as specialty guides—cycling, motoring, etc.

Passport to World Band Radio (International Broadcasting Services). Hour-by-hour, country-by-country listings for world band radio programming; mktg@passband.com [www.passband.com].

The Pocket Doctor: A Passport to Healthy Travel by Stephen Bezruchka, M.D. (The Mountaineers Books). A compact health guide for the traveler.

The Practical Nomad: How to Travel Around the World by Edward Hasbrouck (Avalon Travel Publishing). Essential information on airfare strategies, travel documents, information sources, and more; [www.practicalnomad.com].

Rough Guide: First Time Europe and Rough Guide: First Time Asia (Rough Guides). Practical information, tips, and advice for traveling in these two areas.

Safety and Security for Women Who Travel by Sheila Suan and Peter Laufer (Travelers' Tales). Authors and world travelers help lay to rest fears and provide guidance.

Shawguides [**www.shawguides.com**]. Descriptions of more than 4,100 cooking schools, photo workshops, writers' conferences, art and craft workshops, cultural and language vacations, golf, tennis, and water sports schools and camps, and high performance programs worldwide. Searchable by keyword, name, state, country, region, month, and specialty.

Single-Friendly Travel Directory edited by Diane Redfern. Frequently updated listing of hundreds of tour companies, cruise lines, lodges, spas, resorts, and travel clubs whose functions and pricing are attractive to single and solo travelers. Included with membership to Connecting: Solo Travel Network. Connecting, 689 Park Rd., Unit 6, Gibsons, BC V0N 1V7, Canada; 800-557-1757; [www.cstn.org].

Getting There

Airhitch® [www.airhitch.org]. Get to Europe cheaply by taking advantage of seats left empty on commercial flights.

Airtech [www.airtech.com]. Similar to Airhitch but offers tickets to places outside of Europe.

American Society of Travel Agents [www.astanet.com]. Includes a directory of travel agents who specialize in particular types of trips, as well as international travel information and resources. You can also submit a trip request for bids from different agents.

Council Travel [www.counciltravel.com]. Not just for students and teachers, Council Travel also has good information and rates for regular adult travelers. One of the few places for affordable one-way tickets.

Deutsche Bahn AG [http://bahn.hafas.de/english.html]. Up-to-date timetables for train service in Europe. Well-designed site has options for text-only browsers in English or German.

European Travel Network [www.discountairfares.com]. This nonprofit site is a good place to find budget travel information such as cheap fares and hotels.

Rail Europe [www.raileurope.com]. A good place to plan your European rail travel, buy railpasses and tickets, and see train schedules.

RailServe [www.railserve.com]. Their "Passenger and Urban Transit" links have information and links for rail travel worldwide.

Ticket Planet [www.ticketplanet.com]. Around-the-world ticketing specialists.

Where to Stay

Accommodation Search Engine [www.ase.net]. An online database of hotels, bed and breakfasts, inns, etc. worldwide.

European Hostels.com [www.europeanhostels.com]. Well-organized site lists over 1,550 hostels throughout Europe and rates the top 50.

European Travel Network [www.discountairfares.com]. This nonprofit site is a good place to find budget travel information such as cheap fares and hotels.

Hostelling International [www.iyhf.org]. The "Worldwide Hostels" section lists hostels in 75 countries.

Hostels of Europe [www.hostelseurope.com]. Lists Europe's finest youth hostels and hotels; also offers budget travel links, a travel bookstore, a free electronic newsletter, and more.

Internet Guide to Hostelling [www.hostels.com]. Among the largest directories of hostels in the world; also a bulletin board and travel links.

Places to Stay [www.placestostay.com]. An extensive online reservation service for hotels, bed and breakfasts, inns, and resorts worldwide with up-to-the-minute information on prices and availability.

Travel Planning

American Society of Travel Agents [www.astanet.com]. Includes a directory of travel agents who specialize in particular types of trips, as well as international travel information and resources. You can also submit a trip request for bids from different agents.

Away.com [www.away.com]. Responsible and adventure travel information.

Backpack Europe on a Budget [www.backpackeurope.com]. Backpacking and hosteling information, tips, and links for student and budget travelers planning a trip to Europe.

Budget Travel [www.budgettravel.com]. Geographically indexed contact information for travelers who "don't want to pay 5-star prices."

CNN Travel Guide [www.cnn.com/travel]. Travel news, destination information, booking information, currency converter.

Condé Nast Travel [www.concierge.com]. *Condé Nast's* site has budget travel info and discussion forums as well as other resources for travelers.

Council Travel [www.counciltravel.com]. Not just for students and teachers, Council Travel also has good information and rates for regular adult travelers.

Currency Converter [www.oanda.com/converter/travel]. This site features a program that will do conversions for almost 200 different currencies.

Electronic Embassy Page [www.embassy.org/embassies]. A list of all of the foreign embassies in the U.S.

Embassy World [www.embassyworld.com]. Links to embassies and consulates worldwide.

GoAbroad Home Page [www.goabroad.com]. Offers a searchable database of overseas travel programs.

InfoHub Specialty Travel Guide [www.infohub.com]. Comprehensive, easily searchable database of special interest travel programs.

Izon's Backpacker Journal [www.izon.com]. An extensive list of links and a modest list of free youth/budget travel guides.

Kasbah Travel Information [www.kasbah.com]. A travel search engine with over 100,000 sites listed.

Le Travel Store [www.letravelstore.com]. Travel gear, accessories, publications.

Lonely Planet [www.lonelyplanet.com]. Premier travel book publisher has great content and a sense of humor.

Net News for the Thrifty Traveler [www.thriftytraveler.com]. Information helpful to budget travelers.

Rec.Travel Library [www.travel-library.com]. Personal travelogues and worldwide travel and independent travel information.

Time Out [www.TimeOut.com]. Bars, clubs, hotels, restaurants, shops, galleries, museums, and music venues in the world's major cities, plus interesting original content about each city.

Transitions Abroad [www.TransitionsAbroad.com]. The central hub of alternative travel online with links to the web sites of everyone listed in our resource and program directories.

Travel Document Services [www.traveldocs.com]. Provides visa services for U.S. citizens for most countries for which an entry visa is required; web site also has up-to-date information on most countries and impressive list of travel resources available for purchase.

TravLang [www.travlang.com]. Provides useful tools for the traveler and those interested in learning a foreign language; also links to other places on the net providing related services.

Universal Currency Converter [www.xe.net/currency]. See how many yen your dollar will fetch.

Wide World Books and Maps [www.travelbooksandmaps.com]. Founded in 1976, WWBM was the first travel-only bookstore in the country. Over 14,000 map and book titles in stock.

Worldwide Classroom [www.worldwide.edu]. Travel planning information broken down into 25 categories, plus an extensive list of educational travel programs.

Networking

The Cybercafé Search Engine [http://cybercaptive.com]. Lists over 2,000 cybercafés in 125 countries which offer a multitude of services for the international traveler.

Geotravel Research Center [www.culturebriefings.com]. Web site contains *Culture Briefings* newsletter, which is intended to help travelers understand foreign cultures and customs.

iAgora [www.iagora.com]. A good place to network with other international travelers; offers a good selection of links.

Journeywoman Online [www.journeywoman.com]. This is the premier resource for women who love to travel; a free email newsletter is delivered to you in minutes. [www.Hermail.net] is a directory of women travelers willing to help each other as they travel the world.

Lonely Planet [www.lonelyplanet.com]. Premier travel book publisher has great content and a sense of humor.

Rec.Travel Library [www.travel-library.com]. Personal travelogues and worldwide travel and independent travel information.

Roadnews [www.roadnews.com]. Traveling with your computer? This site has everything you need to stay connected to the "cyberworld" while traveling in the real one.

TravLang [www.travlang.com]. Provides useful tools for the traveler and those interested in learning a foreign language; also links to other places on the net providing related services.

Other Favorites

Arthur Frommer's Budget Travel Online [www.frommers.com]. Information on budget and alternative travel.

No Shitting in the Toilet [www.noshit.com.au]. "A celebration of everything that is perverse about travel." Hilarious.

Passionfruit Magazine [www.passionfruit.com]. New travel publications web site has excellent content and stories for women travelers.

Speaking Vegetarian. The Globetrotter's Guide to Ordering Meatless in 197 Countries by Bryan Geon (Pilot Books). An overview of what to expect—from the vegetarian perspective—in over 197 foreign countries.

Specialty Travel Index. Biannual directory/magazine of special interest and adventure travel listing over 600 tour operators worldwide. $10 per year for 2 issues from Specialty Travel Index, 305 San Anselmo Ave., Suite 313, San Anselmo, CA 94960; 415-459-4900, fax 415-459-4974; [www.specialtytravel.com].

Staying Healthy in Asia, Africa, and Latin America by Dirk G. Schroeder (Avalon Travel Publishing). This is your tool for maintaining good health while living or visiting in developing nations; info@travelmatters.com, [www.travelmatters.com].

There's No Toilet Paper on the Road Less Traveled: The Best of Travel Humor and Misadventure by Doug Lansey (Travelers' Tales). Proving once again that a sense of humor is the one travel tool you shouldn't leave home without.

The Thrifty Traveler, P.O. Box 8168, Clearwater, Fl 33758; 800-532-5731, fax 727-447-0829; editor@thriftytraveler.com, [www.thriftytraveler.com]. Twelve-page monthly newsletter includes a special section for over-50 travelers and a section on Internet travel news.

Tips for the Savvy Traveler by Deborah Burns and Sarah May Clarkson (Storie Publishing). Hundreds of valuable tips from planning to coming home.

Travel Alone & Love It—A Flight Attendant's Guide to Solo Travel by Sharon B. Wingler (Chicago Spectrum Press, $14.95). Instructions on how to plan your own successful solo journey.

Travel and Learn by Evelyn Kaye (Blue Panda Publications) [www.travelbooks123.com]). Over 1,000 exciting learning vacations around the world from art and archaeology to rafting and zoology.

Travel by Cargo Ship by Hugo Verlomme (Cadogon). Practical information and inside tips on traveling by passenger-cargo ship.

Travel Companion Exchange, P.O. Box 833, Amityville, NY 11701; 631-454-0880 or 800-392-1256; tce@whytravelalone.com, [www.whytravelalone.com]. $6 sample newsletter. Widely recommended listings for travelers seeking companions and outstandingly useful newsletter for all travelers. Also check out www. ITAsoftware.com for cheap domestic airfares.

Travel with Others without Wishing They'd Stayed Home by Nadine Nardi Davidson (Prince Publishing). A survival guide to traveling with your spouse, lover, boss, friends, kids, someone else's kids, relatives, pet, and yourself.

Travel with Peace of Mind (International SOS Assistance). Brochure informing individual travelers about medical, personal, and travel assistance when needed while overseas.

The Traveler's Atlas (Barron's Educational Series). A beautiful coffee table book plus a planning guide with regional background information.

Traveler's Tool Kit by Rob Sangster (Menasa Ridge Press). 3rd ed. Practical guide tells you "all you need to know to travel absolutely anywhere."

Traveling Solo by Eleanor Berman (Globe Pequot). Advice and ideas for more than 250 great vacations including language and cooking schools, and active vacations, plus tips for traveling on your own.

Volunteer Vacations by Bill McMillon (Chicago Review Press). 7th ed. More than 500 opportunities worldwide.

Wild Planet! 1,001 Extraordinary Events for the Inspired Traveler by Tom Clynes (Visible Ink). Thorough compendium of festivals, cultural events, and holidays spanning the globe.

Women's Traveller edited by Gina M. Gatta, Ian Philips (Damron Company). Annual. Features thousands of businesses of interest to lesbian travelers, in North America and major European cities. Also a calendar of events and upcoming tours.

Work Your Way Around the World by Susan Griffith (Peterson's Guides). 10th ed. Excellent firsthand information, by country, on short-term jobs to keep you going by *Transitions Abroad* contributing editor.

The World Awaits: Comprehensive Guide to Extended Backpack Travel by Paul Otteson (Avalon Travel Publishing). Practical book with details for life on the road.

World Music, Volumes 1 & 2 from the Rough Guides Series. References and information on music spanning the globe.

World's Most Dangerous Places by Robert Young Pelton and Coskun Aral (Fielding Worldwide). Firsthand experiences, advice on protecting yourself, etc.

Worst-Case Scenario Survival Handbook by David Borgenicht and Joshua Piven (Chronicle Books). Handy book to prepare you to cope with dangers on the road, from escaping from quicksand to wrestling an alligator.

CHOOSING A GUIDEBOOK
HALF YOUR TRIP DEPENDS ON WHAT YOU TAKE WITH YOU

By Ed Readicker-Henderson

Half your trip depends upon your choice of a guidebook. Choose right and it will be like traveling with the best friend you ever had. Choose wrong and you'll go home with a nagging feeling that your trip could have been much, much better.

Fortunately, choosing which guidebook is the one for you is easy. Here are the basic rules:

First and most important, buy a book, not a series. Books are written by individuals, not by companies, and books in any series can be very, very different. At the same time, all series have their unique strengths. If you're going to Europe to eat, Michelin is the standard. If you're looking for noodles in Ayutthaya, Lonely Planet is the place to start. But strong in one area can easily mean weak in another area that's important to you. Look for balance. Which brings us to the next point:

Know yourself. You can't pick right unless you know what you want. Are you out to explore a region's history or to lounge on the beach? Spend some time looking at the things that matter to you, comparing from book to book.

Look up the place you're going in several different books. Of course you don't know which is accurate, but if two books say one thing and the third another, well, maybe number three is a problem. This also gives you a chance to look at the writer's style—is this somebody you want with you on your trip? Check for the vital facts: How do you get from the airport to town without hassle? A random check of books on Belgium showed that only one included this basic bit of information. If it's missing, that's a good indication that other things you need to know are missing as well. This simple test can save you a $50 taxi ride.

Look for purple prose. Many guidebook writers copy huge chunks straight from tourist office brochures. If they talk about the sunset over the beach or the colorful costumes of the locals, drop it.

No books are up to date. With a few exceptions (like those of Rick Steves) a new guidebook is a year old before you ever see it because it takes that long to research and publish. By the time you go, half the restaurants listed have gone bust and all the hotels have raised their prices. Choose a book with a good selection. Some very popular guides only list a few places to stay in big cities; guess what your chance is of getting a spot.

Do not blindly trust your book. If something in your trip is make or break, don't rely on any one source. Before you leave home, go online, make some phone calls, do whatever you have to do to get the very latest information.

When you find the book that fits you, buy it. In the big picture, the cost is a pittance. But whatever book you pick, make it a guide, not a bible. It's sad to go somewhere and see every traveler clutching the same book while they go to the same places. There's plenty of things out there for you to find on your own. And that's the whole point of going, isn't it?

Best Guides by Country

Africa

Bicycling in Africa by David Mozer (International Bicycle Fund, 4887 Columbia Dr. S., Apt. T, Seattle, WA 98108-1919; Tel./fax 206-767-0848; ibike@ibike.org, www.ibike.org). How to do it, with supplements on 17 separate countries.

Asia

Four Dragons Guidebook by Frederick Kaplan (Houghton Mifflin). Covers Hong Kong, Taiwan, Singapore, and Thailand.

Australia

A Traveler's Literary Companion edited by Robert Ross (Whereabouts Press). Modern short stories by Australian authors.

The Australian Bed and Breakfast Book by J. and J. Thomas (Pelican Publishing). Stay in private homes, on farms, and in guest houses with friendly hosts.

Austria

Austria: Charming Small Hotels by Paul Wade (Hunter). A selection of small hotels with character.

Canada

Hidden British Columbia by Eric Lucas. 2nd ed (Ulysses Press). Includes sights, lodging, dining, and outdoor adventures in Vancouver and Victoria as well as more remote areas.

Caribbean

Hidden Bahamas by Richard Harris and Lynn Seldon (Ulysses Press). Covers smaller, out-of-the-way islands as well as the tourist spots of Nassau and Grand Bahama.

Caribbean/West Indies

Adventure Guide to: Barbados, Bermuda, Dominican Republic, Jamaica, Puerto Rico Trinidad/Tobago, and the Virgin Islands (Hunter Publications). Practical guides for the adventurous traveler.

Central America

Costa Rica Traveler's Literary Companion by B. Ras (Whereabouts Press). Compilation of short stories by Costa Rican authors.

Explore Belize by Harry S. Pariser (Hunter Publications). 4th ed. Practical guide for the adventurous traveler.

Hidden Baja by Richard Harris (Ulysses Press). Tourist spots and out-of-the-way locales.

Hidden Cancun and the Yucatan by Richard Harris (Ulysses Press). Covers Cancun as well as more remote areas of the Yucatan peninsula, including listings of sights, lodging, and outdoor adventures.

Hidden Guatemala by Richard Harris (Ulysses Press). Covers natural attractions and small villages and includes lodging, dining, and outdoor adventure listings.

China/Hong Kong

Essential Chinese for Travelers by Fan Zhilong (China Books). Basic phrasebook, dictionary, and cassette, includes sections on hotels, transportation, money, food, and business. Rev. 1996.

Czech and Slovak Republics

Prague Traveler's Literary Companion by P. Wilson (Whereabouts Press). Compilation of short stories by Prague writers.

Europe

Europe 101: History and Art for the Traveler by Rick Steves and Gene Openshaw (Avalon Travel Publishing). Wonderful.

Mona Winks: A Guide to Enjoying Europe's Top Museums by Rick Steves and Gene Openshaw (Avalon Travel Publishing).

Postcards from Europe by Rick Steves (Avalon Travel Publishing). Collection of 25 years of travel tales from veteran European traveler and writer; info@travelmatters.com, [www.travelmatters.com].

Travel Guide to Jewish Europe by Ben Frank (Pelican). 3rd ed. Jewish historical sites, Holocaust memorials, neighborhoods, restaurants, etc.

Traveling Europe's Trains by Jay Brunhouse (Pelican Publishing). 5th ed. Detailed itineraries and what to see along the way.

Understanding Europeans by Stuart Miller (Avalon Travel Publishing). Insights into European behavior, history and cultural heritage.

France

No More Hotels in Paris: How to Find Alternative Accommodations by Cynthia Lynn (Newjoy Press). Finding rentals and other accommodations. Also detailed information about Paris transportation.

TOP-SELLING TRAVEL BOOKS FOR 2001

World Wide Books and Maps (Seattle)

1. Rick Steves' Italy
2. Lonely Planet Cycling France
3. Lonely Planet Italy
4. Worst Case Scenario
5. Atlas of Experience
6. Rick Steves' Paris
7. Rick Steves' France, Belgium & Netherlands
8. Lonely Planet Mexico
9. Rick Steves' Spain & Portugal
10. Where the Pavement Ends

The Savvy Traveler (Chicago)

1. Gusty Women
2. Eyewitness Paris
3. Eyewitness Florence & Tuscany
4. Rick Steves' Italy
5. Eyewitness London
6. Paris Walking Guide
7. Eyewitness Italy
8. Airport Transit Guide
9. Eyewitness Amsterdam
10. Rick Steves' Paris

Amazon.com (Nationwide)

1. Rick Steves' Italy
2. Worst Case Scenario
3. Walking the Bible
4. Coming Home to Jerusalem
5. River Town: Two Years on the Yangtze
6. In Maremma: Life . . . Southern Tuscany
7. Live Well in Mexico
8. Rick Steves' Spain & Portugal
9. Rick Steves' Paris
10. The Paris Shopping Companion

Rick Steves' Paris by Rick Steves (Avalon Travel Publishing). Helps travelers get the most for their time and money while in Paris.

Germany

Traveler's Guide to Jewish Germany by Hirsch and Lopez (Pelican). Sites, synagogues, memorials, and exhibitions.

Greece

Greece: A Traveler's Literary Companion edited by Artemis Leontis (Whereabouts Press). Modern short stories by Greek authors.

Italy

Independent Walker's Guide Italy by Frank Booth (Interlink). Planning and preparation for 35 great walks throughout Italy.

Japan

Tokyo Q: Annual Guide to the City (Stone Bridge Press). A hip insider's guide by long-term residents. Updated annually.

Mexico

The People's Guide to Mexico by Carl Franz (Avalon Travel Publishing). A wonderful read— full of wisdom, too.

Middle East

Israel: Traveler's Literary Companion edited by M. Gluzman and N. Seidman (Whereabouts Press). Short stories by Israeli authors.

Lebanon: A Travel Guide by Reid, Leigh and Kennedy (Pelican Publishing). General guide.

Spectrum Guides (Interlink Publishing). Beautifully photographed, good cultural and background information. Available for: Jordan, United Arab Emirates, Uganda, Tanzania, India, Pakistan, Malawi, Zimbabwe, Maldives, Mauritius, Nepal, Ethiopia.

New Zealand

The New Zealand Bed and Breakfast Book by J. and J. Thomas (Pelican Publishing). Lists over 300 private homes and hotels.

Poland

Polish Cities (Pelican Publishing). A guide to Warsaw, Krakow, and Gdansk.

Russia and the NIS

Language and Travel Guide to Ukraine by L. Hodges (Hippocrene). 3rd ed.

South America

The New Key to Ecuador and the Galapagos by David L. Pearson and David W. Middleton (Ulysses Press). 3rd ed. An emphasis on the outdoors and ecotourism.

Thailand

Diving in Thailand by Collin Piprell (Hippocrene) [www.hippocrenebooks.com]. Best diving sites with information on preparation, facilities, etc.

United Kingdom and Ireland

Independent Walker's Guide to Great Britain and **Independent Walker's Guide to Ireland** by Frank Booth (Interlink) [www.interlinkbooks.com]. Scenic walks through the countryside.

Irish Bed & Breakfast Book by Frank and Fran Sullivan (Pelican Publishing) 504-368-1175, fax 504-368-1195; promo@pelicanpub.com, [www.pelicanpub.com]). 3rd ed.

Rick Steves' London by Rick Steves (Avalon Travel Publishing). New Rick Steves guide that will help travelers get the most for their time and money while in London.

Vietnam

Vietnam: Traveler's Literary Companion edited by J. Balaban and N. Qui Duc (Whereabouts Press). Compilation of short stories by Vietnamese writers.

Around-the-World Travel Guides

The Practical Nomad: How to Travel Around the World by Edward Hasbrouck (Avalon Travel Publishing, 2nd ed., 2000, 652 pp.,$19.95). The most useful and comprehensive book available for planning an extended international trip. Includes an extensive resource guide for travel planning and preparation.

Traveler's Handbook edited by Miranda Haines and Sarah Thorowgood (Globe Pequot, 7th ed., 1997, 940 pp., $21.95). Called "the hitchhiker's guide to the galaxy," this collection of short essays includes a 300-page directory of information sources.

Travelers Tool Kit by Rob Sangster (Menasa Ridge Press, 3rd ed., 2000, 518 pp., $16.95). Practical guide tells you all you need to know to travel absolutely anywhere.

By Kent St. John

There was a time not so long ago when traveling meant time, travel agents, telexes, expensive telephone calls, and "Sorry we have no record of your reservation." Much has improved for the traveler, and the biggest reason is the Internet. To find low fares, I no longer have to buy five newspapers with their Sunday travel sections. I just click and pick, with the speed of Zorro.

Best Portals

Kasbah Travel Information [www.kasbah.com]. A travel search engine with a long history and over 100,000 sites listed. A very helpful forum.

Fares from England [www.deckchair.com]. The English sister site to Kasbah Travel Information is a great site for travelers looking for low fares from London to all points.

PlanetRider Travel Directory [www. planetrider.com]. The "10-minute vacation" section is fast and informative.

Travel-Finder [www.travel-finder.com]. A great portal because of the geographically savvy Spider Finder. Features 8,000 sites and 4,000 hosts.

Airlines of the Web [www.flyaow.com]. Good tips on air travel and the ground transportation links can help you find the best way to and from the airport.

Air Hitch [www.airhitch.org]. If you want super cheap and can be flexible, this airfare site can get you overseas for as little as $169 each way.

Trip.com [www.trip.com]. A travel portal for those with a high tech lifestyle. It can be accessed via Wireless Internet ready phone.

Airwise [www.airwise.com]. The place to get the news that affects airline travelers: good airport guide and discussion forum concerning passengers rights and airline alliances.

Sights, Sounds of Asia [www.gettinghere.com]. For travelers to Southeast Asia the site provides great promotional specials. The sights and sounds of the area's best-loved spots are exceptionally well done.

Last Minute Travel [www.lastminutetravel.com]. Got some sudden free time and not sure where to go? Click on a destination and see what airlines, hotels, and other providers are offering. Perfect for those who suffer from an irresistible travel bug.

Orbitz [www.orbitz.com]. This granddaddy of airfare search sites has just become better. You can't buy the tickets but you can select from dozens of ranked options on traveling anywhere.

Best Airfares Outside the U.S.

www.tiss.com. Discount tickets for flights from cities outside the U.S.

Lowestfares [www.lowestfare.com]. Not always the lowest but check them before buying a ticket. Several times they have come out on top for me. Easy and fast.

Sunday Travel Sections and More [www.johnnyjet.com]. This site offers a lengthy features section for many Sunday newspapers' travel sections.

Travelocity [www.travelocity.com]. Another giant (owned by Sabre) that should be checked, especially if you're looking at Canada, the U.K., or Germany.

Hotwire [www.hotwire.com]. A Priceline-like site for fares but not specific routing.

Ticketplanet [www.ticketplanet.com]. For heavily discounted fares to Asia or the South Pacific visit.

Latin Tickets [www.latintickets.com]. Need to flee South of the Border and quick? You pick your price and they will find the airline for you; if you don't like the price keeping trying.

Costa Rica Fly [www.yeess.com]. The best ticket site for Costa Rica, especially during high season.

Best Sleeps

International Youth Hostel Federation [www.iyhf.org]. The site for the granddaddy for budget travelers worldwide is well designed, well run, and very useful. The news section keeps you well updated on new and renovated hostels.

British Services [www.britishservices.com]. If you're heading to Britain, head to this site. Links to hotels and hostels all over the U.K. take you right to the headquarters of many chains.

Denmark & Copenhagen Guide to Travel [www.danex-exm.dk/links.htm]. Everything imaginable about Denmark (including Greenland): Travel, accommodations, and museums.

Hobo Traveler [www.hobotraveler.com]. Informative and fun. You can spend hours here. The hostel and hotel section is excellent for finding one of a kind lodgings. Many suggestions by hobo readers.

Budget Travel [www.budgettravel.com/hostels.htm]. A place to read others' recommendations. Literally thousands of links.

TuDots [www.tudots.com/hotsites1.htm]. My favorite lodging search spot will link you with lodgings worldwide of various types and cost. Many results from the Amazing Places search are far more reasonable than you would expect and perfect for an unforgettable stay. Web sites ranked in order of their usefulness.

Backpack Europe.com [www.backpackeurope.com]. A site that Arthur Frommer recommends as the best for backpacking in Europe. Thousands of useful links.

Best Information

Travel Library [www.travel-library.com]. Comprehensive information invaluable to dedicated long-term travelers. Covers routes, weather, budgeting, duration, and more. Advice from experienced travelers makes this great site even better. Includes a page full of links to various round-the- world travelers' personal web sites.

The Practical Nomad [www.moon.com/practical_nomad]. Do not even try to book a flight without checking advice from Edward Hasbrouck. He makes experienced travel agents look like they're in first grade. His new book, *Guide to the Online Marketplace*, is a must for any avid traveler.

Transitions Abroad [www.TransitionsAbroad.com]. Near and dear to my heart! The magazine site took me from being a tourist to a traveler with information that just does not exist anywhere else. Their mantra of combining work, study, and living with traveling abroad was a full 20 years ahead of anyone else's. There simply is no better resource for alternative travel anywhere, a gift to those of us truly determined to "find your own thing."

GoNomad [www.gonomad.com]. The *Travel & Leisure* of alternative travel, with a caring and global outlook and opportunities to connect with others who think traveling can be a constructive force. "Loaded with creative, uncrowded destinations, from treetops in Thailand to cooking classes in Europe" (American Airlines magazine).

Planeta [www.planeta.com]. I have never seen such a dedicated and informed devotee to helping both visitors and locals work together to understand Latin America. Ron Mader really cares!

Lonely Planet [www.lonelyplanet.com]. Not only information in their multitude of books on cheap travel; also email newsletters and contacts for live travel events.

http://dir.yahoo.com/Recreation/Travel/ News_and_Media/Magazines to reach a collection of nearly every travel magazine in existence.

TWO

The following specialized tours and programs range from working on organic farms in Australia to conflict resolution in Israel and Palestine. Contact the program directors to confirm dates, costs and other details. Programs based in more than one country are listed under "Worldwide." (For programs with a primary focus on structured learning see chapters 10, 11, and 12.)

Africa

Namibia and Botswana. Low-cost eco-safari, 16 days, 2 countries, with visit to Africa's Foundation HQ in Namibia plus Okavango Delta and Chobe Park, Botswana.
   Dates: May-Jun. **Costs:** $4,484 per person, 16 days, includes air from NY. **Contact:** Keith Tucker, ACACIA Travel, 3272 Rosecrans, San Diego, CA 92110; 800-243-6996, 619-225-1233; travel@acaciatravel.com, [www.acaciatrael.com].

Americas

Healing/Study Vacations. Masters of Oriental and Shamanic medicine guide and instruct tour members in the spiritual, healing, and art practices of the Indigenous tribes encountered. We work in the rainforests, mountains, and seas of Mexico, Cuba, and Belize. This apprentice program attempts to offer a vision of cultural sanity not available in normal hypnotic-style schools which proliferate today in most parts of the world.
   Dates: Nov-Apr. **Costs:** $200 per week. **Contact:** Kirk, East West Center and the Academy of Shamanic Healing; 319-354-1866; kirkstephan@hotmail.com, [www.digivation.com/ec].

Australia

Willing Workers on Organic Farms (WWOOFING). Learn organic growing while living with a host family. Fourteen hundred hosts in Australia or travel the world with over 600 hosts worldwide, on every continent, where you work in exchange for food and board.
   Dates: Year round. **Costs:** AUS$45 single, AUS$50 double (add $5 for postage outside of Australia). **Contact:** WWOOF Australia, Buchan, Victoria 3885, Australia; 011-61-3-5155-0218, fax 011-61-3-5155-0342; wwoof@wwoof.com.au, [www.wwoof.com.au].

Canada

Agawa Canyon Train Tour. Train or fly into our secluded resort on Lake Wabatongushi in the Chapleau Wildlife Preserve, where the only hunting allowed since 1925 is with a camera. Complete packages.
   Dates: May-Sep. **Costs:** Vary. **Contact:** Al Errington, Wilderness Island Resort, Box 22057, 44 Great Northern Rd., Sault St. Marie, Ontario P6B 6H4, Canada; 705-946-2010; vacation@wildernessisland.com, [www.WildernessIsland.com].

Classical Pursuits. An adventure for the mind. For 6 days this summer, pursue your passion for ideas. Discover and discuss meaning in great music, art or literature. **Dates:** Jul 15-Jul 21. **Costs:** CAN$1,000 per seminar. Includes registration, books, continental breakfasts, lunches, special events, and some excursions. **Contact:** Call toll free 877-633-2555; ann.kirkland@utoronto.ca, [www.utoronto.ca/classicalpursuits].

Wilderness Lodging. Purcell Lodge is Canada's finest remote mountain lodge. It sets a new environmental standard in sustainable tourism development. A few miles beyond the crowds of Banff and Lake Louise lies true solitude. A spectacular helicopter flight leaves the familiar far behind. Inside, the comfort of a fine country manor. Outside, your own natural paradise. Peaceful walks in alpine meadows, guided ski tours in stunning surroundings. **Dates:** Late Jun-early Oct, Dec-Apr. **Costs:** All-inclusive American plan $150-$210 per night. **Contact:** Paul Leeson, Manager, Purcell Lodge, Places Less Travelled Ltd., P.O. Box 1829, Golden, BC, Canada V0A 1H0; 250-344-2639, fax 250-344-5520; places@rockies.net, [www.purcell.com].

Wilderness Railway Tours. West Coast Rail Tours is a nonprofit society operating unique "backcountry" railway tours in British Columbia. Ideal for geography, history, railway, and photo enthusiasts. All packages are guided, feature outstanding scenery, vary from 1 to 9 days, year round. **Dates:** Year round. **Costs:** $99-$2,300. **Contact:** West Coast Rail Tours, Box 2790, Stn. Main, Vancouver, BC, V6B 3X2, Canada; 800-722-1233; tours@wcra.org, [www.wcra.org].

China

Cultural Issues and Business. Intensive 6-credit study vacation focuses on how the Chinese conceive and develop business enterprises. Structured program, with classroom activities and site visits. Also includes a general introduction to Chinese culture and the arts and instruction in "survival" Mandarin. Emphasis on understanding change and transition in contemporary China. **Dates:** Jun-Jul. **Costs:** $4,150 includes 4 credit tuition, travel, room and board. **Contact:** Friends World Summer 2001, LIU, 239 Montauk Hwy., Southampton, NY 11968; 631-287-8474, fax 631-287-8463; fw@southampton.liunet.edu, [www.southampton.liu.edu/academic/summer2001/summer.htm].

Costa Rica

Environmental Studies and Spanish. Intensive 6-credit program in environmental issues and Spanish language. Emphasis on the critical study of national environmental policy in Costa Rica and the tension between conservation and development. Immersion Spanish classes individualized to student's level and projects in the community and with the host family. **Dates:** Jun-Jul. **Costs:** $3,950 includes tuition, travel from NY, room and board. **Contact:** Friends World Summer 2001, LIU, 239 Montauk Hwy., Southampton, NY 11968; 631-287-8474, fax 631-287-8463; fw@southampton.liunet.edu, [www.southampton.liu.edu/academic/summer2001/summer.htm].

Homestays. A 10-year-old homestay service helps you get to know Costa Rica as you never would in any other way. We can help you develop a made-to-your-measure itinerary, making reservations for jungle lodges, beach accommodations, day and overnight tours, car rental. Free brochure available. **Dates:** Year round. **Costs:** $30 single; $45 double, breakfasts included, up. Itinerary and reservations complimentary for guests. **Contact:** Marcela and Vernon Bell, Bells' Home Hospitality, P.O. Box 185, 1000 San Jose, Costa Rica; 011-506-225-4752, fax 011-506-224-5884; homestay@racsa.co.cr, [www.homestay.thebells.org].

Horizontes Nature Tours. For more than 16 years, Horizontes has operated quality, personalized travel programs for people interested in nature observation, conservation, education, soft adventure, and meaningful interaction with local people. We operate custom-designed group and individual itineraries for renowned international tour companies, universities, and nonprofit organizations worldwide. Plus a wide selection of package tours. **Dates:** Year round. **Costs:** Call for details. **Contact:** Terry Pratt, Marketing Director, Horizontes Nature Tours, P.O. Box 1780-1002 P.E., San José, Costa Rica; 011-506-222-2022, fax 011-506-255-4513; tpratt@horizontes.com, [www.horizontes.com].

Intensive Spanish with Social Justice Focus. The Institute for Central American Development Studies (ICADS) offers 4-week progressive programs in intensive Spanish language—4 1/2 hours daily, 5 days a week. Small classes (4 or fewer students). Activities and optional afternoon internships or group community service activities that emphasize environmental issues, women's issues, education, healthcare, social justice issues. Supportive learning environment. Homestays, lectures, and field trips. Great alternative for the socially conscious. **Dates:** Programs begin first Monday of each month. **Costs:** $1,500 includes airport pick-up, classes, books, homestay, meals, laundry, lectures, activities, field trips, and internship placements. **Contact:** ICADS, Dept. 826, P.O. Box 025216, Miami, FL 33102-5216; icads@netbox.com, [www.icadscr.com].

Learn Spanish While Volunteering. Assist with the training of Costa Rican public school teachers in ESL and computers. Assist local health clinic, social service agencies, and environmental projects. Enjoy learning Spanish in the morning, volunteer work in the afternoon/evening. Spanish classes of 2-4 students plus group learning activities; conversations with middle class homestay families (1 student or couple per family). Homestays and most volunteer projects are in a small town near the capital, San José.
Dates: Year round, all levels. Classes begin every Monday (except Mar 25-29 and Dec 14-Jan 5), volunteer program is continuous. **Costs:** $345 per week for 26 hours of classes and group activities including Costa Rican dance and cooking classes. Includes tuition, meals, homestay, laundry, all materials, weekly 3-hour cultural tour, and airport transportation. $25 one-time registration fee. **Contact:** Susan Shores, Registrar, Latin American Language Center, PMB 123, 7485 Rush River Dr., Suite 710, Sacramento, CA 95831-5260; 916-447-0938, fax 916-428-9542; lalc@madre.com, [www.madre.com/~lalc].

Living Among the Giant Grasses. Work with and learn about tropical bamboos, one of the world's fastest growing renewable resources while you experience rural Costa Rican life in a wild river setting. This program offers a general orientation on the subject of bamboo, including opportunities to work in a tropical garden, participate in the development of a small bamboo plantation, and assist in the work of a bamboo furniture maker and sculptor.
Dates: Year-round, 1 month sessions, beginning the 1st of each month. **Costs:** $750 for 1st month, $600 each additional month. Includes private sleeping space, shared bath, meals. Airfare not included. **Contact:** Brian Erickson, Apdo. 295-7210 Guapiles, Costa Rica; fax 011-506-710-2264; brieri99@yahoo.com.

Two-Day Pacuare Whitewater Trip. Ride the exhilerating rapids of Costa Rica's most scenic and majestic river. Spend the night in our exotic Pacuare Jungle Lodge, hidden in the middle of an enchanting tropical rainforest. Trip includes ground transfers from San Jose, superior meals, specialist guides, and one-of-a-kind accommodations.
Dates: Year round. **Costs:** $259 per person. **Contact:** Adventuras Naturales, SJO 745, P.O. Box 025216, Miami, FL 33102-5216; 800-514-0411, fax 011-506-253-6934; adventure@adventurecostarica.com, [www.adventurecostarica.com].

Ecuador

Academia Latinoamericana. Proud to be the friendliest Spanish school you have ever known. Family owned and operated. The program offers language study at 9 levels, for complete beginners through advanced. Experienced staff, native Ecuadorians. Carefully selected host families within walking distance of school. Exclusive "Cloud Forest and Galápagos" extension program, volunteer program. U.S. college credit available.
Dates: Year round. **Costs:** $255 per week. Includes 20 hours of lessons, 7 days with host family, 2 meals per day, transfer, services at the school, and teaching material. **Contact:** Suzanne S. Bell, Admissions Director, USA/International, 640 East 3990 South, Suite E, Salt Lake City, UT, 84107; 801-268-4608, fax 801-265-9156; ecuador@access.net.ec, [www.latinoschools.com].

Galapagos Special. Visit the enchanted islands and Ecuador. Three nights in Quito or Guayaquil at a deluxe hotel, city tour, in and out transfers, and a 3-night cruise to the Galapagos Islands on one of our superior first class yachts, Coral 1 or Coral 2.
Dates: Weekly departures year round. **Costs:** Low season (May-Jun, Sep) $1,029 per person; high season $1,167. **Contact:** Vivian Vera, Kleintours, Av. Shyris 1000 y Holanda, Quito, Ecuador; 011-593-2-267-000 (U.S.: 888-50-KLEIN), fax 011-593-2-442-389; market@kleintours.com.ec, [www.galapagosecuador.com].

Europe

Bike Riders Tours. Small group cycling vacations in New England, Canada, and Europe. Self-guided and great chef cooking tours in Europe.
Dates: Year round. **Costs:** $980-$3,000. **Contact:** Bike Riders, P.O. Box 130254, Boston, MA 02113; 800-473-7040, fax 617-723-2355; info@bikeriderstours.com, [www.bikeriderstours.com].

Euro-Bike and Walking Tours. Thirtieth year of providing luxury tours to 15 countries in Europe. Beginner and experienced. See why our customers return year after year. Free brochure. **Dates:** May-Oct, 6-15 day tours. **Costs:** Starting at $1,695. **Contact:** Euro-Bike and Walking Tours, P.O. Box 990, Dekalb, IL 60115; 800-321-6060; info@eurobike.com, [www.eurobike.com].

Innemore Lodge. Cooking and painting courses run at Highland Lodge, set in stunning location. Full board or self-catering. All standards taught, on Isle of Mull, Scotland. Est. 1967. **Dates:** May-Sep. **Costs:** Course from £460 all inclusive. Self-catering from £1,100 (sleeps 12). **Contact:** Andrew Mazur, Innemore Lodge, Pennyghael, Isle of Mull, Scotland, PA70 6HD; Tel./fax 011-44-1681-704282

Language, Arts, and Sports. Active learning vacations: French, Spanish, Italian, Portuguese; cooking, painting, drawing, photography workshops. Combine eduVacational interests: French and sailing or skiing; Spanish and golf; bicycle tours—more countries, more ideas. We match individual needs and interests with programs and options: family stay, apartment, hotel; intensive to total immersion; small groups or study in and live in your teacher's home. **Dates:** Programs run from 1 week to months. **Costs:** Includes room and board, tuition. **Contact:** Mary Ann Puglisi, eduVacations®, 1431 21st St. NW, Suite 302, Washington, DC 20036; 202-857-8384, fax 202-463-8091; eduvacate@aol.com, [www.eduvacations.com].

Sculpture in Italy and Spain. Since 1985 Marble & Art Workshops has offered marble sculpture workshops in the international center of sculpture, Pietrasanta, Italy. Created, organized, and assisted by American sculptor Lynne Streeter, these courses offer the chance to learn classical stone carving techniques in an inspirational and creative environment. For the 4th year, a 2-week workshop will be held near Barcelona, Spain, in an artists' cooperative. Offers an exploration of fundamental sculpture techniques, including hand carving of alabaster, modeling, moldmaking, and casting in clay and plaster, plus innovative finishing options. **Dates:** Pietrasanta, Italy: Session I, May 28-Jun 22; session II, Jul 2-27; session III, Sep. 3-28; session IV, Oct 2-13. Barcelona, Spain: Aug. 13-24. **Costs:** Pietrasanta $1,900 (4 weeks). Barcelona $1,750, $1,900, $1,600 depending on accommodations. **Contact:** Lynne Streeter. Mid-Oct to mid-May each year: P.O. Box 7371, Oakland, CA 94601; 510-533-8893, fax 510-436-0630. Mid-May to mid-Oct each year: Casella Postale 244, 55045 Pietrasanta (LU), Italy; 011-390-584-792004, fax 011-390-584-71198.

Summer School in Archaeology. Introduces participants to the theory and practice of archaeology in general and to Mediterranean and Maltese archaeology in particular. Two-week course is followed by 4 weeks of excavation and finds processing experience. Participants may register for a range of 2- to 6- week options. **Dates:** Jun 10-Jul 19, 2002. **Costs:** From $625-$2,000 includes accommodations. **Contact:** Jean Killick, International Office, Foundation for International Studies, Old Univ. Bldg., St. Paul St., Valletta VLT 07, Malta; 011-356-234121/2, fax 011-356-230538; summerabroad@um.edu.mt.

The Essential Cookery Course. Four-week intensive residential cookery course taking students through methods and principles more frequently covered in a longer course. Progress from basic skills to complex techniques, with the emphasis on practical hands-on cookery. **Dates:** Jan, Feb, May, Jul-Aug, Sep, Oct, Nov. **Costs:** £1,990-£2,390 **Contact:** Cookery at the Grange, Whatley, Frome, Somerset, BA11 3JU, England; Tel./fax 011-44-1373-836579; info@cookery-grange.co.uk, [www.cookery-grange.co.uk].

Yoga for Everyone. Yoga is for everyone. Ruth White has the ability to enable people to see through their limitations and experience a sense of freedom and well-being. As seen on her TV series, she endeavors to adapt her instruction to the needs of her students. Her workshops are popular in Europe, Australia, India, and Greece and are suitable for everyone. **Dates:** Year round. Greek Isle of Lesbos (month of May); **Costs:** Approx. £130 per weekend; £350 1 week in Lesbos. **Contact:** Ruth White, Ruth White Yoga Centre, Church Farm House, Spring Close Ln., Cheam, Surrey SM3 8PU, U.K.; 011-44-208-644-0309, fax 011-44-208-287-5318; [www.ruthwhiteyoga.com].

France

French in France. The French American Study Center was founded 25 years ago in the U.S. Students of any age or any level can be at home in Normandy to study French in real immersion. Seize the opportunity of the high exchange rate of the U.S. dollar. **Dates:** Spring: Mar-May; summer: Jun-Aug; fall: Sep-Nov. **Costs:** From $490 per week (tuition, room and board, and excursions).

Contact: Dr. Alméras, Chairman, French American Study Center, 12, 14, Blvd. Carnot, B.P. 4176, 14104 Lisieux Cedex, France; 011-33-2-31-31-22-01, fax 011-33-2-31-31-22-21; centre.normandie@wanadoo.fr, [http://perso.wanadoo.fr/centre.normandie/].

French Language Learning Vacations. Learn French while discovering the chateaux of the Loire Valley, the secrets of Provence, or the sandy beaches of the Mediterranean. Our programs are designed for independent travelers sharing a passion for the French culture and lifestyle. We offer a choice of locations in Tours, Aix-en-Provence, Montpellier, Paris, or Nice.

Dates: Two or more weeks year round. **Costs:** Two-week packages range from $825-$1,265. Includes classes, housing and fees. **Contact:** Jim Pondolfino, French-American Exchange, 3213 Duke Street, #620, Alexandria, VA 22314; 800-995-5087, fax 703-823-4447; faetours@erols.com, [www.faetours.com].

Horizons in Provence. Provence evokes images of vineyards, olives, sun-filled landscapes, and a profusion of antique monuments. It is all this and more. We'll live in the stunning village of Venasque, ringed by Roman monuments, sleepy wine villages, and a panorama of fertile fields and rolling hills. A week of workshops and excursions. As with all Horizons trips, small groups, great food, and places to stay that have charm and character are the bottom line. Workshops include Painting, Photography, Fabric Printing, and Design—structured for the novice and to challenge those more advanced.

Dates: Apr 20-27; Oct 4-11. **Costs:** $1,545 (lodging, tuition, field trips, all meals except 2 lunches). Air transport package optional. **Contact:** Jane Sinauer, Horizons to Go, Box 2206, Amherst, MA 01004; 413-549-2900, fax 413-549-5995; horizons@horizons-art.com, [www.horizons-art.com].

Provence: The Study of Place. Join Open Roads Open Minds for 8 days of travel, adventure, and writing. Stay in a charming hilltop B and B. Three evening writing workshops facilitated by travel author and teacher. Canoe on the Sorgue, hike in the Cevennes, bike or ride horses in the Camargue. First-time writers welcome.

Dates: May 4-12. **Costs:** $1,595 plus airfare. **Contact:** Open Roads Open Minds, 4824 16th Rd., N., Arlington, VA 22207; 703-527-6535, fax 703-522-0582; roadsinprovence@aol.com, [www.openroadsopenminds.com].

REMPART—Preserving the Past. REMPART aims to preserve the French cultural heritage through the restoration of threatened buildings and monuments. It consists of a grouping of more than 140 autonomous associations organizing workcamps providing a wide variety of work projects involving the restoration of medieval towns, castles, churches, ancient walls, wind/watermills, and industrial sites. Work includes masonry, excavations, woodwork, stone cutting, interior decorating, and clearance work. Opportunities for sports, exploring the region, and taking part in local festivities. Minimum age is 13. Previous experience is not necessary. Some knowledge of French required.

Dates: Workcamps last from 2 to 3 weeks. Most of them are open during Easter holidays and from Jul to Sep. A few camps are open throughout the year. **Costs:** FF230, EURO 35 for insurance, FF40-FF50 per day for food and accommodations. Volunteers help with camp duties, pay their own fares, and should bring a sleeping bag. **Contact:** Union Rempart, 1 rue des Guillemites, 75004 Paris, France; 011-33-1-42-71-9655, fax 011-33-1-42-71-7300; contact@rempart.com, [www.rempart.com].

Summer Program. Summer programs for juniors and adults includes activities and excursions with international groups of students in a very nice and safe place.

Dates: Jun-Sep. **Costs:** Juniors $730 for 2 weeks, adults on request. **Contact:** St. Denis European School, Ph. Minereau, BP 146-37600, Loches, France; 011-33-247-9404-50; euroschool@saint-denis.net, [www.saint-denis.net].

Ghana

The Art and Culture of Ghana. P.O. Box 61435, Honolulu, HI 96839; 877-300-7058, fax 808-247-4113; hea@aloha.net, [http://hawaiiecotourism.org]. Responsible tourism resource network for Hawaii and the Pacific.

Dates: Vary. **Costs:** $2,500 for 14 days. **Contact:** Ellie Schimelman, ABA Tours, 45 Auburn St., Brookline, MA 02446; Tel./fax 617-277-0482; abatours@africancrafts.com, [www.africancrafts.com/abatours].

Greece

Greece Study Vacation Tours. Unique travel experience. Visit the outstanding sites of Greece and the charming Greek islands. Learn about Greek history and culture. Enjoy Greek food and local dancing. Swim at beautiful beaches. Designed for teachers/educators and other interested travelers. Athens-Myoonos-Delos-Paroo-Santorini (Crete). Knowledgeable lecturers. First-class hotels, dinners.

Dates: Jul 10-Aug 2. **Costs:** $2,995. **Contact:** Book with: Educational Tours and Cruises, Att: Marina Cocconi (Tour escort), 94 Prescott St., Medford, MA 02155-3750; 800-275-4109, fax 781-396-3096. In Midwest: Vicky Marin (teacher-tour escort), 144 Frankling Ave., River Forest, IL 60305; 708-366-5346; vjm@edmail.com.; edtours@ed-tours.com, [www.greecestudyvacation.com].

Western Crete Photo Workshops. Discover Chania town and unspoiled Crete with Tony Stone images travel photographer Steve Outram. See all the facets this fascinating area has to offer from ancient ruined sites, to a carpet weaver at his family loom.

Dates: May 7-15; Oct 1-9. **Costs:** $1,890 per person, includes lodging. Airfare not included. **Contact:** Steve Outram, D. Katsifarakis St., Galatas, Chania 73100, Crete, Greece; Tel./fax 011-30-821-32201; mail@steveoutram.com, [www.steveoutram.com].

Greece

Skyros Holistic Vacations. We offer over 200 courses on the beautiful Greek island of Skyros and the Thai island of Ko Samet. Courses range from yoga, Tai Chi, massage, art, personal development, creative writing, and dance to drumming, voicework, drama, and bodywork. Delicious food and spectacular surroundings.

Dates: Jan-Dec. **Costs:** $1,085. **Contact:** Helen Akif, Skyros, 92 Prince of Wales Rd., London NW5 3NE, U.K.; 011-44-207-284-3065, fax 011-44-207-284-3063; connect@skyros.com, [www.skyros.com].

India

Ancient Cultures of the India Himalaya. In a remote region of the India Himalaya, bordering Tibet lies the almost forgotten and somewhat hidden districts of Kinnaur and Spiti Valley. Kinnari people are originally Rajputs of the Khasa clan and maintain a very distinct culture from the Tibetan Buddhists residing in the ancient monasteries. Easy to moderate walks; 4-5 star hotels, and comfortable camping.

Dates: Jul and Aug. **Costs:** From $4,455. **Contact:** Spirit of India, P.O. Box 446, Mill Valley, CA 94942; 888-367-6147, 415-381-5861, fax 415-381-6919; inquire@spirit-of-india.com, [www.spirit-of-india.com].

Art and Architecture of India. Led by Dr. Don Stadtner, PhD, Indian Art History, UC Berkeley, this tour highlights ancient art and architecture of north India including paintings, sculpture, textiles, marble, bronzes, and temples. Special presentations by directors and curators of museums in Delhi, Bombay, and others.

Dates: Feb 11-Mar 3, 2002. **Costs:** From $5,350 double occupancy. **Contact:** Spirit of India, P.O. Box 446, Mill Valley, CA 94942; 888-367-6147, 415-381-5861, fax 415-381-6919; inquire@spirit-of-india.com, [www.spirit-of-india.com].

South India Spiritual Journey. Led by Roland Pargeter. Visits to Mysore Palaces, idyllic beaches, and visits to the ashrams of saints both living and of the past. Arrive in Madras and end in Trivandrum.

Dates: Oct. **Costs:** From $4,950. **Contact:** Spirit of India, P.O. Box 446, Mill Valley, CA 94942; 888-367-6147, fax 415-381-6919; inquire@spirit-of-india.com, [www.spirit-of-india.com].

Tibetan Culture in Exile. Earn 4-6 college credits. After an orientation in Bangalore, visit Sikkim for a unit on Tibetan Buddhism. Proceed to Dharamsala to consider the religion, culture, and politics of the Tibetan diaspora. Program concludes in Delhi.

Dates: May-Jun. **Costs:** $4,600 (4 cr). **Contact:** Friends World Program, Summer 2001, Admissions Office, 239 Montauk Highway, Southampton, NY 11968; 631-287-8474; fw@southampton.liu.edu, [www.southampton.liu.edu/fw].

Indonesia

Experiencing the Arts in Bali. Includes 10 classes in batik, Gamelan music, dance, mask carving, and acrylic painting with Balinese working artists. Quality performances, temple festivals, 4 island tours include all the must-see sights, while residing in Bali's cultural center. We are the experts: 22 years experience. Knowledgeable, caring bilingual guides.

Dates: Jul 5-24, Jul 29-Aug 17. **Costs:** $3,100. **Contact:** Danu Enterprises, P.O. Box 156, Capitola, CA 95010; 888-476-0543; danu@earthlink.net, [www.danutours.com].

Healing Arts of Bali. Explore traditional healing with Balinese shaman, experience traditional massage, herbal medicines, trance rituals, seminars in local customs and religion, mysticism, sacred masks, plus regular yoga and meditation sessions. Seventeen years experience sharing this life-changing experience. Tour dates include unique island-wide festivals. Three expert Balinese/Western guides.

Dates: Jul 29-Aug 11, Aug 12-26. **Costs:** $2,950. **Contact:** Danu Enterprises, P.O. Box 156, Capitola, CA 95010; 888-476-0543; danu@earthlink.net, [www.danutours.com].

Cooking in Thailand

Classes Provide Both a Structure for Travel and Cultural Insight

By Steven Van Yoder

Cooking school vacations are popular worldwide, but in Thailand they have reached a zenith—there are now more than 100 registered cooking schools, 40 in Bangkok alone. Classes provide both a structure for time spent in Bangkok and insight into Thai culture.

The Oriental Hotel's Thai Cooking School, established over a decade ago in a small, restored colonial building across the river from the Oriental Hotel, is widely considered to be the best in Bangkok. Classes cover the entire range of Thai cuisine: snacks, salads, sauces and curries, noodle dishes, condiments, steamed, fried, and grilled foods, and desserts. In classes held four mornings a week, either as a package or singly, students learn to compose a balanced and visually attractive Thai meal, complete with self-created fruit and vegetable carvings.

The school's curriculum is suitable for both experienced and novice cooks. All lessons cover the basic techniques for making fine food that is authentically Thai.

"Our foods can be divided into three categories," says the instructor, Sansern Gajaseni. "The first group contains popular foods—pad thai and other 'fast food' items often found at streetside stalls and curbside stands. Next are provincial or country foods. These are quick, simple dishes meant to feed a large number of people."

The third type he calls "City Thai," a more refined cuisine that dominates Bangkok restaurants. Combining the subtle sauces of the French kitchen, the freshness of nouvelle cuisine, and the careful presentation of the Japanese chef, this is unquestionably the most challenging of Thai cooking styles and most closely reflects the Asian idea of yin and yang—a quest for a harmonious balance that pervades every facet of Thai life.

Thailand is in a geographically enviable location to create some of the world's most interesting food. From mangos, papaya, and pineapple to spices, herbs, and vegetables, Thailand has a lot to work with in the kitchen. And Thailand's location at the crossroad of Asia has contributed to the eclectic and diverse nature of its cooking.

After steeping yourself in Thai cooking in the morning, forays into the city become more meaningful. Whether you head for a shopping spree or a day of sightseeing at the temples, you will have a greater appreciation of the Thai food—pungent, exotic, and omnipresent—that surrounds you on the streets of Bangkok. The Thais have liberated food from the Western straightjacket of breakfast, lunch, and dinner; they snack constantly throughout the day, believing that the time to eat is "when you are hungry." It is not uncommon to find businessmen in suits dining beside the very poor at plastic tables around a noodle vendor's stall.

Although street dining is not something you can take home with you, lessons at the Thai Cooking School will help you summon Thailand wherever you call home.

Israel

Mideast Conflict Studies. Earn 4 college credits in 3 intensive weeks focusing especially on Palestinian Arab identity. A week in Jerusalem: history since Oslo Accords and the place of religion in the conflict; 2 weeks in The Galilee, living in a Palestinian Israeli community. Planned trips include Dead Sea, Haifa, Golan Heights (circumstances permitting).
Dates: Jun 3-24. **Costs:** $4,560 (4 cr). **Contact:** Friends World Program, Summer 2001, Admissions Office, 239 Montauk Highway, Southampton, NY 11968; 631-287-8474; fw@southampton.liu.edu, [www.southampton.liu.edu].

Italy

ARTE|VITA Travel Art Workshops (Tuscany, Florence, and Venice). Intensive studio art and art history courses in heart of Tuscany: Renaissance techniques in a contemporary context. Experienced teaching artists, prominent guest lecturers, and supportive community. Tenth century villa in Chianti on working vineyard with family-run trattoria, olive groves, gardens, and pool. Visit Florence, Siena, and Tuscan hilltowns. Optional Venice trip.
Dates: Jul-Aug: 2-4 weeks in Tuscany, 3 days in Venice. Call for details. **Costs:** $2,600 (2 weeks in Tuscany). Includes housing (double-occupancy rooms with shared bath; single rooms available for supplemental fee); breakfast, lunch, and traditional Tuscan dinner; ground transportation to and from Florence airport and for 2 organized day trips; reading packet; instruction; and admission fees. Fees do not include airfare, meals during excursions, and individual art supplies. $600 (3 days in Venice). Includes 1-way train fare (Florence-Venice); hotel accommodations in Venice; vaporetto ticket; readings and entrance fees, boat tour. Venice fees do not include meals. Prices subject to change. **Contact:** Jessica Houston, ARTE|VITA Travel Art Workshops, 180 Riverside Blvd., 12L, New York, NY 10069; 212-726-1379, fax 212-580-3272; info@artevita.net, [www.artevita.net].

Biking, Hiking and XC Ski Tours. Specializing in Italy for over 10 years, Ciclismo Classico distills the "Best of Italy," offering more unique Italian destinations than any other active vacation company. Educational, full-service tours for all abilities in Umbria, Tuscany, Piedmont, the Dolomites, Puglia, Sicily, the Amalfi Coast, Cinque Terre, Sardegna, Abruzzo, Campania, Corsica, and Elba. Charming accommodations, expert bilingual guides, cooking demonstrations, wine tastings, support vehicle, detailed route instructions, visits to local festivals, countryside picnics—an unforgettable cultural indulgence.
Dates: Apr-Nov (70 departures). Call for specific dates. **Costs:** $1,995-$3,500. **Contact:** Lauren Hefferon, Director, Ciclismo Classico, 30 Marathon St., Arlington, MA 02474; 800-866-7314 or 781-646-3377; info@ciclismoclassico.com, [www.ciclismoclassico.com].

Centro di Lingua Italiana I Malatesta. In the morning we offer group and individual courses, up to 7 lessons a day. In the afternoon, cultural courses such as History of Art, Italy Today, Italian Cookery, Italian for Business, Italian for Tourism, Language of Libretti, History of Opera, Diction.
Dates: One-, 2-, and 3-week classes year round. **Costs:** Costs vary by duration and type of course, starting at LIT530,000 for 1 week. **Contact:** Centro di Lingua and Cultura Italiana, I Malatesta, G. d'Augusto 144, 47900 Rimini, Italy; 011-390-541-56487, fax 011-390-541-21088; imalatesta@tn.nettuno.it, [www.akeor.it/imalatesta].

Experiencing the Arts in Italy. Florence: art museums, churches, and exquisite cuisine. Lucca: graceful piazzas, Roman ampitheater, cathedrals, palazzi, excursion to Pisa. Siena: artistic treasures, contrada halls, churches, museums, Chianti country excursion. Plus one week's classes with Sienese artists in their studios.
Dates: Jun 16-30. **Costs:** Call for details. **Contact:** Danu Enterprises, P.O. Box 156, Capitola, CA 95010; 888-476-0543; danu@earthlink.net, [www.danutours.com].

Hilltowns of Umbria, Tuscany, and Veneto. Crafts, culture, and cuisine—an exploration of 2 regions in Italy to visit small, quaint hidden villages in the remote countryside, sample regional foods and wines. Small group travel. Art instruction and critiques.
Dates: Jun and Sep. **Costs:** $3,195 accommodations, private bus transportation, 6 meals, all breakfasts, full-time bilingual tour director. **Contact:** Personalized Travel for Artists, Roberta Kritzia, 5455 Sylmar Ave., #902, Sherman Oaks, CA 91401; 818-994-2402, fax 818-994-5529 [www.artisttravel.com].

Horizons in Tuscany. Tuscany is studded with panoramic landscapes, ancient walled villages, olive groves, and vineyards and capped by the gorgeous cities of Florence and Siena. A week of workshops and excursions. As with all Horizons trips, small groups, great food, and places to stay that have charm and character are the bottom line. Lodging in a country inn in the heart of Chianti country. Workshops include Painting, Lampworking/Glass Beads, Mosaics, Silversmithing, Jewelry-Making, Photography, Collage. Structured for the novice and to challenge those more advanced.

Dates: Apr 28-May 5; Oct 13-20. **Costs:** $1,545 (lodging, tuition, field trips, all meals except 2 lunches). Air transport package optional. **Contact:** Jane Sinauer, Horizons to Go, Box 2206, Amherst, MA 01004; 413-549-2900, fax 413-549-5995; horizons@horizons-art.org, [www.horizons-art.org].

Landscape Painting-Etruscan Places. Intensive 1-week landscape painting workshop on location in the heart of the Tuscan countryside. Fees include accommodations, meals, workshop, and instruction, field trips to Siena and Volterra, most materials. All levels of experience welcome.

Dates: Eight 1-week sessions May-Oct. **Costs:** $1,375-$1,775 depending on occupancy (2000). **Contact:** Etruscan Places, Joe Vinson/Maddine Insalaco; 212-780-3216; info@landscapepainting.com, [www.landscapepainting.com].

Study Italian in Florence or Tuscan Town. Study Italian in a 16th century Renaissance palace in the center of Florence or in a classic Tuscan town just 30 minutes from the sea. Koiné Center's professional language teachers and small class sizes encourage active participa-tion by each student. Cultural program, guided excursions, choice of accommodations including host families.

Dates: Year round; starting dates each month. **Costs:** Two-week intensive program $325; 3 weeks $395; homestay accommodations from $220 for 2 weeks. **Contact:** In North America: Talking Traveler, 800-274-6007, fax 503-274-9004. In Italy: Dr. Andrea Moradei, Koiné Center, Via Pandolfini 27, 50122 Firenze, Italy; 011-390-55-213881, [www.koinecenter.com].; homestay@teleport.com, [www.talkingtraveler.org].

Tuscany in Watercolor. Nine days watercolor, painting on the Tuscan/Umbrian border. Includes demonstrations of tempera and fresco painting, gilding, and mosaic. Fly from London. ABTA registered travel agent. Tutor: Ian King.

Dates: May **Costs:** Contact sponsor. **Contact:** Angela Dammery, Broadland Arts Centre, 43 The Crossways, Westcliff on Sea, Essex SS0 8PU, U.K.

Japan

Japanese Culture. Earn 3-6 college credits in a unique setting while acquiring useful skills. Take "Teaching ESL for the Nonprofessional" (3 cr), complemented by "Traditional Japanese Arts and Cutlure" (3 cr). Please note these are introductory classes, designed to familiarize students with basic concepts in the field. Does not meet certification requirements.

Dates: May-Jun. **Costs:** $4,200 (3 cr). **Contact:** Friends World Program, Summer 2001, Admissions Office, 239 Montauk Highway, Southampton, NY 11968; 631-287-8474; fw@southampton.liu.edu, [www.southampton.liu.edu/fw].

The Japan-American Student Conference. The Japan-American Student Conference is a 66-year-old nonprofit educational and cultural exchange program for university students from the U.S. and Japan. Thirty-two American and 32 Japanese students spend an intense month of living, studying, and traveling together.

Dates: Jul-Aug. **Costs:** $1,900. **Contact:** Gretchen Donaldson, Japan-America Student Conference, 606 18th St., NW, 2nd Fl., Washington, DC 20006; 202-289-4231, fax 202-789-8265; jascinc@jasc.org, [www.jasc.org].

Mexico

Center for Bilingual Multicultural Studies. Intensive semester or intensive Spanish language programs for executives, bilingual teachers, healthcare professionals, seniors, nurses, high school students. Group-5 system, 40 class hours per week include Spanish class, Latin American courses and lectures, housing with Mexican host family or guest residence; excursions to historical and archaeological sites. Students enrolled may attend the university courses at no additional cost.

Dates: Year round starting every Monday. **Costs:** Registration fee $100; tuition $200 per week; lodging $168 per week, Plan A. **Contact:** Javier Espinosa, President, San Jeronimo #304, Col. Tlaltenango, Cuernavaca, Mor. 62179, Mexico; 011-527-317-10-87, fax 011-527-3-17-05-33; U.S. 800-932-20-68.; admission@bilingual-center.com.mx, [www.bilingual-center.com].

Horizons in Mexico. This program, in what many consider to be the folk art capital of Mexico, will bring you to colorful village markets, introduce you to Mexican artists, and immerse you in this beautiful heartland of a still very much alive pre-Columbian civilization with field trips to numerous archaeological sites in the company of an expert guide. Lodging in a lovely small hotel with wonderful food in the middle of historic Spanish colonial Oaxaca City.

Dates: Jan 4-11. **Costs:** $1,345 includes lodging, meals, guides, excursions. **Contact:** Jane Sinauer, Horizons to Go, Box 2206, Amherst, MA 01004; 413-549-2900, fax 413-549-5995; horizons@horizons-art.org, [www.horizons-art.org].

Intensive Spanish in Cuernavaca.
Cuauhnahuac, founded in 1972, offers a variety of intensive and flexible programs geared to individual needs. Six hours of classes daily with no more than 4 students to a class. Housing with Mexican families who really care about you. Cultural conferences, excursions, and special classes for professionals. College credit available.

Dates: Year round. New classes begin every Monday. **Costs:** $70 registration fee; $680 for 4 weeks tuition; housing $18 per night. **Contact:** Marcia Snell, 519 Park Dr., Kenilworth, IL 60043; 800-245-9335, fax 847-256-9475; mexmarcia@hotmail.com, [www.cuauhnahuac.edu.mx].

Morocco

Culinary Tour. Get to the heart of Moroccan culture through an exploration of its cuisine. Discover the secrets of Moroccan dishes, hear talks in culinary topics, and visit the fabulous and famous souks to learn about herbs, spices, and condiments used on Moroccan cookery. Also see classic tourist sights and have ample free time to shop and explore on your own. Escorted by Joan Peterson, author of *Eat Smart in Morocco* and contributor to *Transitions Abroad.*

Dates: May 21-Jun 5. **Costs:** $3,195 double occ. Airfare included from JFK. Single supplement $610. Those who wish to obtain their own international airfare tickets deduct $800. **Contact:** Joan Peterson, 608-233-5488; joanp@ginkgopress.com.

Nepal

The Kathmandu Valley: An Arts and Cultural Odyssey. Nestled between India and Tibet, Nepal is uniquely rich with thriving cultural and artistic traditions. This ancient Himalayan Kingdom was only opened up to travelers in 1951, and it remains a country that is still mysterious and unspoiled by tourism. Based in the Kathmandu Valley—enjoy a rich array of excursions within Kathmandu itself, and the magical cities of Bhakatapur and Patan, as well as Nagarkot—a hilltop village, surrounded by stunning views of terraced farmland, with the Himalayans as a backdrop. All this and an

opportunity to meet Nepalese artists in their homes, as well, giving you an insider's appreciation of this wonderful country.

Dates: Apr 20-May 4. **Costs:** $2,985 (includes lodging, tuition and field trips, all meals except 1 lunch, 2 dinners, tuition). Optional air package. **Contact:** Jane Sinauer, Horizons to Go, Box 2206, Amherst, MA 01004; 413-549-2900, fax 413-549-5995; horizons@horizons-art.com, [www.horizons-art.org].

New Zealand

Albatross Encounters. Tours to view the albatross and other species of ocean-going birds off the coast of Kaikoura, NZ. Forty out of 92 species of New Zealand's sea birds are commonly sighted here. We provide a unique opportunity for "close up" views of these magnificent sea birds.

Dates: Year round. Weather permitting. **Costs:** NZ$60 adult, NZ$35 per child under 15 years (1999). **Contact:** Lynette Buurman, Manager, Albatross Encounter, 58 West End, Kaikoura 8280, New Zealand; 011-64-3-319-6777, fax 011-64-3-319-6534; info@oceanwings.co.nz, [www.oceanwings.co.nz].

Pacific

Custom Made Individual and Small Group Tours. Travel for the environmentally concerned and intellectually curious.

Dates: Call for details. **Costs:** Call for details. **Contact:** Billie Foreman, Ecotours International, P.O. Box 1853, Pebble Beach, Ca 93953; Tel./fax 831-625-3135; bforeman@netpipe.com.

Poland

Culinary Tour. Enjoy a culinary exploration of Poland's delicious cuisine and discover the secrets of Polish cookery from professional chefs and home cooks. Visit the bustling markets. See the major tourist sights yet still have time to shop and relax. Lodgings include several elegant palaces and castles in tranquil and picturesque park-like settings. All meals included. Escorted by Joan Peterson, *Transitions Abroad* contributor and author of *Eat Smart in Poland.*

Dates: May 9-24, 2001. **Costs:** $2,659 double occ. Includes roundtrip airfare from Chicago/Detroit/DC/NY/Boston/Atlanta. **Contact:** Joan Peterson, 608-233-5488; joanp@ginkgopress.com.

Romania

Transylvanian Traditions. Tour Bucharest and see a Romanian Orthodox church, outdoor village museum, and Ceaucescue's former palace.

CHOOSING A PHOTOGRAPHY TOUR
A CHECKLIST TO HELP YOU MAKE YOUR CHOICE

By Kim Lipker

If taking a photography tour has crossed your mind, don't hesitate for another moment.

A photography tour gives you a hands-on opportunity to develop or polish your skills as a photographer, brings you together with individuals with similar interests, and gives you a unique perspective on a destination you may have visited many times.

Whether you are a professional photographer or a novice with your first camera, there is a trip for you. Tour operators and photography instructors offer a range of custom-designed tours that cater to every traveler's needs. Here's a checklist to help you make your choice.

Expectations. Ask yourself why you are going on a photography tour. Are you expecting technical lessons? Do you want plenty of free time to explore on your own? Are you prepared to spend hours indoors in critiques of your work, or would you rather develop your film at home?

This past October I took my second photography tour of Ireland, this time with Taylor & O'Neill and Focus Adventures. I went on the trip knowing exactly what I wanted to accomplish: to come away with as many written and photographed images of Ireland as possible and to take side trips to off-the-beaten-path places.

Photographic Instruction. Once you know what you want out of a photography tour, start doing your research.

Karen Gordon Schulman with Focus Adventures in Steamboat Springs, Colorado is a teacher with a great amount of technical knowledge. Her trips and workshops focus more on the art of seeing, an approach that appealed to me.

Keep in mind that some photography instructors may ask you to complete a variety of assignments, drop film at night, and spend time in critique the next day. Some instructors may also expect you to have a certain level of experience. Don't be intimidated by this, but be honest about your skills. An instructor like Schulman will take students from those with their first point-and-shoot camera to professional photographers.

Ask what your group size and group ability will be. A tour on a bus with 50 people will be a different experience from one in a van with five people.

Tour Arrangements. If you are going on a trip to Ireland, for example, you want to travel with someone who knows Ireland. Some photography instructors may handle their own destination details, but others let the travel experts handle the particulars. Since I wanted to learn as much as possible about the country through my photography and my writing, I needed a tour operator who was knowledgeable about Ireland.

Clare O'Neill at Taylor & O'Neill in St. Paul, a photographer herself, works with individuals and small groups in planning trips to Ireland. O'Neill has spent her lifetime traveling to Ireland and knows much about the local history and color.

Photography Gear. If your photography instructor does not have a pre-trip checklist or equipment requirements, ask her to put some information together for you. Focus Adventures and Taylor & O'Neill provided my group with an extensive checklist and general information that were invaluable packing tools for the trip.

Schulman recommends that you err on the high side and pack extra film. Her general rule is at least three rolls of 36-exposure film per day. Most instructors will let you use whatever film you want but they will also give you pointers as to what brand and exposure to buy.

Always check your photography gear and bring the owner's manual and spare parts and batteries. Some instructors require a tripod, filters, and flashes. Ask to be sure.

Be prepared with cleaning accessories, notebook, pens, and plastic zipper bags. If you are going to sell your photographs some day, bring model and property releases as well. Contact your photography instructor or tour guide before leaving if you have any questions.

For information on Taylor & O'Neill see [www.tayloroneill.com]. Focus Adventure can be found on the web at [www.focusadventures.com]. To find photography tours I usually consult Shaw Guides, Inc. [www.photoworkshops.shawguides.com] or *Photographers Market, Writer's Digest Books* (workshop or professional organizations section).

Stop at Lazarea Castle and Bicaz George. Travel to Csango villages, Sighisoara, Korund, Cluj, and villages where people still live by treasured traditional customs. End in Budapest with a sunset dinner cruise on the Danube.

Dates: May 9-23. **Costs:** $3,370. **Contact:** Cross-Culture, Inc., 52 High Point Dr., Amherst, MA 01002-1224; 800-491-1148, 413-256-6303, fax 413-253-2303; travel@crosscultureinc.com, [www.crossculture.com].

Russia

Inside Russia Sojourns. Ideal for the traveler interested in truly experiencing the Russian way of life. Offers a variety of ways to interface with Russians—from homestays with Russian hosts, to deluxe custom-designed tours of St. Petersburg led by friendly Russians eager to share their city with you.

Dates: Year round. **Costs:** $1,500 and up. **Contact:** Walton Conway, Golden Cockerel Crafts, 4697 Rich Mountain Rd., Boone, NC 28607; 800-892-5409, 828-297-4653 [www.gccrafts.com].

South America

Amazon Canopy Walkway Special. Three days and 2 nights at ExplorNapo Lodge and Explorama's Canopy Walkway, the world's longest walkway. One-hundred mile river ride on Amazon and Napo rivers, meals, lodging, guided excursions to Canopy Walkway, Ethnobotanical Garden, backwater lakes, pink dolphins, piranha fishing, village visits, birdwatching, and hiking in primary rainforests.

Dates: Every Friday and Saturday in 2001. **Costs:** $395 per person in twin room. **Contact:** Peter Jenson, Explorama Lodges, 340 Ave. La Marina, Box 446, Iquitos, Peru; 011-51-94-25-3301, fax 011-51-94-25-2533; amazon@explorama.com, [www.explorama.com].

Spain

Horizons in Seville and Andalusia. Andalusia—Moorish poets called it an earthly paradise. From the grandeur of the Alhambra, Seville's Alcazar, and the great mosque of Cordoba to mazes of white-washed streets, orange trees and flower-bedecked courtyards—a unique experience in southern Spain. A week of workshops and excursions. As with all Horizons trips, small groups, great food, and places to stay that have charm and character are the bottom line. Lodging in a charming Seville hotel. Workshops include Tile Making and Ceramics, Painting-structured for the novice and to challenge those more advanced.

Dates: Jan 15-Feb 1, 2002. **Costs:** $1,545 (lodging, tuition, field trips, all meals except 1 luncheon, 2 dinners). **Contact:** Jane Sinauer, Horizons to Go, Box 2206, Amherst, MA; 413-549-2900, fax 413-549-5995; horizons@horizons-art.org, [www.horizons-art.org].

Sweden

Uppsala Int'l. Summer Session. Sweden's oldest academic summer program focuses on learning the Swedish language. All levels from beginners to advanced. Additional courses in Swedish history, social institutions, arts in Sweden, Swedish pop music, Swedish film. Excursions every Friday. Extensive evening program includes both lectures and entertainment. Single rooms in dormitories. Apartments at extra cost. Open to both students and adults, who have university eligibility. Credit possible.

Dates: Jun 23-Aug 16; Jun 23-Jul 19; Jul 21-Aug 16, Jul 7-Aug 16. **Costs:** SEK24,400 (approx. $2,300) for the 8-week session, SEK13,200 (approx. $1,250) for the 4-week session. Includes room, some meals, all classes, evening and excursion program. **Contact:** Dr. Nelleke van Oevelen-Dorrestijn, Uppsala Int'l. Summer Session, Box 1972, 751 49 Uppsala, Sweden; 011-31-13-521-23-88 or 011-46-18-10-23-70, fax 011-31-13-521-2389; nelleke.vanoevelen@uiss.org, [www.uiss.org].

Turkey

Culinary Tour. Journey on an exotic culinary odyssey through Byzantine, Ottoman, and modern Turkey. Sample authentic regional cuisine in homes, unpretentious eateries, and elegant restaurants. Watch some of the world's best chefs create materpieces, including Ottoman court classics. Visit wineries and vibrant, bustling markets for exotic spices. Tour also includes visits to historical sites and a boat trip on the Mediterranean. Escorted by Joan Peterson, author of *Eat Smart in Turkey* and *Transitions Abroad* contributor.

Dates: Oct 9-22, 2001. **Costs:** $3,300 double occ. land only (includes 3 domestic flights), $500 single supplement. **Contact:** Joan Peterson, 608-233-5488; joanp@ginkgopress.com.

Gems of the Aegean. Small-group programs to the Southwestern region of Turkey geared for the independent, active, and culturally curious traveler. Escorted by intercultural relations specialists who have a passion for adventure and cultural learning. Program includes transatlantic in-country airfare, accommodations, 2 daily meals, guided excursions to historical sites, boat trips, activities, and more. **Dates:** 2002: 11 consecutive day programs. Limited dates Mar-May, Sep-Oct; weekly dates Jun-Aug. **Costs:** $2,500 double occupancy Mar-May, Oct $2,800 double occupancy Jun-Sep (early booking discount available), $225 single supplement. **Contact:** Patty Brownlee, Global Immersions, Inc., 102 Marshall St., Watertown, MA 02472; Tel: 617-924-2712 or 888-924-2712, fax 617-924-2760; travel@globalimmersions.com, [www.globalimmersions.com].

The Wine and Dine Tour. A combination wine tasting and gourmet tour to sample wonderful Turkish cuisine, take a cooking class, and visit the underrated but excellent Turkish wineries. Package includes all meals. Witness the preparation of *meze* (appetizers), kebab, baklava, and other delicacies. So you don't forget the ingredients, a Turkish guidebook to the cuisine is included. Sightseeing en route. Escorted by Joan Peterson, author of *Eat Smart in Turkey* and contributor to *Transitions Abroad*. **Dates:** Sep 23-Oct 7, 2001. **Costs:** $2,200 includes domestic flight, double occ. Airfare not included. $300 single supplement. **Contact:** Joan Peterson, 608-233-5488; joanp@ginkgopress.com.

United Kingdom and Ireland

An Irish Idyll. From historic Dublin to mountain landscapes, fields of green to quaint villages and dramatic ocean views—this evocative country has a beauty all its own. A week of workshops and excursions. As with all Horizons trips, small groups, great food, and places to stay that have charm and character are the bottom line. Workshops include Painting, Silversmithing and Jewelry Design, Photography, Flameworking/Glass Beads—structured for the novice and to challenge those more advanced. **Dates:** May 12-19; Sep 15-22. **Costs:** $1,545 (lodging, tuition, field trips, all meals except 2 lunches). Air transport package optional. **Contact:** Jane Sinauer, Horizons to Go, Box 2206, Amherst, MA 01004; 413-549-2900, fax 413-549-5995; horizons@horizons-art.org, [www.horizons-art.org].

British Culture and Institutions. On-site examination of British ideas and culture, media, political and legal institutions, in addition to usual tourist attractions. London-based, with trips to Cantebury, Hastings, Brighton, Salisbury, Stonehenge, and Bath. Retracing steps of Jack the Ripper, Sherlock Holmes, Dickens, Rumpole, Beckett, Hobbes, More, Mill, Churchill, etc. New: Tours of *London Times* and BBC. **Dates:** Jul 20-Aug 10. **Costs:** $3,100 all-inclusive, includes airfare. **Contact:** Dr. Walter Mead, International Studies Program, Campus Box 6120, Illinois State Univ., Normal, IL 61790-6120; 309-829-7009 or 309-438-5365, fax 309-438-3987; wbmead@ilstu.edu

Diversity Issues: London and Ireland. Exploration of diversity in the U.K. in 3 intense weeks. Opportunity for 6 college credits. Experiential focus with community visits and meetings with local leaders. Two weeks in London followed by a week in Northern Ireland for a look at peace and reconciliation efforts. Visits integrated with seminars and readings. **Dates:** Jun-Jul. **Costs:** $4,360 includes tuition, travel from NY, room and board. **Contact:** Friends World Summer 2001, LIU, 239 Montauk Hwy., Southampton, NY 11968; 631-287-8474, fax 631-287-8463; fw@southampton.liunet.edu, [www.southampton.liu.edu/academic/summer2001/summer.htm].

Edinburgh Univ. Summer Courses. Summer courses for adults at the Univ. of Edinburgh. Subjects include archaeology, literature, Scottish culture, creative writing, nature, environment, drama, film, music, Edinburgh festival arts, and philosophy. Accommodations and social program available. **Dates:** Late Jun-end Aug. **Costs:** Variable. Please contact for details. **Contact:** Ursula Michels, International Summer Courses, CCE, Univ. of Edinburgh, 11 Buccleuch Pl., Edinburgh EH8 9LW, Scotland, U.K.; 011-44-0-131-650-3073, 011-44-0-131-662-0783, fax 011-44-0-131-667-6097; cce@ed.ac.uk, [www.cce.ed.ac.uk/summer].

Explore Medieval England. Bed and breakfast in a 200-year-old converted Kentish barn. Explore Sissinghurst, Bodiam, and Leeds castles; Rye, Canterbury, Tenterden. See the sights of medieval England. **Dates:** Year round. **Costs:** Contact sponsor. **Contact:** Bethersden Old Barn B and B; 011-44-870-740-1180, fax 011-44-1233-820-547; barn@ukpages.net, [www.ukpages.net/barn.htm].

Irish Theater Summer School in Ireland. Gaiety School of Acting Summer Program. Study Irish Theater in Ireland, 1 month program (July). Practical acting classes. Beckett, O'Casey, Friel, and Synge. Academic and extensive social program. Ireland's premier drama school. Founder Joe Dowling AD Guthrie Theater.

MOUNTAIN BIKING THE ALPS

COMBINE A VACATION ABROAD WITH A GRATIFYING PHYSICAL ACTIVITY

By Mark Diorio

Mountain biking is the ultimate way to combine a vacation abroad with a gratifying physical activity. The rider is intimately exposed to the people of the region and to its customs, beliefs, and culture. A network of huts spaced along the trails are places of temporary communal living for "intimate strangers."

The practical benefits of alpine huts are obvious: The first is cost; the average price is around $15 dollars a night, and the accommodations are much more pleasant than camping. The huts also serve wonderful food at a reasonable cost, so cooking utensils and supplies do not need to be packed. An additional benefit is that the bedding is included (except for your own sleeping bag liner, which is required), so all that the traveler needs to bring are personal belongings.

The starting point of most trails is usually near a town and can be reached by train, but locating the cycling trails takes planning. (I recently found a web site, [www.maps.com], that carries an English version of the Alps Region map by the company Reise Und Verkehrsverlad.) Other good Alps maps are produced by Michelin. I found mine at a local bookstore. Since the biking trails are shared with hikers, books such as the Sierra Club's Adventuring in the Alps are useful. This book, and many other alternative travel books are available from the Adventurous Traveler Bookstore [www.adventuroustraveler.com]. Adventurous Traveler also has books on using the huts. Additional hut information can be found at the GORP web site, [www.gorp.com/gorp/activity/Europe/Alps.htm]. The Austrian government has a web site with advice on mountain biking and general hut courtesies [www.austrianalps.environment.gov.au/codes/bikecode.html].

If finding the network of trails is a concern, consider using a touring company. I booked my trip through AlpsTours, [www.alpstours.de], based in Munich, Germany. The cost of the trip was under $600 for eight days, and that included all lodging and some meals. They provide a guide and make housing arrangements; the riders are responsible for everything else. Once the trek begins, there is no further assistance from the company. An American presence is rare (I was the only American that ever rode with Alps Tours).

Dates: Jul 2-27. **Costs:** $3,200 includes accommodations. **Contact:** Patrick Sutton, Gaiety School of Acting, Meeting House Sq., Temple Bar, Dublin 2, Ireland; 011-353-1-6799277, fax 011-353-1-6799568; gaiety.school@indigo.ie, [www.gaietyschool.com].

Kiltartan Hedge School. An informal but comprehensive exploration of W.B. Yeats' Coole Park and Ballylee writings in the landscape that inspired them. Attention is paid to the influence of local folklore and the writings of Lady Gregory.

Dates: Jul 7-14. **Costs:** Irish £50. **Contact:** Dr. Louis Muinzer, 33 Jameson St., Belfast BT7 2GU, Northern Ireland; Tel./fax 011-44-28-90649010

Landscape Painting in the Burren. Professional art tutors take painters outdoors on location for sketching and painting in the famous Burren country of North Clare: rockscapes, seascapes, streetscapes. Media include oils, watercolors, pastel, gouache, acrylics. Accommodations in Irish Tourist Board approved B and B. Studio, materials, and equipment available.

Dates: May-Sep weekly and weekends. **Costs:** From $450 per week. Includes tuition, accommodations, and full breakfast. **Contact:** Christine O'Neill, The Burren Painting Centre, Lisdoonvarna, Co. Clare, Ireland; 011-353-65-7074208, fax 011-353-65-7074435; isclo@indigo.ie, [http://indigo.ie/~isclo].

Special Interest Vacations. Some 50 theme itineraries for individuals or small groups covering such interests as antiques and collectibles, gardens, literary associations, railways, art galleries, theater, stately homes, culinary courses, American heritage, etc. **Dates:** Year round. **Costs:** Land costs from approx. $120 per day. **Contact:** Cheryl Hedgpeth, Sterling Tours, 2707 Congress St., Suite 2-G, San Diego, CA 92110; 800-727-4359, 619-299-3010, fax 619-299-5728; sterlingtours@worldnet.att.net, [www.sterlingtours.com].

Summer Studies in London. An exceptional opportunity to study alongside U.K. students and enjoy a taste of British academic life. The summer program offers 75 credit-bearing courses across a broad range of subject areas including humanities, drama, criminology, health, and business. **Dates:** Early Jul-mid-Aug. **Costs:** Approx. $3,415 includes tuition, orientation, meal plan, accommodations, social programs. **Contact:** Anita Mascarenhas, Summer School Office, Middlesex Univ., Trent Park Campus, Bramley Rd., London N14 4YZ, U.K.; 011-44-20-8411-5782, fax 011-44-20-8411-2297; sschool@mdx.ac.uk, [www.summer.mdx.ac.uk].

The Heatherley School of Fine Art. Fine art courses. Painting, drawing, sculpture, printing, watercolor, pastels. Open studio. Foundation/portfolio. Diploma in portraiture. Continuing studies. Diploma in sculpture. Summer courses. Part-time and full-time. **Dates:** Contact organization for details. **Costs:** Contact organization for details. **Contact:** The School Office, The Heatherley School of Fine Art, 80 Upcerne Rd., Chelsea, London SW10 0SH, U.K.; 011-44-207-351-4190, fax 011-44-207-351-6945; info@heatherleys.org, [www.heatherleys.org].

The Joe Mooney Summer School. Traditional Irish Music, Song, and Dance and daily workshops in fiddle, flute, tin whistle, uilleann pipes, button accordion, piano accordion, harp, banjo, concertina, bodhran, traditional singing, and set dancing. Evening lectures, recitals, concerts and céilthe. **Dates:** Jul 20-27. **Costs:** EURO 40. **Contact:** Nancy Woods, Joe Mooney Summer School, Drumshanbo, Co. Leitrim, Ireland; 011-353-78-41213; nwoods@ie.

Univ. of Cambridge Summer Schools. Intensive study in Cambridge as part of an international community. Plenary lectures and special subject courses are offered, together with evening activities and excursions. Both multi-disciplinary and specialist-subject programs are available. **Dates:** Jul and Aug. **Costs:** Tuition from £510-£740, accommodations from £285-£1,040 (2001 prices, 2002 TBA). **Contact:** International Division, Univ. of Cambridge, Madingley Hall, Cambridge CB3 8AQ, U.K.; 011-44-1954-280398, fax 011-44-1954-280200; intenq@cam.ac.uk, [www.cont-ed.cam.ac.uk/IntSummer].

Walking in Ireland. Southwest Walks Ireland offer hassle-free, fun-filled, and relaxing walking holidays. We pride ourselves in our ability to immerse people in the nature and culture of this wonderful land. The holidays we offer are guided, self-guiding, and special interest. **Dates:** Apr-Oct. **Costs:** From $300. **Contact:** John Ahern, Southwest Walks Ireland, 40 Ashe St., Tralee, Co. Kerry, Ireland; 011-44-353-066-7128733, fax 011-44-353-066-7128762; swwi@iol.ie, [www.irishtourism.com/swwi.htm].

Walking Tours in England and Scotland. Walking and hiking tours with sightseeing in the beautiful countrysides of England and Scotland. Local guides and talks by experts. Lodging at splendid country hotels and inns with sumptuous food. All meals and all sightseeing included. Since 1985.

Dates: Apr-Oct, weekly. **Costs:** $1,700-$1,900, 7 to 8 days, all inclusive (1999). **Contact:** Seth Steiner, English Lakeland Ramblers; 800-724-8801, fax 212-979-5342; Britwalks@aol.com, [www.ramblers.com].

Worldwide

Active Journeys. Cycling, walking, hiking, sea kayaking tours available in Europe, Canada, Asia, Latin America, and the Pacific. Independent and escorted tours as well in Bhutan, Ireland, France, Switzerland, Italy, France, and Austria.

Dates: Year round. **Costs:** From $750 per week. **Contact:** Active Journeys, 4891 Dundas St., W., Toronto, Canada M9A 1B2; 800-597-5594, fax 416-236-4790; info@activejourneys.com, [www.activejourneys.com].

Anderson Ranch Arts Center Summer Workshops and Field Expeditions. Year-round field expeditions take participants to places that inspire them through contact with other cultures, landscapes, and disciplines. Regular expeditions include trips to Nepal, Jamaica, Ireland, and the American Southwest.

Dates: Jamaica (painting) Apr 21-29, (photography and painting) Nov 3-11; Nepal (ceramics) Jan 30-Feb 20. **Costs:** Contact organization for details. **Contact:** Anderson Ranch Arts Center, P.O. Box 5598, Snowmass Village, CO 81615; 970-923-3181, fax 970-923-3871; info@andersonranch.org; [www.andersonranch.org].

California Academy of Sciences Travel Program. Academy-led tours place participants in the context of specifically chosen natural environments. Teaching, understanding, and conservation are our goals.

Dates: Programs vary in length from 7 days to 3 weeks. **Costs:** Approx. $2,000-$10,000. **Contact:** Kathie Harvey, Academy Travel Office, 965 Brewster Ave., Redwood City, CA 94063; 800-853-9372, fax 650-365-6303; calacademy@hcptravel.com.

Cultural Adventures in Russia, Central Asia, and Beyond. Customized trips for individuals and special interest groups are our specialty. Destination specialists offering over 35 sensational "off the beaten path" small group adventures and 50 independent travel itineraries to choose from (Russia, Central Asia, Mongolia, China). On-site offices in Russia, Ukraine, Uzbekistan. Call for a free catalog featuring the legendary Trans-Siberian Railway, the Silk Route, Mongolia, and more.

Dates: Year round for custom and independent programs; scheduled departures for tours. **Costs:** Homestays from $40 a night. Full escorted tours from $1,850. **Contact:** MIR (the Russian word meaning "peace" and "world"), 85 S. Washington St., Suite 210, Seattle, WA 98104; 800-424-7289 or 206-624-7289, fax 206-624-7360; info@mircorp.org, [www.mircorp.com].

Cultural Immersion Tours. Unique small group, cultural adventures in Japan, China, and Scotland with emphasis on arts, architecture, and interaction with local culture.

Dates: May, Oct, and Jul (2-week trips). **Costs:** $3,985-$5,300. **Contact:** Journeys East, P.O. Box 1161, Middletown, CA 95461; 800-527-2612, fax 707-987-4831; trips@journeyseast.com, [www.journeyseast.com].

Custom Group Tours. Student, adventure, vacation, senior, and theme group travel arrangements worldwide. Interesting and exciting destinations are easy with our custom itineraries and careful planning.

Dates: Year round. **Costs:** Vary. **Contact:** Ralph Joksch, Cruise Tours, 2201 Pillsbury Rd., B-1A,Chico, CA 95926; 800-248-6542, fax 530-895-8255; cruise-tours@pobox.com.

First Choice for Home Exchange. Vacation Homes Unlimited offers the ideal travel alternative for people who want not only to see an area but to experience it. Cut your travel costs dramatically and join the thousands who have found home exchange to be comfortable, convenient, and earth friendly. Directory and Internet memberships available.

Dates: Year round. **Costs:** $65 per year directory membership, $30 per year Internet membership, $95 per year directory and Internet. **Contact:** Anne Pottinger, Vacation Homes Unlimited, P.O. Box 1562, Santa Clarita, CA 91386; 800-VHU-SWAP, 661-298-0376, fax 661-298-0576; admin@exchangehomes.com, [www.exchangehomes.com].

Global Volunteers. The nation's premier short-term service programs for people of all ages and backgrounds. Assist mutual international understanding through ongoing development projects throughout Africa, Asia, the Caribbean, Europe, the Pacific, North and South America. Programs of 1, 2, and 3 weeks range from natural resource preservation, light construction, and painting to teaching English, assisting with health care, and nurturing at-risk children. No special skills or foreign languages are required.

Dates: Over 150 teams year round. **Costs:** Tax-deductible program fees range from $450 to $2,395. Airfare not included. **Contact:** Global Volunteers, 375 E. Little Canada Rd., St. Paul, MN 55117; 800-487-1074, fax 651-482-0915; email@globalvolunteers.org, [www.globalvolunteers.org].

Home Exchange Vacations. Swap your home for all the comforts of another home (for free!). Home Base Holidays (est. 1985 London) posts new exchange offers daily on the web site with a particularly large choice in England. Three directories are also published annually. Enjoy the best bargain accommodations-and a vacation to remember.

Dates: All year (directories published Nov, Mar, and Jun). **Costs:** 1) Internet only £38; 2) Internet and directories £70. **Contact:** Lois Sealey, Home Base Holidays, 7 Park Ave., London N13 5PG, England; 011-44-20-8886-8752, fax 011-44-20-8245-9532; homeexchange@btinternet.com, [www.homebase-hols.com].

Independent Homestay Program. Independent Homestay Programs focus on the homestay experience. These programs are ideal for independent teen and adult travelers desiring full immersion in another culture for a short period of time.

Dates: One to 4 weeks, year round. **Costs:** Approx. $800-$1,300. **Contact:** Outbound Department, 17 N. 2nd Ave., St. Charles, IL 60174; 888-227-6231, fax 630-377-2307; info@cci-exchange.com, [www.cci-exchange.com].

Member's Travel Program. The Minneapolis Institute of Arts Member's Travel Program offers a wide variety of opportunities to explore the world's most important examples of art and architecture. Ranging in length from 1 day to several weeks, our tours provide an indepth, behind the scenes exploration of both international and domestic destinations.

Dates: Vary. **Costs:** Vary. **Contact:** Diane Hilliard, The Minneapolis Institute of Arts, Member's Travel Program; 800-229-8407, 612-333-1440; diane.hilliard@lander.com.

Nature Expeditions International. Educational soft adventure programs since 1973. Trips to over 20 countries in Africa, Asia, Australia, and Latin America. Full range of adventure cruising programs. Each expedition offers upscale accommodations, unique cultural activities, and 3-4 different soft adventures. Specializing in creating distinctive itineraries led by expert guides. Flexible, guaranteed departure dates.

Dates: Year round. **Costs:** Call for details. **Contact:** Nature Expeditions, International, 7860 Peters Rd., Suite F-103, Plantation, FL 33324; 800-869-0639 or 954-693-8852, fax 954-693-8854; info@naturexp.com, [www.naturexp.com].

Painting Workshop Tours for Artists. A variety of painting workshop (noncredit) tours for artists, each led by a qualified and experienced art teacher who provides workshop instruction, demonstrations, and critiques along the way. Painting is outdoors, usually with studio available in case of bad weather. Accommodations in small, local hotels, rooms with private bathrooms. In 2000 locations include Mexico, France, Italy, England, and Ireland.

Dates: Feb-Sep. **Costs:** Vary. **Contact:** Webster's World, P.O. Box 2057, Falls Church, VA 22042; 800-952-9641, fax 703-836-0308; websterw@patriot.net, [www.webstersworld.net].

PAX Abroad. Offers opportunities for high school students; homestay programs in Ecuador, France, Germany, and Spain for 1 semester or full year. Some custom academic programs available. Summer adventures to Australia, Ecuador, Spain, and Brazil for soccer.

Dates: Semester or full year. Summer. **Costs:** Varies. **Contact:** PAX Abroad, PAX-Program of Academic Exchange, 71 Arch St., Greenwich, CT 06830; 800-555-6211, fax 203-629-0486; academicexchange@pax.org, [www.pax.org].

Penn Summer Abroad. Academic programs granting Univ. of Pennsylvania credits. Courses focusing on language, culture, economics, theater, anthropology, cinema, art history, traditional folk medicine, performing arts, and religion. Several programs offer homestays, some offer internships.

Dates: Mid-May-late Aug (2-8 weeks). **Costs:** Tuition: $1,695 per course. Living costs vary. **Contact:** Elizabeth Sachs, Penn Summer Abroad, College of General Studies, Univ. of Pennsylvania, 3440 Market St., Suite 100, Philadelphia, PA 19104-3335; 215-898-5738, fax 215-573-2053; summerabroad@sas.upenn.edu, [www.sas.upenn.edu/CGS].

Photo Explorer Tours. Custom tours to the world's best photographic opportunities for small groups of amateur and professional photographers.

Dates: Year round. **Costs:** Vary. **Contact:** Dennis Cox, Photo Explorer Tours; 800-315-4462, fax 734-996-1481; decoxphoto@aol.com, [www.photoexplorertours.com].

Sugarcraft Tuition. Professional Sugarcraft tuition. All levels from beginners to advanced. Royal icing, sugarpaste, floral, modeling, novelty, pastillage, and many others aspects of Sugarcraft. One-, 2- or 5-day courses or individual tuition. Top tutors and friendly environment.

Dates: One- and 2-day tuition year round. Five-day schools in Mar and Jul. **Costs:** £65 per day or £350 for 5-day schools. **Contact:** Course Coordinator, Squires Kitchen School, 3 Waverley Ln., Farnham, Surrey GU9 8BB, U.K. 011-44-1252-711749, fax 011-44-1252-714714; school@squires-group.co.uk, [www.squires-group.co.uk, www.squires-shop.com].

WorldTeach. Teach in Africa, Asia, Latin America. Based at Harvard Univ. for 15 years, WorldTeach provides opportunities for individuals to make a meaningful contribution to international education by living and working as volunteer teachers in developing countries in Africa, Asia, and Latin America. Offers 8-week summer teaching programs to qualified adults 18 years of age and older, involving either English or basic computer/internet instruction. WorldTeach also offers 1 year and semester teaching placements for college graduates.

Dates: Jun 20-Aug 20 (summer); long-term programs depart through the year. **Costs:** Summer $3,990; year/semester $4,990-$5,990. Includes international roundtrip airfare, health insurance, orientation and training, room and board, and full-time in-country staff support. **Contact:** WorldTeach, Center for International Development, Harvard Univ., 79 John F. Kennedy St., Cambridge, MA 02138; 800-483-2240 or 617-495-5527, fax 617-495-1599; info@worldteach.org, [www.worldteach.org].

Women Welcome Women World Wide. We aim to foster international friendship by enabling women to visit one another. Members (2,800) are of all ages and backgrounds and come from many parts of the world.

Costs: Recommended minimum donation: £20. **Contact:** 5W, 88 Eston St., High Wycombe, Buckinghamshire HP11 1DJ; Tel./fax 011-44-1494-465441 [www.womenwelcomewomen.org.uk].

Women's Travel Club. Largest women's travel club in the U.S., room share guarantees, small groups, cultural and spa vacations.

Dates: Year round. **Costs:** $325-$4,500. **Contact:** Phyllis Stoller, The Women's Travel Club 21401 NE 38 Ave., Aventura, FL 33180; 800-480-4448; womantrip@aol.com, [www.womenstravelclub.com]].

THREE

SENIOR TRAVEL
BEST RESOURCES AND PROGRAMS

Today's senior travelers are more health-conscious and demand more intellectual and physical challenges: museums, concerts, festivals, archaeological digs, and scientific expeditions. They no longer want just basic tours. They opt for less group travel and more independence. However, they still want efficient schedules and arranged transfers. Program listings start on page 46. Programs in more than one country are listed under "Worldwide."

Senior Home and Hospitality Exchanges

Senior Citizens Stopovers Planet Earth [www.chariot.net.au/~annet/]. Be a guest or a host in a hospitality exchange.

Seniors Abroad International Homestays. 12533 Pacato Circle North, San Diego, CA 92128; fax 858-487-1492; haev@pacbell.net. Three or 4 homestays of 6 days each are arranged for active persons over age 50 between U.S. and New Zealand, Australia, Japan, and U.K. Americans may volunteer to host a couple or a single for 6 days.

Senior Publications

Archaeology Abroad, 31-34 Gordon Sq., London WC1H OPY, England; fax 011-44-020-7383-2572; arch.abroad@ucl.ac.uk, [www.britarch.ac.uk/archabroad]. Two bulletins per year list worldwide archaeological digs with details of staffing needs and costs.

At Sea at Sixty: Reflections from a Round the World Voyage by Catharine Stewart-Roache and Patrick J. Roache. (Hermosa Publications, Albuquerque, NM 87119. $15.95). The 60-year-old authors describe their voyage around the world on Semester at Sea Program. Order from: Hermosa Publishers, P.O. Box 9110, Albuquer-

que, NM 87119; fax 505-866-5323; [www.Hermosa-pub.com/Hermosa].

Britain on Your Own: A Guide for Single Mature Travelers by Dorothy Maroncelli (West Wind Books. 2nd ed. $15.95; www.bookzone.com/feature/britain.htm).

Marco Polo Magazine. A quarterly geared to travelers age 50 plus. Contact 727-735-9455; info@travelroads.com.

Travel Tips for Older Americans (Dept. of State Pub. 10337; fax 202-647-3000; http://travel.state.gov/olderamericans.html). Everything from discount airfares to passports and visas to health insurance.

Travel Unlimited: Uncommon Adventures for the Mature Traveler by Alison Gardner (Avalon Travel Publishing). Selected travel opportunities for travelers over 50.

World's Top Retirement Havens: How to Relocate, Retire, and Increase Your Standard of Living edited by Margaret J. Goldstein (Avalon Travel Publishing).

Senior Tour Sponsors

Alaska Snail Trails, P.O. Box 210894, Anchorage, AK 99521. Eleven-day, 6-day, and 5-day Alaskan tours; 800-348-4532, 907-337-7517, fax 907-337-7517, [www.aksnailtrails.com].

Eldertreks, 597 Markham St., Toronto, ON, Canada M6G 2L7; 800-741-7956, 416-588-5000, fax 416-588-9839; eldertreks@eldertreks.com, [www.eldertreks.com]. An adventure travel company dedicated to over-50 travelers. Small group trips, limited to 16.

Golden Escapes, Inc., a Canadian travel company specializing in escorted vacations to 4 continents, 75 The Donway West, Suite 710, Toronto, ON M3C 2E9, Canada; admin@goldenescapes.com, [www.goldenescapes.com].

Live in Costa Rica Tours by Christopher Howard (Costa Rica Books, Suite 1 SJO 981, P.O. Box 025216, Miami, FL 33102-5216; 619-461-6131; crbooks@racsa.co.cr, www.liveincostarica.com). Guided exploratory tours to Costa Rica for people who are thinking of living there full- or part-time.

Odysseys Unlimited, 85 Main St., Suite 101, Watertown, MA 02472; 781-370-3608, fax 781-370-3699; corp@odysseys-unlimited; [www.odysseys-unlimited.com]. Small group tours worldwide.

Photo Explorer Tours. Up to 12 programs annually include: China, Tibet, Turkey, India, Nepal, Ethiopia, Guatemala, South Africa, Bhutan, New Zealand, Ireland. Photo Explorer Tours, 2506 Country Village, Ann Arbor, MI 48103; 800-315-4462, fax 734-996-1481; decoxphoto@aol.com, [www.photoexplorertours.com].

Senior Women's Travel, 136 E. 56th St., New York, NY 10022; 212-838-4740, fax 212-826-8710; maryann@poshnosh.com, [www.poshnosh.com]. For senior women travelers who "want it all." Europe and other destinations.

Senior Transportation

Senior Fare Bargain Report by Jens Jurgen (Travel Companion Exchange, Inc., P.O. Box 833, Amityville, NY 11701; 631-454-0880; tce@whytravelalone.com, www.whytravelalone.com). $3, 2 copies $4 postpaid, check must accompany order. This 8-page booklet covers all details of the various senior airfares offered by most airlines for domestic and some international travel.

Senior Travel Web Sites

Arthur Frommer's Budget Travel Online [www.frommers.com/vacations/special_travelers/senior] features a section on senior travel with articles and information links.

Third Age Travel, a resource guide with an on-line community, travel companions matching service, feature stories and travel related subjects geared to seniors: [www.thirdage.com/travel].

Elderhostel[www.elderhostel.org]. Begin your adventures in lifelong learning from this stalwart friend of active seniors. Free catalog: 11 Avenue de Lafayette, Boston, MA 02111-1746; 877-426-8056.

Over the Hill Gang [www.skiersover50.com]. Ski trips, hiking, bicycle trips, and other travel opportunities from this membership organization ($40 per year) for active senior travelers.

Wired Seniors [www. wiredseniors.com/cgi-bin/seniorssearch/dir/page.asp?cn=15]. A general web site of interest to seniors with a section on tours featuring "senior friendly" itineraries.

Senior Travel Programs

Central Europe

Central European Teaching Program. Teach conversational English (or German, French, and other subjects) in schools in Hungary, Poland, and Romania. Live and work for a year in this rapidly changing part of the world, and immerse yourself in a new culture. Salary, housing, and health insurance are provided. Program support services.

    Dates: Sep-Jun or Jan-Jun. **Costs:** Placement fee: $2,000. **Contact:** Amy Berigtold, CETP, Beloit College, 700 College St., Beloit, WI 53511; 608-363-2619; cetp@beloit.edu, [www.beloit.edu/~cetp].

Costa Rica

Enjoy Learning Spanish Faster. Techniques developed from our ongoing research enable students to learn more, faster, in a comfortable environment. Classes of 2-4 students plus group learning activities; conversations with middle-class homestay families (1 student or couple per family). Homestays are in a small town near the capital, San José.

    Dates: Year round. Classes begin every Monday at all levels (except Mar 25-29, Dec 14-Jan 5). **Costs:** $345 per week for 26 hours of classes and group activities including Costa Rican dance and cooking classes. Includes tuition, 3 meals per day, 7 days per week, homestay, weekly 3-hour cultural tour, laundry, all materials, and airport transportation. $25 one-time registration fee. **Contact:** Susan Shores, Registrar, Latin American Language Center, PMB 123, Suite 710, 7485 Rush River Dr., Sacramento, CA 95831-5260; 916-447-0938, 916-428-9542; lalc@madre.com, [www.madre.com/~lalc].

By Arline Wills

A growing senior travel trend is to include extended family members in trips abroad. That way, grandparents whose earlier vacations were quick getaways now have time to enjoy sights and experiences through younger eyes. However, when a whole 3-generation family goes off together, one group may want to do the museums, another take a cooking class, and still another wants to explore caves. Havoc could reign. Mutually agreed upon plans might prevent later problems.

The first priority is to agree upon the purpose of the trip. Is it just a family vacation in another setting? An introduction to the culture, language, and way of life of other people? Here it's wise to defer to those who are bankrolling the trip, often the grandparents. It might be better to break up the group or take different family age levels at different times. While this may defeat the idea of a family reunion overseas, it may well improve family harmony in the long run.

When parents are not included, how do seniors cope with the demands of little ones on a trip? It depends on the kids' ages and interests, but one easy solution is a cruise. Many cruise lines offer on-board diversions and entertainment for children. Still, it's hard to see how children benefit from days they spend at sea.

Better options include specialty tours with combinations of language or art programs.

One of the best arrangements that we know from experience is to rent a house in an area where there's plenty of activities and attractions for a variety of ages. When we did this the first time, in Brittany, we and our children and grandchildren were about 10 miles apart, each in our own quarters but near enough to enjoy day trips and some meals together. Staying in one location, especially for the first venture abroad, makes children feel comfortable and gives them opportunities to make acquaintances and get a foot in the culture. Agents all over Europe and points beyond are eager to place you in their apartments, farms, private homes, villas, and castles.

Family Travel Guides

Before signing up for a conventional tour with the grandkids, check out the following:

Family Travel Guides Catalog (Carousel Press, P.O. Box 6038, Berkeley, CA 94706-0038; 510-527-5849; info@carousel-press.com, www.carousel-press.com). *Family Travel* by Evelyn Kaye (Blue Panda Press) includes educational trips with children as well as houseswaps. *France for Families* (A Touch of France, 660 King George Rd., Fords, NJ 08863; 800-738-5240, fax 732-738-0917; www.atouchoffrance.com). For grandparents who want to introduce the kids to France, this program arranges hands-on activities. *How to Take Great Trips With Your Kids* by Sanford Portnoy and Joan Flynn Portnoy (Harvard Common Press). *Take Your Kids to Europe* by Cynthia Harriman (Globe Pequot Press). This immensely popular book, now in its 3rd printing, gives practical and sensible advice on travel with all ages.

World Pen Pals (P.O. Box 337, Saugerties, NY 12477; Tel./fax 914-246-7828). Connect grandchildren with a child of the same age and gender near your destination early in the trip-planning stage. A personal meeting may even be possible. Send $3 and a SASE for each connection and encourage the child to follow through.

Family Tours

Just about every tour company now offers some opportunity to take the kids along. Children can easily get bored hanging around with adults, so try to find just the right balance of education, interaction with people and cultures, recreation, and fun. Here are some of my favorites:

Familyhostel (6 Garrison Ave., Durham, NH 03824; 800-733-9753; www.learn.unh.edu). This offshoot of Elderhostel and Interhostel organizes families-only vacations in foreign and domestic locations combining learning with recreational, cultural, and social activities. You receive a reading list relating to chosen activities and destinations before you go. An average 10-day Familyhostel trip costs about $2,600 per child and $3,000 per adult including all meals, accommodations, and airfare.

Grand Travel (6900 Wisconsin Ave., Suite 706, Chevy Chase, MD 20815; 800-247-7651, fax 301-913-0166; www.grandtrvl.com) offers travel vacations for grandparents and their grandchildren in Europe, Africa, and Australia. Guides are teachers who bring cultural experiences down to each child's age level.

Special Expeditions (720 5th Ave., 6th Fl., New York, NY 10019; 800-762-0003; www.expeditions.com) offers a selection of trips that include learning combined with scavenger hunts and educational puzzles for kids. Small company-owned ships go to remote island locations where all generations can study wildlife and nature.

Family Travel Made Easy (424 Bridge St., Ashland, OR 97520; 800-826-7165, fax 541-488-3067; www.about-family-travel.com) will custom plan an intergenerational trip catering to the specific interests of everyone. Suggestions include a Bible history tour of Israel and a painters' tour of Italy.

Earthwatch Institute (680 Mt. Auburn St., P.O. Box 9104, Watertown, MA 02472; 800-776-0188). Each year 3,500 volunteers work with scientists and conservationists on 1- to 3-week field research projects in over 60 countries. No special skills are necessary.

Global Volunteers (375 E. Little Canada Rd., St. Paul, MN 55117; 800-487-1074, fax 651-407-5163; www.globalvolunteers.org) encourages families to join together in short-term tax-deductible volunteer programs in Asia, Africa, Europe, the Pacific, South America, and the Caribbean. Work includes healthcare, teaching, light construction, and natural resource preservation. No special skills or foreign language required.

The Parker Company (Seaport Landing, 152 Lynnway, Lynn, MA 01902; 800-280-2811; italy@theparkercompany.com, www.theparkercompany.com). In addition to finding rental properties for travelers, the Parker Company arranges homestays combined with wine tours, cooking and painting classes, and creative writing programs, all in Italy. This is one of the best agencies for finding villas, cottages, castles, farmhouses, and apartments in Italy.

Property Rentals Holiday Home Pages (info@holiday-home-pages.co.uk, www.holiday-home-pages.co.uk) is an international Internet directory of hundreds of rental property suppliers, organized by country and region.

Idyll, Ltd. (P.O. Box 405, Media, PA 19063; 888-868-6871, fax 610-565-5142; info@untours.com, www.untours.com) arranges apartment rentals for families and provides local contacts for orientation.

British Travel Int'l. (800-327-6097, www.britishtravel.com.city) lists city apartments in Paris and London as well as country cottages in the rest of Europe. Send for their catalogs.

Rentals in Italy (800-726-6702, www.rentvillas.com) lists 800 properties in Tuscany alone.

Tuscany Now [www.tuscanynow.com] lists over 60 private villas and apartments in Tuscany, all with swimming pool.

Holiday-Rentals.com [www.Holiday-Rentals.com] is a useful web site for booking rentals directly with the owners. The company claims to have listings for over 2,000 properties in 40 countries.

Home Exchange (P.O. Box 30085, Santa Barbara, CA 93130, 805-898-9660, fax 805-898-9199; admin@HomeExchange.com, www.HomeExchange.com). The largest open system Internet exchange program has no catalog, just web sites, with an annual listing fee of $30. Also available from them is the book Home Exchange Vacationing by Mary and Bill Barbour.

Italy Farm Holidays (547 Martling Ave., Tarrytown, NY 10591; 914-631-7880, fax 914-631-8831) lists about 50 working farms that offer accommodations and meals. Some provide bikes and horseback riding. Usually require 3- to 7-day stays. Great for young kids.

Friends Overseas (68-04 Dartmouth St., Forest Hills, NY 11375) is a hospitality program for singles and families who want to meet Scandinavians and perhaps foster a return visit and friendship. Send a business size stamped, self-addressed envelope. Inquire about a similar program with Friends Overseas Australia if that's your destination.

Hospitality Exchange (Wayne and Kathy Phillips, Editors, Box 561, Lewiston, MT 59457; 406-538-8770; hospitalityex@hotmail.com) is a traveler's directory of people in 20 countries who offer each other hospitality in their homes. Each listing gives details on members' interests and the hospitality they can provide. They put out two directories a year, $20 for one year and $35 for two years.

Europe

Cradle of Catholicism Tour. Fully escorted 16-day tour of France and Italy emphasizing sights important to the past and present of Catholicism, while experiencing the treasures of western Italy and southern France. Includes all breakfasts, 9 dinners, sightseeing, accommodations, tour manager/driver, taxes, tips, and service charges. Air and land inclusive prices available from over 200 departure cities.
Dates: Apr 22, Sep 9, Oct 14. **Costs:** $2,260 land only. Early booking discounts available. **Contact:** Image Tours, Inc., 2828 Kraft Ave., SE, Grand Rapids, MI 49512-2076; 800-964-3170.

Heart of Europe Tour. Fully escorted 15-day tour of Holland, Belgium, Germany, Austria, Italy, Switzerland, and France. Includes all breakfasts, all but 4 dinners, sightseeing, accommodations, taxes, tips, and service charges. Air and land inclusive prices available from over 200 departure cities.
Dates: Apr-Nov. **Costs:** $1,780 land only. Early booking discounts available. **Contact:** Image Tours, Inc., 2828 Kraft Ave., SE, Grand Rapids, MI 49512-2076; 800-964-3170.

World War II Memorial Tour of Europe. Fully escorted 16-day tour of Holland, Germany, Belgium, Luxembourg, and France focusing on WWII where it happened. Gain a unique perspective as you visit famous battle sights, museums, and war memorials. Take in dramatic history of the war as well as the charm of the Old World. Includes all breakfasts, 9 dinners, sightseeing, accommodations, tour manager/driver, taxes, tips, and service charges. Air and land inclusive prices available from over 200 departure cities.
Dates: Apr-Oct. **Costs:** $2,120 land only. Early booking discounts available. **Contact:** Image Tours, Inc., 2828 Kraft Ave., SE, Grand Rapids, MI 49512-2076; 800-964-3170.

France

French in France. The French American Study Center was founded 25 years ago in the U.S. Students of any age or any level can be at home in Normandy to study French in real immersion. Seize the opportunity of the high exchange rate of the U.S. dollar.
Dates: Spring: Mar-May; summer: Jun-Aug; fall: Sep-Nov. **Costs:** From $490 per week (tuition, room and board, and excursions). **Contact:** Dr. Alméras, Chairman, French American Study Center, 12, 14, Blvd. Carnot, B.P. 4176, 14104 Lisieux Cedex, France; 011-33-2-31-31-22-01, fax 011-33-2-31-31-22-21; centre.normandie@wanadoo.fr, [http://perso.wanadoo.fr/centre.normandie/].

Immersion Course in French. Intensive 2-4 week course for professional adults in Villefranche (next to Nice) overlooking the French Riviera's most beautiful bay; 8 hours a day with 2 meals. Audiovisual classes, language lab, practice sessions, discussion-lunch. Evening film showings, evening outings with teachers, excursions to cultural landmarks. Accommodations in comfortable private apartments.
Dates: Courses start Jan, Feb, Mar, May, Jun, Aug, Sep, Oct, Nov, Dec. **Costs:** Tuition fees: Dec-Apr EURO200/4 weeks; May-Nov EURO2,650/4 weeks. Accommodations: Dec-Apr EURO300-800/4 week; May-Nov EURO350-900/4 weeks. **Contact:** Frédéric Latty, Institut de Francais, 23, avenue General Leclerc, 06230 Villefranche Sur Mer, France; 011-33-493-01-88-44, fax 011-33-493-76-92-17; instfran@aol.com, [www.institutdefrancais.com].

Italy

Language Courses by the Sea. The courses: conversation course (2 hours a day); main mini-groups (4 hours a day); intensive (main course plus 6 private lessons); indvidual tuition. Special courses: tourist industry, commercial Italian for import/export; small group (max. 6 students). Sports (sailing, catamaran, surfing); excursions (Calabria, Sicily). Accommodations in apartments.
Dates: Mar 6-Nov 24. **Costs:** Two-week course includes single room LIT1,010,000. **Contact:** Caffè Italiano Club, Largo A. Pandullo 5, 89861 Tropea (VV), Italy; 011-390-0963-60-32-84, 011-390-0963-61786; caffeitaliano@tin.it, [www.paginegialle.it/caffeital].

Study Italian in Florence or Tuscan Town. Study Italian in a 16th century Renaissance palace in the center of Florence or in a classic Tuscan town just 30 minutes from the sea. Koiné Center's professional language teachers and small class sizes encourage active participation by each student. Cultural program, guided excursions, choice of accommodations including host families.
Dates: Year round; starting dates each month. **Costs:** Two-week intensive program $325; 3 weeks $395; homestay accommodations from $220 for 2 weeks. **Contact:** In North America: Talking Traveler, 800-274-6007, fax 503-274-9004. In Italy: Dr. Andrea Moradei, Koiné Center, Via Pandolfini 27, 50122 Firenze, Italy; 011-390-55-213881, [www.koinecenter.com]; homestay@teleport.com, [www.talkingtraveler.org].

Seniors Travel Solo
Try Joining Group for First-Time Travel on Your Own

By Arnie Wills

It's a fact that seniors as a group have more disposable income and more time to spend it than ever before. If that's true for you, what's keeping you from packing up?

Perhaps a spouse can't travel any more and you have no one with similar interests to travel with? Or perhaps you're concerned about safety and health or problems with unfamiliar languages and cultures?

If it's too scary to think of heading off alone, try joining a tour group the first time, one where you're likely to meet people with similar interests. Find a group that allows for free time to explore on your own and follow your interests. Being alone in a group combines the best elements of solo and accompanied travel. You always have people in the group to talk with and eat with, but you can also explore on your own, close your door, and savor your privacy.

Solo travel arrangements usually require paying some penalties in the form of financial supplements. If this is a deterrent or you don't like the idea of going with a group, look for an organization that will supply you with a companion of your age and gender (see Solo Travel Resources box on next page). The risk is that you may not "click" with that person. But think of it as a short-term commitment: you've at least got to where you want to go and you may even have found a longer-term friend.

Real solo travel—where you decide the destination, read up on it, get your own tickets, and head off alone—is another matter. This is where you weigh concerns for personal safety and where women feel especially vulnerable (nearly all the solo travel advice is directed at women). While it might not be wise to strike out on your own to, say, Burundi, a shake-down visit to a more familiar culture like Mexico will get you started.

Perhaps the most important goal to keep in mind is to learn as much as possible about the people and places you'll be visiting before you leave home and go out of your way to meet the locals when you're there. You can do this in small ways: by admiring a gardener's work, offering to take someone's picture, asking for information about local landmarks, accepting an invitation into a family home for a meal, etc. (see hospitality exchange organizations, above.)

People everywhere, travelers and locals alike, are more willing to take up with singles than with pairs. So leave your shyness at home, pack your bag (preferably a rolling carry-on), and go for it!

Spain

Courses for Mature Students. Designed for students over 50. The small group classes are focused on practical, everyday communication in Spanish with emphasis on listening and speaking, as well as cultural and social aspects, rather than grammar analysis and writing.

Dates: Mar 19, May 21, Oct 29. **Costs:** $494 for 2 weeks. Includes transfer from Seville airport or train station upon arrival, welcome drink, 20 classes in small groups, social and cultural activities on 4 afternoons/evenings per week. Entrance tickets are included for a full-day excursion (Sat), a theater evening, and one dinner with teacher per course. **Contact:** Spanish Dept., CLIC IH Seville, C/ Albareda 19, 41001 Sevilla, Spain; 011-34-954-502131, fax 011-34-954-561696; training@clic.es, [www.clic.org].

Spanish for Seniors. Widely recognized to be one of Spain's leading language schools, Malaca Instituto has a special program designed for seniors who want to improve their Spanish to enjoy holidays in Spanish-speaking countries. Lessons in Spanish of everyday situations combined with cooking lessons, gallery and museum visits, small excursions, dance classes, etc.

Dates: Sep 24; Oct 8, 22; Nov 5; starting Feb 11, 25; Mar 11, 25; Apr 8, 22; May 6, 20; Jun 3, 2002. **Costs:** PTS69,000 for 2-week course and activities. **Contact:** Bob Burger, Malaca Instituto, c/Cortada 6, 29018 Malaga, Spain; 011-34-95-229-3242, fax 011-34-95-229-6316; espanol@malacainst-ch.es, [www.malacainst-ch.es].

Turkey

Anatolia's Civilizations. A popular and comprehensive tour of Turkey with visits to cultural, archaeological, and historical sites in Istanbul, Canakkale, Troy, Pergamum, Izmir, Ephesus, Sardis, Pamukkale, Aphrodias, Antalya, Konya, Cappadocia, Ankara, and Bursa.

Dates: Mar-Oct. **Costs:** From $1,390. **Contact:** ATC Anadolu, 420 Madison Ave., New York, NY 10017; 888-ANADOLU.

United Kingdom and Ireland

British Studies at Oxford. This program of study in one of the world's most prestigious universities offers undergraduate and graduate credit in art history, business, communication, drama, education, English literature, history, and political science taught by Oxford Univ. professors. The participants live in private rooms tidied daily by the college staff, who also serve 3 bountiful and tasty meals a day in the Great Hall. Field trips are an integral part of each course as well as group trips to the theater in Stratford-upon-Avon and London.

Dates: Summer: Jun 30-Jul 20; Jul 21-Aug 10; or Jun 30-Aug 10. **Costs:** $3,350 for 3 weeks; $6,050 for 6 weeks. Includes 4 or 8 credits, travel in Britain for course related events, theater, entrance to museums, dinners in country inns, and many field trips. Overseas travel not included. **Contact:** Dr. M.B. Pigott, Director, British Studies at Oxford, 322 Wilson Hall, Oakland Univ., Rochester, MI 48309-4401; 248-652-3405 or 248-370-4131, fax 248-650-9107; pigott@oakland.edu, [www.oakland.edu/oxford].

Worldwide

Language Programs for All Ages. For all ages and all Spanish levels. Spanish classes, excursions, cultural activities. One week to 6 months. Various settings: beaches, mountains, small towns, large cities, etc. Countries: Mexico, Costa Rica, Guatemala, Panamá, Argentina, Chile, Ecuador, Peru, Uruguay, Venezuela, Puerto Rico, Dominican Republic, Bolivia, Spain. Also Portuguese in Brazil!

Dates: Programs start every week or every month. **Costs:** Depends on location. Prices start at $200 per week and include classes, homestay, travel insurance, most meals, some cultural activities. **Contact:** AmeriSpan Unlimited, P.O. Box 40007, Philadelphia, PA 19106; 800-879-6640, fax 215-751-1100; info@amerispan.com, [www.amerispan.com].

Travel-Study Seminars. Center for Global Education at Augsburg College. Through study tours, learn from people of diverse backgrounds about their economic, political, and social realities. Emphasis on those working on the grassroots level. Programming in Mexico, Central America, South Africa, and Cuba. Call for a free listing of upcoming seminars.

Dates: Ongoing. **Costs:** $1,000-$4,500 depending on destination and length of trip. **Contact:** Center for Global Education, Augsburg College, 2211 Riverside Ave., Box TR, Minneapolis, MN 55454; 800-299-8889, fax 612-330-1695; globaled@augsburg.edu, [www.augsburg.edu/global].

FOUR

FAMILY TRAVEL
BEST RESOURCES

Parents often approach overseas travel with trepidation. "We're thinking of going to Switzerland with our two-year-old. Are we nuts?" Or "Our 14-year-old barely speaks to us. Will two weeks in Mexico help, or will we all end up hating each other?" Go for it. The experience is well worth it. Just know the basic whys and hows of traveling with kids:

• **Stay put for at least part of your trip.** *Parents who contact us after an overseas trip with kids rave about the time they spent "living" instead of "traveling."*

• **Explore normal life as much as possible.** *Spend time in grocery stores picking out local foods or in toy stores comparing the wares with those at home.*

• **Make history and culture digestible to your kids.** *Buy a disposable camera for each child and encourage them to "collect" gargoyles, roof gables, or church towers. When you visit a museum, start with the gift shop and let each kid choose two postcards, then set out to find the kids' "own" works. Balance each day physically, with a morning cathedral visit, for instance, followed by renting bikes in the afternoon. Let family members take turns choosing the day's itinerary.*

• **Most importantly, don't leave the human side of family travel to chance.** *Brainstorm all the ways you can engineer meetings with other families. And get started now. Savor the process as you open the mailbox or email every day to welcome responses to your friendly overtures to other families.*

Family Travel Publications

Adventuring with Children by Nan Jeffrey (Avalon House Publishing, $14.95). Great overseas and domestic advice for active families who want to backpack, camp, sail, bicycle or canoe.

Children's Books in Print (RR Bowker, annual). Don't buy this one: Your public library should have it. Look up the countries you'll be visiting in the subject index, then read as many books as you can with your kids before you go!

Clan of the Cave Bear by Jean Auel (Bantam Books, 1984). Great background reading for visiting prehistoric caves in France, even though the book is based elsewhere.

Découvrir Paris est un Jeu d'Enfant by Isabelle Bourdial and Valeri Guidoux (Editions Parigramme/CPL, 28 rue d'Assas, 75006 Paris, France. 1994, FF98). A great guide in French, to buy on arrival or from [www.amazon.fr].

The Family Travel Guide: An Inspiring Collection of Family-Friendly Vacations edited by Carole Terwilliger Meyers (Carousel Press, 1995). First-hand family travel accounts from all over the world. Helps you picture your trip—and includes additional suggestions of places to go and things to see.

Florence for Kids by Stefano Filipponi and Annalisa Fineschi (Fratelli Palombi Editori, 1998, www.palombieditori.com). A thin, colorful guide to Florence written at an upper-elementary level. Only available in Italy.

French or Foe? Getting the Most Out of Visiting, Living & Working in France by Polly Platt (Cultural Crossing, 1998, $16.95); [www.pollyplatt.com]. Fascinating to any Francophile.

Le Guide de la Science en France (Hachette, Paris, 1994, FF98). A wonderful guide to nature parks and all things scientific in France. Includes editors' top picks. In French; buy it on arrival or from [www.amazon.fr].

Le Guide du Routard Junior...Paris et ses environs avec vos enfants (Hachette, Paris, 1999, FF79). Widely available in Paris. Includes activities, restaurants, and shops recommended for kids.

Have Children Will Travel, P.O. Box 152, Lake Oswego, OR 97034; toll free 877-699-5869. Online family newsletter of travel resources and tips; deb@havechildrenwilltravel.com, [http://havechildrenwilltravel.com].

The History of Art for Young People by H.W. and Anthony Janson (Abrams, 1997, $49.50). Expensive but good. Try your library before you go and let your kids "shop" for masterpieces they'd like to see in Europe.

Ireland for Kids by Derek MacKenzie, Derek (Trafalgar Square Publishing, 2001). Comprehensive; includes activities, museums, hotels, restaurants throughout the Republic and Northern Ireland.

Italy with Kids by Barbara and Michael Pape (Open Road Publishing, 2000, $14.95). Parent-tried advice with sections for Rome, Venice, Verona, Tuscany, Naples and Amalfi, and Milan and Lakes Region.

Kids' London by Simon Adams (DK Publishing, 2000). All the great pictures of a DK guide with kid-level text.

Kids Love Israel; Israel Loves Kids by Barbara Sofer. New 2nd ed. includes lodging, camps, language, food, plus over 300 sightseeing ideas for the whole country. $17.95 from Kar-Ben Copies, 6800 Tildenwood Ln., Rockville, MD 20852; 301-984-8733. Kept current on publishers web site: [www.karben.com].

Kids' Trips in Tokyo: A Family Guide to One-Day Outings by Ivy Maeda, Kitty Kobe, Cynthia Ozeki, and Lyn Sato (Kodansha International). Organized by 1-day itineraries, with info for infants and older kids. Excellent resource.

London for Families by Larry and Michael Lain (Interlink Publishing Group, 2000, $14.95). Finally a London guide you can buy in the U.S.

Paris for Families by Larry and Michael Lain (Interlink Publishing Group, 2000, $14.95). Very comprehensive; even includes info on short-term apartments and sample letters in French to help you book.

Take the Kids London by Joseph Fullman (Cadogan Guides, 2000, $16.95). A very thorough city guide.

Take the Kids Paris by Helen Truszkowski (Cadogan Guides, 2000, $16.95). Useful.

Take the Kids Traveling by Helen Truszkowski (Cadogan Guides, 2000, $16.95). More geared to U.S. and Europe than *Travel with Children*.

Take Your Kids to Europe by Cynthia Harriman (Globe Pequot, 4th ed., 2001). Intercultural guide to how and why to do it.

Travel with Children by Maureen Wheeler (Lonely Planet, 1995, $11.95.) Advice for hard-core family travelers, especially those heading to Third World countries; will make travel in Europe seem like a snap.

Usborne Book of Europe by Rebecca Treays (Usborne, 1994, £7.65). Available online from W.H. Smith at [www.bookshops.co.uk]. Comprehensive enough for parents, but written for kids to read, too. Good overview of the Continent.

Usborne Book of London by Moira Butterfield (E.D.C. Publications, 1987, $9.95). Available from [www.amazon.com]. The history and landmarks of London for kids 10 and older.

Family Travel Web Sites

Family Travel Forum [www.familytravelforum.com] is dedicated to the ideals, promotion, and support of travel with children. Their web site includes a selection of family travel titles available through amazon.com.

Quinwell Travel [www.quinwell.com]; 800-339-8892. Information and booking services for traveling with children on cruise ships and family travel in general.

www.travelwithyourkids.com features tips from real parents on how to travel internationally (or just long distances) with children. Topics covered include: getting kids ready to travel, health and safety, getting passports and visas, the best seats on a plane for families, sections on traveling while pregnant, international adoptions, and a special section on moving and living abroad.

TRAVEL WITH CHILDREN
DON'T FORGET LEASHES AND VALIUM!

By Rick Steves

My wife, children, and VW van have traveled with me from Norway to Naples and Dublin to Dubrovnik. It's not hell, but it's not terrific travel, either. Still, we'd rather change diapers in Paris than in Seattle. And an international adventure is a great foundation for a mountain of family memories.

Young European families, like their American counterparts, are also traveling, babies and all. You'll find more and more kids' menus, hotel playrooms, and kids-go-crazy zones at freeway rest stops all over Europe. Babies are great icebreakers—socially and in the Arctic.

Here are some of the lessons we've learned from whining and giggling through Europe with our kids.

Baby Gear

Since a happy baby on the road requires a lot of gear, the key to survival is either to have a rental car or stay in one place. Of course, pack as light as you can. But if you figure you'll need it, trust your judgment.

Bring a car seat, borrow one or buy one in Europe, or see if your car rental company can provide one. If you'll be driving long hours while the baby sleeps, try to get a car seat that reclines.

A stroller is essential. An umbrella model is lightest, but a heavy-duty model with a reclining back works better for naps. Ours served as a luggage cart for the Bataan death march parts of our trip when we had to use public transportation. Carry the stroller onto the plane—you'll need it in the airport. Big wheels handle cobblestones best.

A small travel crib was a godsend. No matter what kind of hotel, pension, or hostel we ended up in, as long as we could clear a 4-by-4-foot space on the floor, we'd have a safe, clean, and familiar home for our kids to sleep and play in.

If a baby backpack works for you at home, bring it to Europe. (I just use my shoulders.) Rucksacks are great for parents who wish they had the hands of an octopus. Prepare to tote more than a tot—a combo purse/diaper bag with shoulder straps is ideal. Be on guard—purse-snatchers target mothers (especially while busy and off guard, as when changing diapers). Thieves aside, in most of Europe a mother with a small child is given great respect. Europeans love children. You'll generally be offered a seat on crowded buses and allowed to go to the front of the line at museums.

There's lots more to pack. Encourage bonding to a blanket or stuffed critter and take it along. We used a lot of Heinz dehydrated food dumped into zip-lock baggies. Tiny Tupperware containers were great for crackers, raisins, and snacks. You'll find plenty of disposable diapers, wipes, baby food, and so on in Europe, so don't take the whole works from home. Before you fly away, be sure you've packed ipecac, a decongestant, acetaminophen, and a thermometer. For a toddler, bring a few favorite books and a soft ball (easy on hotel rooms). Buy little European toys as you go. As our children got older, activity books and portable video games kept them occupied for what might have been countless boring hours. Also, a daily holiday allowance as a reward for assembling a first-class daily picture journal gave our children reasons to be enthusiastic about every travel day.

Parenting at 32,000 Feet

You'll pay 10 percent of the ticket cost to take a child under the age of two on an international flight. The child doesn't get a seat, but many airlines have flying baby perks for moms and dads who ask for them in advance—roomier bulkhead seats, hang-from-the-ceiling bassinets, and baby meals. After age two, a toddler's ticket costs 70 to 90 percent of the adult fare; from age 12 on, kids pay full fare. (Railpasses and train tickets are free for kids under age four; those under 12 ride the rails for half price.)

Gurgling junior may become an airborne Antichrist as soon as the seat belt light goes off. Ask your pediatrician about sedating your baby for a 10-hour intercontinental flight. We think it's only merciful (for everyone involved). Dimetapp, Tylenol, or Pediacare have also worked well for us.

Prepare to be 100 percent self-sufficient throughout the flight. Expect cramped seating and busy attendants. Bring extra clothes (for you and the baby), special toys, and familiar food. Those colored links are handy for attaching toys to the seat, crib, highchairs, jail cells, and so on. The in-flight headphones are great entertainment for flying toddlers.

Landings and takeoffs can be painful for ears of all ages. A bottle, a pacifier, or anything to suck helps equalize the baby's middle-ear pressure. For this reason, nursing moms will be glad they do when it comes to flying. Remember, crying is a great pressure equalizer. Bring earplugs for nearby passengers.

Once on foreign soil, you'll find that your footloose and see-it-all days of travel are over for a while. Go easy. Traveling with a tyke is tiring, wet, sticky, and smelly. Your mobility plummets.

Be warned—jet lag is nursery purgatory. Our kids took it hard. Luckily, we settled in good hotels and most of the guests were able to stay elsewhere.

Accommodations

We slept in rooms of all kinds, from hostels (many have family rooms) to hotels. We weren't charged for the kids' accommodations until they turned five. While we always used our own bedding, many doubles have a sofa or extra bed that can be barricaded with chairs and used instead of the crib.

Childproof the room immediately on arrival. A roll of masking tape makes quick work of electrical outlets. Anything breakable goes on top of the free-standing closet. Proprietors are generally helpful to considerate and undemanding parents. We'd often store our bottles and milk cartons in their fridge, ask (and of course pay) for babysitting, and so on.

Every room had a sink where kids could pose for cute pictures, have a little fun, make smelly bubbles, and get clean. With a toddler, budget extra to get a bath in your room—a practical need and a fun diversion. Toddlers and campgrounds— with swings, slides, and plenty of friends—mix wonderfully.

Self-catering flats rented by the week or 2-week period, such as gîtes in France and villas in Italy, give a family a home on the road. Many families prefer settling down this way and side-tripping from a home base.

Food

While Europeans are warm to children, we found European restaurants and their customers cool to noisy babies. Highchairs are rare. We ate happiest at places with outdoor seating and at the many McDonald's-type, baby-friendly fast food places. Outdoor or hotel room picnics work great. In restaurants (or anywhere), if your infant is making a disruptive fuss, apologetically say the local word for teeth and annoyed locals will become more sympathetic.

Nursing babies are easiest to feed and travel with. Remember, some cultures are uncomfortable with public breastfeeding. Be sensitive.

We stocked up on munchies (fruit, pretzels, and tiny boxes of juice—which double as squirt guns). A 7 a.m. banana worked wonders, and a 5 p.m. snack made late European dinners workable. In restaurants we requested extra plates for the kids, who just nibbled from our meals. We ordered "fizzy" (but not sticky) mineral water (call it "pop"), and the many spills were no problem. With all the candy and sweet temptations at toddler-eye level in Europe, you can forget a low-sugar diet. While gelati and pastries are expensive, our kids' favorite suckers, Popsicles; hollow toy-filled chocolate eggs were cheap and available everywhere.

Plan to spend more money. Use taxis rather than buses and subways. Hotels can get babysitters, usually from professional agencies. The service is expensive but worth the splurge when you crave a leisurely, peaceful evening sans bibs and cribs.

We arranged our schedule around naps and sleep time. Well-rested babies are worth the limitation. Driving during the kids' naps worked well. As they became toddlers, however, the kids stayed up very late, playing soccer with new Italian friends on the piazza or eating huge ice creams in the hotel kitchen with the manager's kids. We gave up on a rigid naptime or bedtime, and we enjoyed Europe's evening ambience as a family.

OK, you're there—watered, fed, and only a little bleary. Europe is your cultural playpen, a living fairy tale, and a sandbox of family fun and adventure. Grab your kids and dive in.

Family Travel Programs

Abercrombie & Kent, 1520 Kensington Rd., Suite 212, Oak Brook, IL 60523; 800-323-7308. fax 630-954-3324, [www.abercrombiekent.com]. A wide range of itineraries tailored to families traveling during summer and school vacation.

AmeriSpan Unlimited, P.O. Box 40007, Philadelphia, PA 19106; 800-879-6640; info@AmeriSpan.com, [www.AmeriSpan.com]. Family, teen, senior, and adult language programs in 14 countries in Mexico, Spain, Central and South America. Housing with a host family.

ExperiencePlus!, 415 Mason Court, Unit 1, Ft. Collins, CO 80524; 800-685-4565, fax 970-493-0377; tours@experienceplus.com, [www.Experienceplus.com]. Walking and bicycling tours in Europe, Central America, and Canada for families with teens.

Family Travel Forum, FTF Membership Dept., Cathedral Station, P.O. Box 1585, New York, NY 10025-1585; 888-FT-FORUM, fax 212-665-6136; [www.familytravelforum.com]. Membership organization ($48 per year) publishes newsletter and web site on global family travel—including destinations, health and parenting tips, travel deals, family tour operators—and provides customized travel information.

Familyhostel, 6 Garrison Ave., Durham, NH 03824; 800-733-9753; [www.learn.unh.edu]. Reasonably-priced family educational visits to various destinations with an emphasis on cultural learning.

France for Families. A Touch of France, 660 King George Rd., Fords, NJ 08863; 800-738-5240, fax 732-738-0917; [www.atouchoffrance.com]. Arranges family tours or "`a la carte" activities—from art to cooking to perfume-making—for kids in Paris and elsewhere in France.

Hostelling International (AYH), 733 15th St., NW, Suite 840, Washington, DC 20005; 202-783-6161; hiayhserv@hiayh.org [www.iyhf.org] or [www.hiayh.org]. Many hostels have private family rooms. Advance reservations are required.

Idyll, Ltd., P.O. Box 405, Media, PA 19063; 888-UNTOUR1, fax 610-565-5142; info@untours.com, [www.untours.com]. Home rentals with hand-holding: Idyll arranges apartments and includes low-key orientation at your destination.

Sister Cities International, 1424 K St., Suite 600, Washington, DC 20005; 202-347-8630, fax 202-393-6524; [www.sister-cites.org]. Check the web site directory of existing city pairs, or to find out how to set up a sister city program.

Society for the Protection of Nature in Israel, 28 Arrandale Ave., Great Neck, NY 11024; 212-398-6750, fax 212-398-1665; [www.amitravel.com/spni]. Operates 1-14-day hikes and nature explorations—even a camel tour—in different parts of Israel. Expert environmental guides and low costs. Accommodations are in the group's field study centers or hostels. Children age 10 and up welcome.

World Pen Pals, P.O. Box 337, Saugerties, NY 12477; Tel./fax 845-246-7828; [www.world-pen-pals.com]. Promotes international friendship and cultural understanding through correspondence between young people under age 23. Pen friends offered by gender and continent but for specific countries phone first to verify availability. Send $3 and SASE for each pen pal desired.

Family Camping Resources

Continental Sites Guide. Available from The Caravan Club, East Grinstead House, East Grinstead, W. Sussex RH19 1UA, U.K.; 011-44-1342-32-69-44, fax 011-44-1342-41-02-58; [www.caravanclub.co.uk]. Excellent 2-volume campground guide covers sites in Europe, with readers' reports, good directions.

Country-by-Country Booklets. Many national tourist offices in Europe provide excellent free camping guides or maps; contact the national tourist offices.

Europa Camping and Caravaning (Drei-Brunnen, Stuttgart, Germany, 1999). Available from [www.amazon.de]. A great European guide to campgrounds available with maps, ferry information, and currency exchange tips.

Europe by Van and Motorhome by David Shore and Patty Campbell (Shore/Campbell Publications, 1994/2001, $13.95 plus $1 s/h). A comprehensive resource to everything involved with buying, renting, or simply surviving in an RV or camper in Europe.

Family Campers and Rivers, 4804 Transit Rd., Bldg. 2, Depew, NY 14043-4704; 800-245-9755; [www3.pgh.net/~dscott/ferv.html]. Family memberships in this camping organization are $25 and include children under 18. For an additional $15 members can purchase an International Camping Carnet.

RV Rentals: Auto Europe (Italy, Spain, Germany, France, U.K.), 800-223-5555; [www.autoeurope.com].

Traveler's Guide to European Camping by Mike and Teri Church (Rolling Homes Press, call 425-822-7846.) Lots of campground listings.

By Ann McDuffie

Traveling with children can be difficult. Here are some tips to make it easier:

Preparation

It helps to prepare the children weeks before the flight. A big map and a tiny airplane make a great visual aid. Read the children stories from the region and show them picture books to help prepare them for the change.

Don't Worry, Be Happy

You may be feeling stressed, but it's important that you convey a sense of security, says Maureen Wheeler, author of *Travel with Children* (Lonely Planet). Try not to let the children feel your own insecurity.

"As a parent you are, of course, expected to know everything. You are the source of all wisdom and strength. Now is not the time to unburden yourself to your child," Wheeler warns.

On our last trip from Kuwait—the one with the pets, the excess baggage, and no husband—I was feeling slightly overwhelmed. But I didn't let on. Instead, we talked about our destination, pointed out interesting cloud formations and scenery, played travel games. It helps to involve the kids and keep them informed of your plans-where you're going, how you're getting there. Details are not only interesting but also convey a sense of security.

Baggage Claim

Whether it's a permanent transfer or a leisurely vacation, you'll need to plan carefully what to take along. Make a list. Pack enough essential items to get you through the flight and a little extra in case shopping is inconvenient. But not so much that you're overburdened. Pack sample-size containers of shampoo, powder, lotion. To prevent leaks, pack medicines and toiletries in resealable plastic bags. Engage children in packing their own backpacks or carry-ons with toys, games, books, and other comforting items.

Carry a favorite stuffed toy or doll looped with an elastic to the child's wrist to prevent the tragedy of leaving it behind. One mother I know gift-wrapped a few new toys and tucked them inside her carry-on.

Notify the airline in advance that you'll be traveling with children. They often offer special services for children such as kid's meals served first and free travel souvenirs. Bring along your own snacks and carry a water bottle.

Bring a stroller so you can strap baby in between flights.

Final Boarding Call

Ask the flight attendant if there are spare seats, giving the kids room to stretch out.

If possible, book nonstop flights to avoid changing aircraft and racing to another gate with children and baggage in tow. When that's impossible, allow enough of a layover to let kids run and stretch in the airport, many of which are now equipped with playgrounds or nurseries. During her 7-hour layover in Amsterdam, one friend checked in at the airport hotel with her two children for a rest and a change of scenery.

Large, crowded airports hold lots of attractions for curious kids. Discuss with your children what to do if you get separated. For little ones you might write the flight information on a tag and put it in their pocket. You tag your luggage, why not your children?

FIVE

DISABILITY TRAVEL
BEST RESOURCES AND PROGRAMS

We hope readers with disabilities will consider all the incredible opportunities listed in Transitions Abroad *and will ask the organizer of each program that interests them about how their needs could be accommodated. If we are traveling to create a better and more just world, then let's be sure that we are including all its citizens. The following resources will be a big help. A selection of best programs begins on page 65.*

Disability Travel Organizations

International disability-related organizations offer opportunities to volunteer or work abroad and may be able to assist with accommodations, provide referral to local disability-related resources, locate personal assistants, sign interpreters and guides, and advise program participants and travelers on accessibility and what to expect in the host country. They may also be a good resource for finding housing as their members may already have accessible housing and be interested in hosting a person with a disability from another country. The following organizations have affiliate members around the world and their web sites list member organizations worldwide:

Accessible Europe, 011-39-0113096363, fax 011-39-011-3091201; [www.accessibleeurope.com]. Arranges special tours in Europe for disabled travelers.

Center for International Rehabilitation Research Information and Exchange (CIRRIE), State Univ. of New York at Buffalo, Center for Assistive Technology, 515 Kimball Tower, Buffalo, NY 14214-3079; 716-829-3141 ext. 149, fax 716-829-3217; kmorgan@buffalo.edu, [http://cirrie.buffalo.edu]. Facilitates exchange

opportunities for professionals in the rehabilitation field through travel grants. The hosting institution must apply for the grant.

Council of International Programs (CIP), 1700 E 13th St. SE, Suite 4ME, Cleveland, OH 44114-3213; 216-566-1088, fax 216-566-1490; cipusa@compuserve.com, [www.cipusa.org]. Brings mid-career professionals from around the world into the U.S. for practical training in fields such as human services, education, law, non-profit management, and public administration. CIP welcomes participants with disabilities and representatives of disability organizations and also arranges homestays with families that have members with disabilities. Scholarships are sometimes available.

Council on International Education Exchange (CIEE), 633 3rd Ave., 20th Fl., New York, NY 10017; 888-COUNCIL or 212-822-2600, fax 212-822-2699; info@ciee.org, [www.ciee.org]. Offers work, study, and volunteer programs in many countries around the world.

Disabled Peoples' International (DPI), 101-7 Evergreen Pl., Winnipeg, Manitoba R3L-2T3, Canada; 204-287-8010, TTY 204-284-2598, fax 204-453-1367; dpi@dpi.org, [www.dpi.org]. A worldwide organization of people with disabilities who advocate for the right to full participation and equality and control over services that affect their lives. DPI has representatives for African, Asian, European, Latin American, and North American regions.

Gazette International Networking Institute (GINI), 4207 Lindell Blvd., Rm. 110, Saint Louis, MO 63108-2915; 314-534-0475, fax 314-534-5070; gini_intl@msn.com, [www.post-polio.org]. Network of people that gathers and disseminates information to survivors of polio and users of home mechanical ventilators. Web site lists international post-polio resources.

Hesperian Foundation, 1919 Addison St., Suite 304, Berkeley, CA 94704-1144; 510-845-1447, fax 510-845-9141; hesperian@hesperian.org, [www.hesperian.org]. Nonprofit organization committed to improving the health of people in poor communities throughout the world by making health information accessible. Contact organization for current volunteer opportunities.

Mobility International USA (MIUSA), P.O. Box 10767, Eugene, OR 97440; Tel./TTY 541-343-1284, fax 541-343-6812; info@miusa.org, [www.miusa.org]. A nonprofit organization dedicated to expanding equal opportunities for people with disabilities in international exchange, leadership development, disability rights training, and community service.

National Clearinghouse on Disability and Exchange (NCDE). See MIUSA, above, clearinghouse@miusa.org. A project managed by MIUSA and sponsored by the Bureau of Educational and Cultural Affairs of the U.S. Department of State. Strives to increase the participation of people with disabilities in the full range of international exchange opportunities by providing free information and referrals to individuals, disability organizations, and exchange programs. Web site has database of disability organizations and exchange programs worldwide.

Rehabilitation International (RI), 25 East 21st St., New York, NY 10010; 212-420-1500, TTY 212-420-1752, fax 212-505-0871; rehabintl@aol.com, [www.rehab-international.org]. An organization that works to promote the prevention of disability, rehabilitation, and the equalization of opportunities for people with disabilities worldwide. Publishes an array of periodicals and reports on disability issues.

Society for Accessible Travel & Hospitality, 347 5th Ave., Suite 610, New York, NY 10016; 212-447-7284; sathtravel@aol.com, [www.sath.org]. Publishes Open World magazine and informa-

tion booklets on trip planning for persons with disabilities. Their web site has a good selection of links and information.

World Blind Union, c/o CBC ONCE, La Coruna 18, 28020 Madrid Spain; 011-34-19-571-3685, fax 011-34-19-571-5777; umc@once.es, [http://umc.once.es]. Focuses on human rights and equal opportunities for blind and visually impaired people worldwide.

World Federation of the Deaf, Magnus Ladulaadsgatan 63, 4th Fl., S-11827 Stockholm Sweden; Tel./Fax 011-46 8 442-1499; info@wfdnews.org, [www.wfdnews.org]. International, non-governmental central organization of national associations of the Deaf.

Disability Travel Publications

Building Bridges. More than 200 pages of suggestions and creative ideas for including, recruiting, and accommodating people with disabilities in international programs. Includes information on volunteer service programs and legal issues for international advisers. Available in alternative formats. $20. Accompanying open-captioned video, $49. Audio description upon request. Contact Mobility International USA (above).

The Diabetic Traveler, P.O. Box 8223, Stamford, CT 06905; 203-327-5832. $18.95 per year. A newsletter with articles and information of particular interest to travelers with diabetes.

Easy Access Australia by Bruce M. Cameron. Easy Access Australia Publishing Ltd., 512 pp., $27.45. [http://homevicnet.net/au/~bruceeaa]. A travel guide to Australia for people with disabilities.

Emerging Horizons. A newsletter that provides unbiased views of accessible travel options. Sample copies from: P.O. Box 278, Ripon, CA 95366; fax 209-599-9409; horizons@emerginghorizons.com, [www.candy-charles.com/Horizons].

Holiday Care, Imperial Buildings, 2nd Floor, Victoria Rd., Horley, Surrey, RH6 7PZ, U.K.; 011-44-1293-774-535, fax 011-44-1293-784-647; holiday.care@virgin.net, [www.holidaycare.org.uk]. The U.K.'s central source of holiday information for disabled persons and their personal assistants.

Holidays in Britain and Ireland 2001: A Guide for Disabled People by Royal Association for Disability and Rehabilitation (RADAR), 12 City Forum, 250 City Rd., London EC1V 8AF, U.K.; 011-44-20-7250-3222, fax 011-44-20-7250-

0212; radar@radar.org.uk, [www.radar.org.uk]. Over 1,000 places to stay in all parts of the U.K. and Republic of Ireland. £15 postpaid. RADAR also offers a number of other useful guides and publications.

Home Is in the Heart. Video on accommodating people with disabilities in the homestay experience. Provides information and ideas for exchange organizations. Discusses how to recruit homestay families, meet accessibility needs, and accommodate international participants with disabilities. Open captioned. $49 from Mobility International USA (above).

Hostelling International Directories. Printed guides have symbols indicating accessible hostels. In U.S. contact Hostelling International, 733 15th St., NW, Suite 840, Washington, DC 20005; fax 202-783-6171; hostels@hiayh.org, [www.hiayh.org]. International guides are $13.95 and North American Guide is free to members, nonmembers $3. A list of locations is also available on both web sites.

Institute on International Education (IIE), 809 United Nations Plaza, New York, NY 10017-3580; 212-8838-200, fax 212-984-5452; info@iie.org, [www.iie.org]. Provides information on most topics related to international study and volunteer opportunities. IIE produces numerous exchange-related publications that can be found through their web site. They also administer the Fulbright and other grant programs.

Loud, Proud & Passionate: Including Women with Disabilities in International Development Programs by MIUSA. Contact MIUSA (above) for ordering information, $30 (members 10% discount), international orders add $10 s/h. Includes guidelines to ensure inclusion of women with disabilities in the development process, as well as personal experience stories and resources. Alternate formats available upon request. Available in English, Russian, and Spanish. LPP Video $49.

Paralyzed Veterans of America, Distribution Center, P.O. Box 753, Waldorf, MD 20604-0753; 888-860-7244; info@pva.org, [www.pva.org]. Publishes many resources including the brochures New Horizons Information for the Air Traveler with a Disability.

Wheelchair Through Europe. Graphic Language Press, P.O. Box 270, Cardiff by the Sea, CA 92007; 760-944-9594; graphiclanguage@yahoo.com, [http://wheelchairtravel.tripod.com]. $13. Resources on accessible sites in Europe, including hotels, transportation, and resources.

A World Awaits You (Away). Annual journal devoted to exchange opportunities for people with disabilities, including personal stories, tips, and current exchange opportunities. For a free copy contact Mobility International USA (see Organizations, above).

Disability Travel Web Sites

Access Abroad [http://disserv3.stu.umn.edu/abroad]. Lists accessibility information for over 40 international sites in 25 different countries. Also has tips for students with disabilities planning to go abroad and resources for study abroad advisers.

Access-Able Travel Source, 303-232-2979, fax 303-239-8486; [www.access-able.com]. Free Internet information service for mature and disabled travelers. Online database of resources including accommodations, transportation, attractions, adventures, doctors, and equipment rental and repair. Searchable by country, state, province, and city. Site also has a comprehensive list of disability links, publications, specialty travel agents, travel tips, and more.

Armchair [www.armchair.com/tour/hc/handcap.html]. For phone contacts and information on tours with disabled travelers in mind.

Arthur Frommer's Budget Travel Online [www.frommers.com/vacations/special_travelers/dis]. Includes section on resources for travelers with disabilities.

Disibility Net: Travel [www.disabilitynet.co.uk/info/holidays/index.html]. Links, news, and information for disabled travelers.

Disabled Person's Guide to Tokyo [www.jwindow.net/LWT/TOKYO/REDCROSS/redcross_index.html].

Dtours [http://Ireland.iol.ie/infograf/dtour]. A visitors guide to Ireland for persons with disabilities.

European Union. Travel guides for tourists with disabilities for many European countries available online at: [http://europa.eu.int/comm/enterprise/services/tourism/tourism-publications/documents/guides.htm].

Global Access: Disabled Travel Network, [www.geocities.com/paris/1502]. Personal stories, access guides and extensive links to international disability travel resources.

REACH OUT TO YOUTH WITH DISABILITIES

WAYS TO INCLUDE YOUTH WITH DISABILITIES IN INTERNATIONAL EXCHANGE

By Pamela Houston

Here are a few simple ideas to begin or enhance outreach to youth with disabilities and make programs more welcoming. To discuss these ideas further or get more information, contact the National Clearinghouse on Disability and Exchange, P.O. Box 10767, Eugene, OR 97440; 541-343-1284 (Tel./TTY), fax 541-343-6812; info@miusa.org, [www.miusa.org].

Include photographs and comments of youth with different kinds of disabilities in your publicity materials—this sends a message that they are welcome.

Advertise your programs through local or national disability organizations—most have newsletters and/or web sites.

Make your information available in alternative formats such as on cassette, diskette, or in large print.

Get lists of local sign language interpreters for interviews and orientation meetings.

A basic, sturdy ramp can be built where there are one or two steps into a home or building or between different rooms.

Bathrooms and bedrooms in a dorm or homestay can be made accessible by temporarily removing the doors and hanging a curtain in their place.

Web sites can be made accessible to people with disabilities. Contact the Web Accessibility Initiative for more information at wai@w3.org or visit their web site at [www.w3.org]. Submit your web site to be assessed for accessibility for free at [www.cast.org/bobby].

Organizations that provide international alternative travel opportunities can recruit individuals with disabilities as volunteers, staff, and board members.

For more information on accessibility and the Americans with Disabilities Act, contact the Disability Rights Education and Defense Fund at 800-466-4232 (voice/TTY) or on the web at [www.dredf.org].

Half the Planet [www.halftheplanet.org]. Comprehensive, reliable information ideas, products, and services for people with disabilities including an extensive travel section.

IIE Passport [www.iiepassport.org]. A searchable online database of 5,000 U.S. education abroad programs.

International Volunteer Programs Association [www.volunteerinternational.org]. An alliance of nonprofit, non-governmental organizations based in the Americas that are involved in international volunteer and internship exchanges. Web site features a comprehensive database of volunteer and intern opportunities worldwide.

Mobility International USA [www.miusa.org]. Wealth of information on international exchange for disabled travelers.

Moss Rehab ResourceNet [www.mossresourcenet.org]. A web-based information center for people with disabilities. Includes national and international travel resources and tips.

New Horizons: Information for the Air Traveler with a Disability [www.faa.gov/acr/dat.htm]. Information from the U.S. Department of Transportation on the rights and responsibilities of travelers with disabilities.

Tourism for All [http://andi.casaccia.enea.it/hometur.htm]. Database of information on accessible sites. Currently includes Italy, Sweden, France, Germany, and Spain, with more to come.

Tours and Programs

Access/Abilities, P.O. Box 458, Mill Valley, CA 94942; 415-388-3250, fax 415-383-8718; elieber@accessabil.com, [www.accessabil.com]. Offers custom searches on accessible travel opportunities as well as information on travel destinations, including programs, services, accommodations, and transportation.

Accessible Journeys. Howard J. McCoy, 35 W. Sellers Ave., Ridley Park, PA 19078; 800-846-4537, fax 610-521-6959; sales@disabilitytravel.com, [www.disabilitytravel.com]. Travel arrangements for slow walkers and wheelchair travelers, friends, and family.

AFS Intercultural Programs, 198 Madison Ave., 8th Fl., New York, NY 10016; 800-AFS-INFO or 212-299-9000, fax 212-299-9090; afsinfo@afs.org, [www.afs.org]. Offers exchanges for high school students and educators to a variety of countries and has extensive experience accommodating participants with a range of disabilities.

Calvert Trust Exmoor, Wistlandpound, Kentisbury, Barnstaple, Devon, EX31 4SJ, U.K. Offers holidays for people of all abilities. Both self-catering and catered accommodations. Outdoor activities and indoor pool. Fax 011-44-1237-431684; calvert.exmoor@btinternet.com, [www.calvert-trust.org.uk]. The Calvert Trust also has centers at Keswick in Cumbria and at Keilder (see web site).

Camphill Associations, c/o Camphill Assn. of North America, Triform Camphill Community, 20 Triform Rd., Hudson, NY 12534; info@camphillassociation.org, [http://camphillassociation.org]. Camphill operates schools and intentional communities for people with mental disabilities in the U.S., Canada, and several other countries. They accept volunteers and interns from around the world. *The Global Directory* of international sites is available on the Camphill U.K. web site [www.camphill.org.uk].

Directions Unlimited, 123 Green Ln., Bedford Hills, NY 10507; 800-533-5343 or 914-241-1700, fax 914-241-0243; cruiseusa@aol.com. Specializes in arranging vacations and tours for persons with disabilities.

Disability Rights/Leadership Development. Mobility International USA (MIUSA) coordinates programs for people with and without disabilities focused on disability rights, leadership development and cross-cultural learning. Through the National Clearinghouse on Disability and Exchange, MIUSA also provides information and referrals for other international exchange requests.

Dates: Summers, 2-4 weeks.**Costs:** $500-$1,000 program fees. **Contact:** Stephanie Gray, Exchange Coordinator, Mobility International USA, P.O. Box 10767, Eugene, OR 97440; 541-343-1284 (V/TTY), fax 541-343-6812; info@miusa.org, [www.miusa.org].

Guided Tour, Inc., 7900 Old York Rd., Suite 114B, Elkins Park, PA 19027-2339; 215-782-1370, fax 215-635-2637; gtour400@aol.com, [www.guidedtour.com]. Programs for persons with developmental and physical challenges.

Handicapped Scuba Association International, 1104 El Prado, San Clemente, CA 92672; 949-498-4550, fax 949-498-6128; hsa@hsascuba.com, [www.hsascuba.com]. Offers information on dive trips and where you can learn to dive. Conducts 2 accessible dive travel adventure vacations per year.

Institute on Independent Living, Peterséns Väg 2, 127 41 Stockholm-Skärholmen, Sweden; 011-46-8-740-42-00, fax 011-46-8-740-45-00. Web site [www.independentliving.org/VacationHomeSwap.html] provides information on swapping vacation homes with other people with disabilities, as well as a long list of accessible guides for places around the world.

Japan-U.S. Community Education and Exchange (JUCEE), 1440 Broadway, Suite 501, Oakland, CA 94612; 510-267-1920, fax 510-267-1922; info-us@jucee.org, [www.jucee.org]. Offers internship exchanges between Japan and the U.S. for individuals seeking development in the nonprofit sector, including disability organizations.

Keli Tours, 19 Hacharoshet St., P.O. Box 2176, Keidar-Center, Raanana, Israel; 011-972-9-740-9490, fax 011-972-9-740-9408; info@keli-tours.co.il, [www.keli-tours.co.il]. Offers tours of the Middle East and Israel for people with and without disabilities.

Philanthropy Host Families, P.O. Box 7781, Santa Rosa, CA 95407; 770-569-8171; Phyllis@inreach.com. Provides homestay exchanges to Ghana focusing on community service. Working to establish deaf-related program.

SERVAS/U.S. SERVAS Committee, 11 John St., Suite 407, New York, NY 10038-4009; 212-267-0252, fax 212-267-0292; info@servas.org, [www.servas.org]. An international network that links travelers with hosts in many countries with the hope of building world peace through understanding and friendship. SERVAS actively encourages people with disabilities to join, and it has a specially prepared listing of accessible and semi-accessible homes with hosts able to accommodate either hearing, vision, or mobility impaired travelers.

The United States Peace Corps, 1111 20th St., NW, Washington, DC 20526; 800-424-8580, [www.peacecorps.gov]. Offers long-term volunteer service opportunities throughout the world. The Peace Corps actively recruits people with disabilities for their programs.

Wheelchair Travel, Ltd., Trevor Pollitt, 1 Johnston Green, Guildford, Surrey, GU2 9XS, England; 011-44-1483-233640, fax 011-44-1483-237772; trevor@wheelchairtravel.co.uk, [www.wheelchairtravel.co.uk]. A self-drive rental, taxi, and tour service specifically for disabled people, especially wheelchair-users.

WorldTeach, c/o Center for International Development, Harvard Univ., 79 John F. Kennedy St., Cambridge, MA 02138; 800-483-2240 or 617-495-5527, fax 617-495-1599; info@worldteach.org, [www.worldteach.org]. Participants are placed in 6-month to 1-year assignments teaching China, Costa Rica, Ecuador, South Africa, Honduras, or Namibia. (Countries may change; some shorter-term placements are available.) WorldTeach encourages people with disabilities to apply to its programs.

Youth for Understanding, 3501 Newark St., NW, Washington, DC 20016-3199; 800-TEENAGE or 202-966-6800, TTY 800-787-8000, fax 202-895-1104; admissions@us.yfu.org, [www.yfu.org]. Provides summer, semester, or school year high school programs in Asia, Europe, North America, South America, and the Pacific. YFU encourages students with disabilities to apply to their programs.

SIX

RESPONSIBLE TRAVEL
BEST RESOURCES AND PROGRAMS

As people take an ever-greater interest in their environment and other cultures, travel is changing. Readers looking for appropriate alternatives to conventional tourism will find the following publications, web sites, and organizations most helpful. A listing of best programs starts on page 75.

Responsible Travel Publications

Active Woman Vacation Guide by Evelyn Kaye (Blue Panda Publications). True stories by women travelers and complete information on adventure vacations worldwide. More information available at [www.travelbooks123.com].

Adventures in Nature by William Friar (Avalon, 2001). The book deftly summarizes conservation efforts in Panama and provides in-depth profiles of natural destinations throughout the country. The Panama Canal is a featured attraction and beautifully described in this book.

Adventuring with Children by Nan Jeffrey (Avalon, 2001). Her approach to this book is a must for anyone who wants to explore places overseas with their kids.

American Indians and National Parks by Robert Keller and Michael Turek (Univ. of Arizona Press, 2001). Examines the relationship of parks and Indian cultures, a story never told. A must read.

Backpacking and Hiking in Chile and Argentina by Tim Burford (Globe Pequot Press, 2001). Second edition of a great hiking and trekking book.

Beyond Safaris: A Guide to Building People-to-People Ties With Africa by Kevin Danaher

(Africa World Press). Global Exchange, 2017 Mission St., Suite 303, San Francisco, CA 94110; 415-255-7296. 1991. $12.95. A bit old but still one of the best resources for socially conscious travelers in Africa. Lists organizations.

Defending Our Rainforest: A Guide to Community-Based Ecotourism in the Ecuadorian Amazon by Rolf Wesche and Andy Drumm (Accion Amazonia, Quito, 1999). A welcome guide produced by Ecuador's Fundacion Accion Amazonia (acciona@ecnet.ec). Available from Accion Amazonia as well as through South American Explorers.

Earth-friendly Inns: Northeast (Sandbar Willow Press, 2000). Guide to "green" hotels in the U.S. Northeast. This is the first in a series. Highly recommended. Author web site [www.earthfriendlyinns.com].

Ecotourism and Sustainable Development by Martha Honey (Island Press, 1999). The most thorough and up-to-date account available of the promise and pitfalls of ecotourism.

The Ecotourist's Guide to the Ecuadorian Amazon by Rolfe Wesche. The Pan-American Center for Geographical Studies and Research, 3er piso, Apdo 17-01-4273, Quito, Ecuador; 011-593-245-1200.

The Ecotraveller's Wildlife Guides by Les Beletsky (Academic Press). Titles include *Costa Rica* (1998), *Belize and Northern Guatemala* (1998), *Tropical Mexico* (1999), *Hawaii* (1999), *Ecuador and the Galapagos Islands* (1999). $27.95 each. Each book provides information on natural history, ecology, conservation, and species identification.

Ecuador and the Galapagos Islands by Rob Rachowiecki (Lonely Planet Publications, 2001). Fifth edition of this terrific guidebook. Highly recommended.

E/The Environmental Magazine. The Earth Action Network, P.O. Box 5098, Westport, CT 06881; 203-854-5559, fax 203-866-0602; [www.emagazine.com]. Bimonthly magazine with a focus on environmental issues and awareness.

Footprint Mexico and Central America edited by Peter Hutchison (Footprint Handbooks, 2001). Reliable information about general tourism as well profiles of national parks and reserves. Highly recommended.

Footprint South America edited by Ben Box (Footprint Handbooks, 2001). A terrific guide. Highly recommended.

The Green Holiday Guides The 16 Green Holiday Guides provide more than 1,500 addresses of a variety of ecological farms and other environmentally friendly places to lodge or camp. $10 per guide from ECEAT International, P.O. Box 10899, 1001 EW Amsterdam, the Netherlands; 011-31-20-6681030, fax 011-31-20-4630594; eceat@antenna.nl, [www.eceat.nl].

The Green Host Effect: An Integrated Tourism and Resort Development by James Sweeting, Aaron Bruner, and Amy Rosenfeld (Conservation International, 1999). A thorough review of the tourism industry and the potential of ecotourism. The conclusions and recommendations are sound, though they could be more specific.

The Gringo Trail by Mark Mann (Summersdale Publishing, U.K., 1999). This riotous mix of humor and scandal documents the travels of three Brits who go to South America for different reasons.

Green Travel Sourcebook by Daniel Grotta and Sally Wiener Grotta. (John Wiley & Sons, 1992).

Green-Travel Mailing List. For green travel resources on the Internet. To subscribe contact majordomo@igc.apc.org.

Holidays That Don't Cost the Earth by John Elkington and Julia Hailes. Victor Gollancz Ltd., 14 Henrietta St., London, WC2E 8QJ, U.K.

1992. £5.99. A worldwide guide to environmental vacations.

Inside Indonesia Magazine edited by Dr. Gerry van Klinken. P.O. Box 1326, Collingwood 3066, Australia; 011-61-3-9419-4504, fax 011-61-3-9419-4774; admin@insideindonesia.org, [www.insideindonesia.org]. Fosters active links with Indonesians working for change. Includes information on ecotourism and human rights economics.

La Mosquitia: A Guide to the Land of Savannas, Rain Forests and Turtle Hungers by Derek A. Parent (Intrepid Traveller). The first guidebook to Honduras.

Last Resorts: The Cost of Tourism in the Caribbean by Polly Pattullo (Monthly Review Press). Excellent review of the tourism industry in the Caribbean.

Moon Handbooks: Honduras by Chris Humprhey (Moon Publications, 2000). This 2nd edition revises the nuts-and-bolts information about traveling in Honduras and provides an entertaining read for anyone heading to Central America.

New Frontiers. Anita Pleumarom, Coordinator, Tourism Investigation and Monitoring Team, P.O. Box 51, Chorakhebua, Bangkok 10230, Thailand; fax 011-66-2-519-2821. A bimonthly newsletter for briefing on tourism, development, and envrionment issues in the southeast Asian Mekong region.

The New Key to Costa Rica by Beatrice Blake and Anne Becher (Ulysses Press, 2000). Good all-around guide to Costa Rica with an ecology focus.

The Other Guide to Toronto (Green Tourism Association, 2000). Pioneering guide to Toronto's parks and gardens.

The Other Side of Paradise by Susan Stonich (Cognizant Communication, 2000). Excellent academic review of tourism, conservation, and development in the Bay Islands. Documents the negative impacts on the communities and the local ecosystems.

Periplus Action Guides $24.95 each. Also publishes *Periplus Adventure Guides,* $19.95 each; *Discover Indonesia Series,* 9.95 each; *The Hitchhiker's Guide to Japan,* $12.95 each. Charles E. Tuttle Co., 153 Milk St., 5th Fl., Boston, MA 02109.

Planeta [www.planeta.com], a synthesis of environmental news and travel information from the Americas. Articles range from practical field guides to academic work on ecotourism. Contact Ron Mader; ron@planeta.com.

Rethinking Tourism and Ecotravel: The Paving of Paradise and How You Can Stop It by Deborah McLaren. Kumarian Press, 14 Oakwood Ave., West Hartford, CT 06110-2127; 800-289-2664, fax 860-233-6072; [www.kpbooks.com]. 1997. $21.95. Useful information about the global tourism industry and creative alternatives. Use some of the hundreds of resources listed in this book and you will never travel the same way again.

Rough Guide to Belize by Peter Eltringham (Rough Guides, 2001). A superb 2nd edition that details the best of ways of exploring Belize (and nearby Tikal and the Bay Islands). What Belize First calls "a tour de force" is a must-read for travelers heading to this country.

Travel Unlimited: Uncommon Adventures for the Mature Traveler by Alison Gardner (Avalon Travel Publishing, 2001). This travel encyclopedia offers abundant suggestions on alternative travel including ecotourism, educational vacations, and volunteering. Author web site [www.travelwithachallenge.com].

Traveler's Venezuela Companion by Dominic Hamilton (Globe Pequot Press, 2001). We've waited several years for this excellent guidebook. Author web site [www.dominichamilton.com].

Working with the Environment by Tim Ryder. 2000. (Vacation Work, U.K., 1996, £10.99). Guide to careers that involve working with the environment. Includes a chapter on environmental tourism.

The World Awaits by Paul Otteson (Avalon Travel Publishing). This "comprehensive guide to extended backpack travel" is an excellent guide for beginners.

Responsible Tourism Organizations

Airline Ambassadors, 19 South B Street, Suite 1, San Mateo, CA 94401; 650-347-3500, fax 650-347-3882. Or contact Carl E. Oates at 214-361-1488, fax 650-347-3882 info@airlineamb.org, [www.airlineamb.org]. Group brings sustainable tourism discussions to the U.N. and medical supplies abroad.

Asia Tourism Action Network (ANTENNA), 15 Soi Soonvijai 8, New Petchburi Rd., Bangkok 10310, Thailand. A network in Asia and the Pacific promoting locally controlled tourism; publishes a newsletter.

Badri Dev Pande, Environmental Education and Awareness, P.O. Box 3923, Kathmandu, Nepal. Developing a sustainable tourism master plan of Manaslu region of Nepal.

The Bospas Forest Farm c/o Casa Dobronski, Calle Guanhuiltagua N34-457, Quito, Ecuador; bospas22@hotmail.com, [www.ecuativer.com/bospas]. The 15 hectares Bospas family farm, growing fruit and vegetables organically in a scenic Andean valley, welcomes travelers and interns/volunteers.

Center for Global Education, Augsburg College, 2211 Riverside Ave., Minneapolis, MN 55454; 800-299-8889; globaled@augsburg.edu, [www.augsburg.edu/global]. Sponsors travel seminars and semester programs in which participants learn from people of diverse backgrounds about their economic, political, and social realities. Emphasis on those struggling for justice. Programming in Mexico, Central America, Southern Africa, and Cuba.

Center for Responsible Tourism, D. Donnelly and Virginia Hadsell, 1765-D Le Roy, Berkeley, CA 94709; dodyhd@aol.com. An educational group dedicated to informing the U.S. public of the prostitution of children and women in Asian tourism.

Center for the Advancement of Responsible Travel (CART), 70 Dry Hill Park Rd., Tonbridge, Kent TN10 3BX, U.K. Center of information on responsible tourism in Europe.

Earthwatch Institute, 3 Clocktower Pl., Suite 100, Box 75, Maynard, MA 01754-0075; 800-776-0188; info@earthwatch.org, [www.earthwatch.org]. Offers working vacations with scientists around the world.

Ecumenical Coalition on Third World Tourism (ECTWT), c/o CPDC, P.O. Box 284, Bridgetown, Barbados; contours@caribnet.net; or ECTWT European office: 19 Chemin des Palettes, CH-1212 Grand Lancy, Switzerland; 011-41-22-794-49-59, fax 011-41-22-794-47-50; contours@geneva-link.ch. Only international Third World NGO focusing on impact of tourism. Publishes a quarterly magazine called *Contours*.

Elderhostel, 11 Ave. de Lafayette, Boston, MA 02111-1746; 877-426-8056; [www.elderhostel.org]. For travelers over 50. Environmentally friendly educational travel programs for seniors.

EQUATIONS: Equitable Tourism Options, No. 198, II Cross, Church Rd. (behind old KEB office), New Thippasandra, Bangalore 560 075, India; 011-9180-528-2313; admin@equation.ilban.ernet.in. Responsible tourism advocate; helps travelers locate environmentally and culturally sensitive projects in India.

Global Exchange, 2017 Mission St., Suite 303, San Francisco, CA 94110; 415-255-7296; gx-info@globalexchange.org, [www.globalexchange.org]. Reality tours focus on social, cultural, environmental issues in Third World countries.

Global Service Corps, 300 Broadway, Suite 28, San Francisco, CA 94133; 415-788-3666 ext. 128, fax 415-788-7324; gsc@igc.apc.org, [www.globalservicecorps.org]. Service-learning and cultural immersion in Costa Rica, Tanzania, or Thailand. Live with a village family while assisting grassroots organizations on community service and development projects.

Green Visions, Terezija bb (Skenderija shopping complex-Dom Mladih), Office 32, Sarajevo 71000, Bosnia and Herzegovina; Tel. 011-387-33-207-169; sarajevo@greenvisions.ba, [www.greenvisions.ba]. Provides information on ecotourism opportunities in Bosnia, Herzegovina, and Serbia.

Indonesia Resources and Information Program (IRIP), P.O. Box 190, Northcote 3070, Australia; 011-61-3-481-1581. Fosters active links with Indonesians working for change.

Institute for Central American Development Studies (ICADS) Dept. 826, P.O. Box 025216, Miami, FL 33102-5216, or ICADS, Apartado 3-2070, Sabanilla, San Jose, Costa Rica; 011-506-225-0508, fax 011-506-234-1337; icads@netbox.com. Interdisciplinary internship programs focusing on development issues from ecological and socio-economic perspectives.

International Bicycle Fund, 4887 Columbia Dr. S, #T-9, Seattle, WA 98108; 206-767-0848; ibike@ibike.org, [www.ibike.org/bike]. Promotes bicycle transport; links with autofree and bicycling organizations around the world; publishes essays on environmentally and culturally friendly traveling; sponsors bicycle tours throughout Africa and Cuba.

International Institute for Peace Through Tourism, Fox Hill 13, 685 Cottage Club Rd., Stowe, VT 05672; [www.iipt.org]. Facilitates tourism initiatives that contribute to international peace and cooperation.

ISEC/Ladakh (India) Project, P.O. Box 9475, Berkeley, CA 94709; 510-548-4915. An educational program that supports innovative grassroots development efforts of the Ladakhi people who live on the western edge of the Tibetan Plateau in India. Good resource materials. Provides Westerners with an opportunity to work on a Ladakhi farm in the summer months.

Lost Valley Educational Center, 81868 Lost Valley Ln., Dexter, OR 97431; 541-937-3351; info@lostvalley.org, [www.lostvalley.org]. Founder Dianne G. Brause, a well-known writer and leader in the field of responsible and sustainable travel (and contributing editor for *Transitions Abroad*), offers opportunities in Central America for participants to live, learn, and work with local people.

Okologischer Tourismus in Europa (OTE), Bernd Rath, Am Michaelshof 8-10, 53177 Bonn, Germany; oete-bonn@t-online.de, [www.ote.de]. Responsible tourism organization; resources in German.

Our Developing World, 13004 Paseo Presada, Saratoga, CA 95070-4125; 408-379-4431; fax 408-376-0755; odw@magiclink.net; www.magiclink.net/~odw]. Educational project bringing Third World realities to North Americans. Community programs, teacher training materials, resources library. Study tour to South Africa July/August 2002.

Responsible Tourism Network, RTN Coordinator, P.O. Box 34, Rundle Mall, Adelaide, SA, Australia 5000; 011-618-232-2727, fax 011-618-232-2808; bwitty@ozemail.com.au, [www.caa.org.au/travel/rtn/]. Responsible tourism by Australians. Works with tourists, travel industry, and host communities. Publishes *Travel Wise* and *Travel Smart,* practical tips for responsible tourists.

Rethinking Tourism Project, 366 North Prior Ave., Suite 203, St. Paul, MN 55104; 651-644-9984, fax 651-644-2720; RTProject@rethinkingtourism.org, [www.rethinkingtourism.org]. An educational and networking project for indigenous peoples. Offers some volunteer opportunities and internships, mainly in U.S.

Tourism Concern, Stapleton House, 277-281 Holloway Rd., London N7 8HN, U.K.; 011-44-0207-753-3330, fax 011-44-0207-753-3331; info@tourismconcern.org.uk, [www.tourismconcern.org.uk]. Excellent resource on issues related to tourism: land rights, displacement, general responsible tourism information.

Tourism With Insight (Arbeitsgemeinschaft Tourismus mit Einsicht), Hadorter Str. 9B, D-8130 Starnberg, Germany. Responsible tourism study group.

Transitions Abroad $28/6 issues. P.O. Box 1300, Amherst, MA 10014-1300; 800-293-0373, fax 413-256-0373; info@TransitionsAbroad.com, [www.TransitionsAbroad.com]. Bimonthly resource guide to work, living, study, and travel abroad advocates and publishes information on culturally and ecologically responsible travel.

University Research Expeditions Program, Univ. of California, 1 Shields Ave., Davis, CA 95616; 530-752-0692; urep@ucdavis.edu, [http://urep.ucdavis.edu]. Field research expeditions worldwide for travelers of all ages. The program uses its own codes of conduct for researchers and travelers visiting indigenous lands.

Ecotourism Organizations

Alaska Wilderness Recreation and Tourism Assn. (AWRTA), 2207 Spenard Rd., Suite 201, Anchorage, Alaska 99503; 907-258-3171, fax 907-258-3851; info@awrta.org, [www.awrta.org]. Membership organization of small, locally-owned ecotour operators and native-owned ecotourism programs. Promotes the protection of Alaska's wild places.

Annapurna Conservation Area Project (ACAP), ACAP Headquarters Ghandruk, Ghandruk Panchayat, Kaski District, Nepal. An international project that uses trekkers' fees to protect the environment and culture of the Gurung people in north central Nepal.

Asociación Ecuatoriana de Ecoturismo (ASEC) Diego Andrade, Calle Victor Hugo E10-111 y Isla Pinzon, Ciudadela Jipijapa, Quito, Ecuador; 245-055 y 466-295; asec@accessinter.net, [www.planeta.com/ecotravel/south/ecuador/asec.html].

Asociación Ecuatoriana de Ecoturismo (ASEC), Calle Victor Hugo E10-111 y Isla Pinzon, Ciudadela Jipijapa, Quito, Ecuador; 011-245-055 y 466-295; asec@accessinter.net, [www.planeta.com/ecotravel/south/ecuador/asec.html]. Contact: Diego Andrade.

Asociación Méxicana de Turismo de Aventura y Ecoturismo (Mexican Association of Adventure Travel and Ecotourism - Amtave) AMTAVE; info@amtave.com, [www.amtave.com] is a group of about 80 plus travel providers who work in the fields of ecotourism and adventure tourism. The association produces an annual catalog and boasts a useful web site. Currently, the organization is run by 8 co-presidents who are in charge of various regions in Mexico.

Baikal Reflections, Inc., P.O. Box 310, Mesa, CO 81643-0310; 970-268-5885, fax 970-268-5884; baikal@ITI2.net. Offers programs to Siberia.

Belize Ecotourism Association (BTIA), 195A Vista Del Mar, Ladyville 025-2806, Belize; [www.belizeecotourism.org]. Formed on Earth Day, 1993, by a small group of members of the Belize Tourism Industry Association, BETA serves as an advocate for conservation and ecologically-sound development of tourism within BTIA and Belize.

Bhutan Tourism Authority, Bhutan Tourism Corporation Ltd., P.O. Box 159, Thimphu, Bhutan; 011-975-2-22854/24045/22647; [www.kingdomofbhutan.com/travel.html]. The Bhutanese government is implementing a new ecotourism management program in the Jigme Dorji National Park.

Bina Swadaya Tours, Jln. Gunung Sahari III/7, Jakarta 10610, P.O. Box 1456, Jakarta, 10014, Indonesia; 011-62-21-420-44-02, fax 011-62-21-425-65-40; bst@cbn.net.id, [www.ecoclub.com/bst]. Travelers visit rural community to learn about Indonesia's daily life and ethnic tribes, and experience village stays to observe community's income-generating development projects. Destinations include Java, Bali, Sumatra, and Kalimantan (Borneo).

Conservation International, Eco-Escuela de Espanol 2501 M St., NW, Suite 200, Washington, DC 20037; 800-429-5660 ext 264, fax 202-887-5188; s.vigilante@conservation.org, [www.ecomaya.com]. Daniel Vizcaino; vizcaino@conservation.org. Conservation International believes that carefully planned and implemented tourism development can be a sustainable economic alternative. Works with the Ixcán Biological Station in Chiapas; Una Ecopark and Fazenda Rio Negro in Brazil; Chalalán Ecolodge in Bolivia and Eco Maya in Guatemala.

COOPRENA (National Eco-Agricultural Cooperative Network of Costa Rica), Apdo. 6939-1000 San Jose, Costa Rica; 011-506-286-4203; cooprena@racsa.co.cr, [www.agroecoturismo.net/english/index.htm]. Consortium of cooperatives developing eco-agro tourism and small farms.

The Cousteau Society, 870 Greenbriar Cir., #402, Chesapeake, VA 23320; 757-523-9335; cousteau@cousteausociety.org, [www.cousteausociety.org]. Good marine guidelines and information about threats to the world's oceans.

Departamento de Recursos Naturales/ICT (Costa Rican Tourism Institute) San Jose, Costa Rica; 506-223-1733, ext. 328; info@turismo-sostenible.co.cr, [www.turismo-sostenible.co cr]. Contacts: Rodolfo Lizano and Alberto Sanchez. A Costa Rican government office which is developing certification standards for green hotels.

Earth Island Institute, 300 Broadway, Suite 28, San Francisco, CA 94133; 415-788-3666; [www.earthisland.org]. Provides organizational support to individuals in developing projects for the conservation and restoration of the global enviornment. Thirty projects worldwide including Baikal Watch and ecotours to eastern Russia, [www.earthisland.org/baikal/baikal.html].

Earthstewards Network, PeaceTrees Vietnam P.O. Box 10697, Bainbridge Island, WA 98110; 206-842-7986, fax 206-842-8918. For PeaceTrees projects contact Chuck Meadows; chuckm@peacetrees.vietnam.org, [www.earthstewards.org].

ECOCLUB.com. An international ecotourism club. Free membership for ecotourists, genuine ecotourism providers, eco-professionals, academics, and students. Travel advice, news, networking, and discounts in ecotours, ecolodges, and eco-products. Ecoclub SA, P.O. Box 65232, Psihico, Athens 15410, Greece; 011-30-1-671-9-671, fax 011-30-1-671-9-251; [www.ecoclub.com].

Ecotourism Association of Australia, GPO Box 268, Brisbane, Queensland 4001; 011-61-7-3229-5550, fax 011-61-7-3229-5255; mail@ecotourism.org.au, [www.ecotourism.org.au].

Ecoventure, Ronald Ziegler, Washington State Univ. Libraries, Pullman, WA 99164-5610; fax 509-335-6721; ziegler@wsu.edu, [[www.wsulibs.wsu.edu/ecoventure/ !ecovent.htm]. Ecoventure has a database, BaseCamp, to provide travelers with information on ecotourism.

Europe Conservation, Via Fusetti, 14-20143 Milano, Italy; 011-390-2-5810-3135.

European Center for Eco Agro Tourism, P.O. Box 10899, Amsterdam 1001 EW, The Netherlands. Promotes eco-agro tourism, a sustainable tour option for people with green thumbs.

Euroter, 82, rue Francois Rolland, F 94130 Nogent-sur-Marne, France; 011-331-4514-6421. Publishes principles for developing green tourism in European villages.

eXito Latin America Travel Specialists, Inc. 1212 Broadway, Suite 910, Oakland, CA 94612; 800-655-4054, 510-655-2154; 108 Rutgers St., Ft. Collins, CO 80525; 800-809-9878, 970-490-1114; ecotravel@wonderlink.com, [www.exitotravel.com]. Airline ticket consolidator offering travel arrangements, advice for budget travelers, and tour packages that support local economies and environmentally conscious operation instead of quick profits.

Friends of MalaeKahana, P.O. Box 305, Laie, HI 96762; 808-293-1736. Native Hawaiian civic group operates ecotourism and low-impact tourism along historic beach. Native Hawaiian group operates MalaeKahana State Recreation Area. Ecotourism-based campground/cabin management for the state of Hawaii.

Golondrinas Cloudforest Conservation Project, Calle Isabel La Catolica 1559 (n24-679), Quito, Ecuador; 011-593-2-226-602; manteca@uio.satnet.net, [www.ecuadorexplorer.com/golondrinas]. A conservation organization conserving 25,000 hectares of cloudforests on the northwest slopes of the Andes. They have volunteer and educational programs, including a 4-day trek through the Cerro Golondrinas area.

Hawaii Ecotourism Association, P.O. Box 61435, Honolulu, HI 96839; 877-300-7058; hea@aloha.net, [http://hawaiiecotourism.org]. Responsible tourism resource network for Hawaii and the Pacific.

INDECON Foundation, Jl. Taman Margasatwa No. 61, Jati Padang, Jakarta 12540, Indonesia; 011-62-21-788-38624, fax 011-62-21-780-0265; indecon@indosat.net.id, [http://indecon.i-2.co.id/index.html]. Helps link ecotourists with a wide range of opportunities throughout Indonesia.

The International Ecotourism Society, P.O. Box 668, Burlington, VT 05402; 802-651-9818, fax 802-651-9819; ecomail@ecotourism.org, [www.ecotourism.org]. A nonprofit membership organization representing the ecotourism industry.

Journeys International, 107 Aprill Dr., Ann Arbor, MI 48103; 734-665-4407 or 800-255-8735; [www.journeys-intl.com]. A well-established ecotour operator. Guides are either natives or residents of the countries they visit. Part of their profits support environmental preservation. Destinations include Asia, Africa, the Middle East, Australia, the Pacific, South and Central America, Europe and the Mediterranean, and the polar regions.

Kiskeya, P.O. Box 109-Z, Zona Colonial, Santo Domingo, Rep. Dominicana; 809-537 89 77; kad@kiskeya-alternative.org, [http://kiskeya-alternative.org/cangonet]. Enterprising organization focusing on ecotourism as well as indigenous dance. Works mostly in the Caribbean.

Kodukant Ecotourism Initiative, SAARISOO, EE 3482 Joesuu, Parnumaa, Estonia; 011-372-446-6405. A network of small tour operators living in or near protected areas.

Lisle, Inc., 900 County Rd. 269, Leander, TX 78641-9517; 800-477-1538, fax 512-259-0392; lisle@utnet.utoledo.edu, [www.lisleinternational.org]. Pioneer people-to-people program. Destinations include Costa Rica, Bali, Turkey, and India.

Oceanic Society Expeditions, Fort Mason Center, Building E, San Francisco, CA 94123; 415-441-1106, fax 415-474-3395; [www.oceanic-society.org]. Promotes environmental stewardship, education, and research through ecotourism.

Pax World Tours/Mercy Corps, 3015 SW First Ave., Portland, OR 97201; 800-292-3355 ext. 250, fax 503-796-6843; info@mercycorps.org, [www.mercycorps.org]. Works for peace and justice through innovative programs that encourage peacemaking and community-based development. Promotes people-to-people links and responsible tourism.

School for Field Studies, 16 Broadway, Beverly, MA 01915; 800-989-4435 , fax 978-927-5127; admissions@fieldstudies.org, [www.fieldstudies.org]. Field studies and hands-on opportunities for high school and college students concerned about the environment.

Sea Turtle Restoration Project, P.O. Box 400, Forest Knolls, CA 94933; 415-488-0370; rarauz@sol.racsa.co.cr, [www.seaturtles.org]. STRP advocates responsible fishery practices, marine reserves, and environmental regulations in world trade and pursues these goals internationally. Environmental internship available Aug 15-Jan 15 in which participants learn about sea turtles and patrol their nesting beach while working with Costa Rican conservationists and biologists.

Sierra Club, 85 2nd St., 2nd Fl., San Francisco, CA 94105; 415-977-5500, fax 415-977-5799; information@sierraclub.org, [www.sierraclub.org/]. Publishes good travel guides, offers conservation focused tours around the world.

Sikkim Biodiversity and Ecotourism Project, P.O. Tadong, Sikkim 737102, India; 011-91-3592-31046, fax 011-91-3592-31090; tmisikk@dte.vsnl.net.in. Develops and implements regional ecotourism program with local communities in the Sikkim Himalayas.

South American Explorers (SAE), 126 Indian Creek Rd., Ithaca, NY 14850; 607-277-0488; explorer@saexplorers.org, [www.saexplorers.org]. Promotes ecologically responsible tourism. Has clubhouses in Quito, Ecuador and Lima and Cusco, Peru. Publishes quarterly magazine and sells books and maps.

Toledo Ecotourism Association (TEA), San Miguel Village, Toledo District, Belize. Contact Pabzo Ack, BTB Information Center, Punta Gorda, P.O. Box 180, Belize; 011-501-72-2531, fax 011-501-72-2199; tide@btl.net, [www.public.usit.net/plenty1/TEA.html]. Network of indigenous farm cooperatives in pristine Mayan lands.

Tour de Cana, P.O. Box 7293, Philadelphia, PA 19101; 215-222-1253, fax 215-222-1253 then press *21; tourdecana@aol.com. An outgrowth of the organization Bikes Not Bombs, this group is a proponent of responsible tourism and, with the International Bicycle Fund, organizes bike-study tours to some islands of the Caribbean that are, at least temporarily, less accessible to U.S. citizens.

Travel Quest, 5050 Sepulveda Blvd., Sherman Oaks, CA 91430; 919-789-6080; 74732.3153@compuserve.com. Promotes greater care and understanding of the planet, people, and other beings.

Tropical Biodiversity Center, Apdo 8-3870, San Jose 1000, Costa Rica; 011-506-291-0862, fax 011-506-253-4963; hjimenez@racsa.co.cr, [www.geocities.com/rainforest/9148]. Courses on Tropical Birding and Tropical Dendrology every year, in Spanish (April) and English (March, June, August).

Turismo Ecologico y Cultural del Pueblo Maya, San Cristobal de las Casas, Chiapas, Mexico. An indigenous-owned alternative ecotour group.

Wildland Adventures, Inc., 3516 NE 155th St., Seattle, WA 98155; 800-345-4453, 206-365-0686; info@wildland.com, [www.wildland.com]. Ecotour operator offers group travel, customized trips, rainforest workshops, and responsible trips such as conservation projects and community services. Contributes part of profits to conservation and community development at the local level.

Wildlife Conservation International, P.O. Box 68244, Nairobi, Kenya; 011-222254-221-699. Information about ecotourism projects in Kenya.

World Wildlife Fund, 1250 24th St., NW, Washington, DC 20037; 800-CALL-WWF; [www.worldwildlife.org]. Offers ecotours throughout the world. Useful information about the global tourism industry and creative alternatives.

Ecotour Operators

Adventure Life Journeys, P.O. Box 956, Missoula, MT 59806; 800-344-6118 and 406-541-2677, fax 406-541-2676; info@adventure-life.comm, [www.adventure-life.com]. Contact: Brian Morgan. Shows travelers the true colors of the Andes, Amazon, Galapagos and Central America. Small groups, family-run hotels, local transportation, and local guides intimate with the area are the foundations of the company's travel philosophy. Trips explore local culture, ecology, and life in remote villages, wild jungles, and breathtaking mountains.

Alandaluz. Eco-minded hotel and education center on the Pacific coast. Reservations in Quito: Banquedano 330 y Reina Victoria; 011-593-2-505-084; info@alandaluz.com and alandalu@ecuanex.net.ec, [www.alandaluz.com].

America Tours Av. 16 de Julio (El Prado), 1490 Efidicio Avenida, Oficina #9, La Paz, Bolivia; 011-591-2-374204, fax 011-591-2-310023; jmiranda@ceibo.entelnet.com, [www.america-ecotours.com]. Contact: Jazmin Caballero. Specializes in quality ecotourism throughout Bolivia.

Bahia Dolphin Tours Calle Bolivar 1004 y Riofrio, Bahia de Caraquez, Ecuador; 011-593-5-692-097 or 692-086, fax 011-593-5-692-088; archtour@telconet.net, [www.qni.com/~mj/bahia/index.html]. Contact: Patricio Tamariz. Eco cultural tour operator for Chirije (beautiful beachfront cabins on a secluded beach on an important archaeological site surrounded by Dry Tropical Forest). Economical packages.

Costa Rica Expeditions, Calle Central & Avenida 3, San Jose, Costa Rica. Mailing address: PO Box 025216. Dept 235, Miami, FL 33102-5216; 506-257-0766, fax 506-257-1665; costaric@expeditions.co.cr, [www.costaricaexpeditions.com]. Recommended by more guidebooks than any other company in Costa Rica.

Durham-San Ramon Sister Communities, Apartado 28, Matagalpa, Nicaragua; 505-612-5003. U.S.: 1320 Shepherd St., Durham, NC 27707; 919-489-1656; info@durham-sanramon.org and herma@ibw.com.ni, [www.durham-sanramon.org]. D-SRSC is a partnership between Durham, NC and San Ramon, Nicaragua involving ecotourism trips, organic shade-grown coffee, homestays, health, water, and education projects.

Eco Paraiso, Celestun, Yucatan, Mexico; 011-(991-621-00 and 620-60; info@ecoparaiso.com, [www.ecoparaiso.com]. Eco-friendly hotel on the Gulf of Mexico with guided tours to the nearby Celestun Biosphere Reserve.

Ecocolors, Camaron #32, SM 27, Cancun, Quintana Roo; Tel./fax 011-98-84-95-80 and 011-84-36-67; ecoco@cancun.com.mx, [www.cancun.com.mx/ecocolors]. Contact: Kenneth Johnson. Ecotourism in the Maya World.

Ecotrackers Network Foundation, Av. Amazonas, N21 - 217, 21•4 Floor and Roca Sts., Quito, Ecuador; 011-593-2Ê-55-98-13Ê/Ê 56-48-40; ecotrackers_ecuador@hotmail.com, [www.ecotrackers.8k.com]. Volunteers live in a local community for a week or more, learn Spanish, help to preserve the culture and environment.

Ecoturismo Yucatan, Calle 3 #235 (between 32-A and 34), 97219 Merida, Yucatan; 011-99-25-21-87 and 011-99-20-27-72; alfonso@ecoyuc.com, [www.ecoyuc.com]. Contacts: Alfonso Escobedo and Roberta Graham de Escobedo. Package and custom tours of the world of the Maya including archaeology, culture, birdwatching, kayak and bicycle tours.

Himalayan High Treks, 241 Dolores St., San Francisco, CA 94103-2211; 800-455-8735; effie@himalayanhightreks.com, [www.himalayanhightreks.com]. A small trekking company that specializes in trips to Bhutan, India, Nepal, and Tibet; publishes newsletter.

La Cooperativa de los Guias Alta y Baja Tarahumara, Municipal de Guachochi, Norogachi, MPO de Guachochi, Chihuahua, Mexico; 011-51-50-1003. Contact: Martha Garcia, P. O. Box 203, Bozeman, MT 59771; 406-587-3585, fax 253-550-5387. Contact: Santiago James Barnaby, santiago@coppercanyonguide.com, [www.coppercanyonguide.com]. Homestay, custom trips for individuals or small groups offering a focus on culture, natural history, or canyoneering adventures in the Copper Canyon, Chihuahua, Mexico.

Marlene Ehrenberg Tours, Mexico City; marlene_ehrenberg@hotmail.com, [http://marlene366.tripod.com]. Specialized tours that focus on the ecology and culture of Mexico.

Mayatours, 2608 N. Ocean Blvd., Suite 108, Pompano Beach, FL 33062; 954 942-6262, fax 954-783-7414; info@mayatour.com, [www.mayatour.com]. Contact: Robert Beels. Archaelogical tours to Maya sites, ecological and traditional tours, scuba diving and vacation packages to Central America.

Pantera Excursions, Apdo Postal 670, 34000 Durango, Durango, Mexico; 011-18-25-0682; pantera@omanet.com.mx, [www.aventurapantera.com.mx]. Contact: Walter Bishop. Offers tours of Sierra Tarahumara, Baja California, and Sierra Madre.

Rainforest Expeditions, Ave. Aramburu, 166, 4b, Miraflores, Lima, Peru; 011-511-4218347, fax 011-511-421-8183. U.S. contact: Mario Corvetto, mlcorvetto@aol.com, [www.perunature.com]. Contact: Luis Zapater. Rainforest tours to Tambopata Research Center (13 rooms) and Posada Amazonas (24 rooms) located in the Connecticut-sized southeastern Peruvian Amazon reserve of Tambopata Candamo.

Savvy Travel, 1325 Howard Av., #416, Burlingame, CA 94010; 650-342-4887 or 800-276-8328, fax 650-342-4891; savvytravl@aol.com, [www.savvytravel.net]. Eco-ethno adventures throughout South America. Active small groups, unique itineraries.

Tierra Dentro, Reforma 528-B, 68000 Oaxaca, Oaxaca, Mexico; 011-9-514-9284. U.S. fax 603-375-8434; info@tierradentro.com, [www.TierraDentro.com]. Contact: Livingston Monteverde and Gloria Gracida. Specializing in rock climbing and mountaineering; expeditions to the Mexican volcanos.

The Travel Specialists, M.J. Kietzke and Susan McGonagle, 120 Beacon St., Somerville, MA 02143; 800-370-7400 ext 51; mj@tvlcoll.com or susan@tvlcoll.com, [www.travelcollaborative.com/pages/directory/index.htm]. Evaluates travel programs, operators, and the travel industry; arranges alternative trips and programs worldwide, full-service travel agency.

Tread Lightly Limited, 37 Juniper Meadow, Washington Depot, CT 06794; 800-643-0060 or 860-868-1710, fax 860-868-0298; PaTread@aol.com, [www.treadlightly.com]. Contact: Audrey Patterson. Focus on Central America.

Tropic Ecological Adventures, Av. Republica E7-320 y Diego de Almagro, Edifico Taurus, Dpt 1-A; 011-593-2-234-594/225-907, fax 011-593-2-560-756; sdtropic@uio.satnet.net, [www.tropiceco.com]. Contact: Sofia Darquea. An award-winning ecotourism operator offering nature and culture-based trips in the Amazon, Andes, and the Galapagos Islands.

The Best Ecotravel Web Sites

The Ecotourism Explorer [www.ecotourism.org] is a well-organized site of interest to ecotravelers and eco-professionals alike.

The Ecotravel Center site [www.ecotour.org], sponsored by Conservation International, has lists of tour operators, resources, and destinations. Also has a Travel Forum chat room where you can exchange information and ideas with other travelers.

Gonomad.com [www.gonomad.com] offers resources, trip planning advice, and discussions among active travelers.

The Great Outdoor Recreation Pages (GORP) site [www.gorp.com] is one of the webs most content-rich travel sites. They have loads of information on a multitude of destinations and adventure travel topics.

The Green-Travel Directory of Organizations [www.green-travel.com/] is the Web's pioneering global directory of ecotravel organizations with links to email and web sites.

Planeta [www.planeta.com]. A synthesis of environmental news and travel information from the Americas. Articles range from practical field guides to academic work on ecotourism. The site hosts more than 50 different email forums focusing on individual countries as well as topical subjects. Contact: Ron Mader, ron@planeta.com.

Tourism Concern [www.tourismconcern.org.uk/] is a membership network set up in 1989 to bring together people concerned about tourism¹s impact on communities and the environment. Their site has a good resource section.

The Vegetarian Vacations site [www.vegetarian-vacations.com/] has a list of tours, holidays, and courses which offer exclusively vegetarian or vegan cuisine.

Responsible Travel Programs

Canada

Strathcona Park Lodge and Outdoor Education Center. Alpine to Ocean Adventures take you to wilderness settings where you come across few other travelers, whether it be sea kayaking, canoeing, trekking, backpacking, mountaineering, rock climbing.

Dates: Mar to Nov. **Costs:** From $50 per person per day. **Contact:** Strathcona Park Lodge C.O.L.T., P.O. Box 2160, Campbell River, BC, V9W 5C5, Canada; 250-286-3122, fax 250-286-6010; info@strathcona.bc.ca, [www.strathcona.bc.ca].

Caribbean

Tacaribe Tour Operators Ltd. Inbound. Adventure travel, bird watching, nature trails, rainforest, hiking, cave explorations, natural history, agritourism, turtle watching, scuba diving, kayaking, sightseeing, etc.

Dates: Contact organization for details. **Costs:** Contact organization for details. **Contact:** Dominic Salvary, Tacaribe Tour Operators, Ltd., LP50 Esperanza Dr., Champ Fleurs, Trinidad and Tobago, West Indies; tacaribe@tstt.net.tt.

Central America

Nicaragua Work Trips. El Porvenir, a nonprofit dedicated to sustainable development, offers 1-week and 2-week work trips to Nicaragua. Work in small groups (10 or less) in a rural community with local families constructing simple water and sanitation or reforestation projects. Get to know other parts of Nicaragua in recreational/educational side trips. Construction skills or Spanish are not required. Accompanied by bilingual U.S. staff.

Dates: Jan 7-21; Feb 9-18; Jul 13-27. **Costs:** $750 plus airfare. **Contact:** Carole Harper, El Porvenir, 2508 42nd St., Sacramento, CA 95817; 916-736-3663; info@elporvenir.org, [www.elporvenir.org].

Costa Rica

Costa Rica Rainforest Outward Bound. CRROBS offers everything from 15-day treks to our 85-day tri-country semester course. The courses feature such activities as white-water rafting, canopy/rock climbing, village homestays, rainforest trekking with indigenous guides, surf adventures, and cave exploring.

Dates: Year round. **Costs:** Contact sponsor. **Contact:** Costa Rica Rainforest Outward Bound School, P.O. Box 243, Quepos, Costa Rica; 011-506-777-1222; info@crrobs.org, [www.crrobs.org].

Learn Spanish While Volunteering. Assist with the training of Costa Rican public school teachers in ESL and computers. Assist local health clinic, social service agencies, and environmental projects. Enjoy learning Spanish in the morning, volunteer work in the after-noon/evening. Spanish classes of 2-4 students plus group learning activities; conversations with middle class homestay families (1 student or couple per family). Homestays and most volunteer projects are in a small town near the capital, San José.

Dates: Year round, all levels. Classes begin every Monday (except Mar 25-29 and Dec 14-Jan 5), volunteer program is continuous. **Costs:** $345 per week for 26 hours of classes and group activities including Costa Rican dance and cooking classes. Includes tuition, meals, homestay, laundry, all materials, weekly 3-hour

cultural tour, and airport transportation. $25 one-time registration fee. **Contact:** Susan Shores, Registrar, Latin American Language Center, PMB 123, 7485 Rush River Dr., Suite 710, Sacramento, CA 95831-5260; 916-447-0938, fax 916-428-9542; lalc@madre.com, [www.madre.com/~lalc].

Cyprus

The Laona Project. A sustainable development project assisting the economies of small rural communities in northwestern Cyprus. Visitors stay in comfortable, carefully-renovated village houses or inns in beautiful scenery and experience the quiet rhythm of a traditional way of life.

Dates: Year round. **Costs:** Approx. $40 per day (low season) to $55 (high season). **Contact:** The Laona Project, P.O. Box 50257, 3502 Limassol, Cyprus; 011-357-5-369475, fax 011-357-5-352657; ccf@dial.cylink.com.cy.

Ecuador

Galápagos Travel. Workshops in the Galápagos Islands. Specializing in comprehensive, educationally-oriented, professionally-led natural history tours of the Galápagos Islands. Each trip spends 11 days to 2 full weeks in the Galápagos, touring all the significant outer islands, and allowing for a maximum of wildlife observation. Three distinct itineraries available.

Dates: Monthly departures on 16-passenger yachts. **Costs:** Approx. $3,400-$4,200. Airfare not included. **Contact:** Galápagos Travel, 783 Rio Del Mar Blvd., Suite 47, Aptos, CA 95003; 800-969-9014, fax 831-689-9195; galapagostravel@compuserve.com, [www.galapagostravel.com].

Europe

Explore Europe by Bicycle. A leisurely way of seeing beautiful regions in Europe.

Dates: Mid Apr-mid Oct. **Costs:** $1,390-$1,830. **Contact:** International Bicycle Tours, P.O. Box 754, Essex, CT 06426; 860-767-7005, fax 860-767-3090; bikeibt@worldnet.att.net, [www.internationalbicycletours.com].

Self-Guided: Cycling/Walking. Travel at your own pace, with support behind the scenes. No group to slow you down or rush you. Route instructions, accommodations, luggage transfers, emergency support provided. Bike included on cycling tours. Flexible itineraries. Stay in B and B's family-run hotels, country manors. Unique Drive, Hike, and Stroll tours, as well as a variety of Short Escapes.

Dates: Year round; start almost any day—your choice. **Costs:** Vary by tour and number of days. **Contact:** Randonnée Tours, 62 Albert St., #100, Winnipeg, MB, Canada R3B 1E9; 800-465-6488, 204-475-6939, fax 204-474-1888; info@randonneetours.com, [www.randonneetours.com].

India

Responsible Travel Programs. Itineraries within India, Nepal, Bhutan, and Sikkim, Tibet, with emphasis on small and deluxe hotels, visiting families, meeting locals at all levels, no hotel meals. Transportation ranges from deluxe motorcoaches to cars to horse carts to camel carts to cycle rickshaws; elephant and camel rides; visiting jungles and villages; walks and visiting local market places and schools.

Dates: Various. **Costs:** $3,995-$4,495 each from West coast with hotels, sightseeing, most meals and tips, airfare. (1999). **Contact:** Suraj Zutshi, CTC, Unique Journeys, 71 Keystone Ave., Reno, NV 89503; 775-323-0110, fax 775-323-6914. [www.uniquejourney.com].

Mexico

Eco-Adventure Resort. Adventure trips, snorkeling, fishing, whale watching, kayaking, horseback riding, surfing, and mountain biking.

Dates: Year round. **Costs:** $98-$118 per night double occupancy. **Contact:** Reservations 800-365-7613. 224 Avenida del Mar, Suite D, San Clemente, CA 92672; getaway@costaazul.com.

Mar de Jade Ocean-front Center, Chacala, Nayarit. Celebrating our 20th year as a center for responsible tourism, we are located in the fishing village of Chacala on its beautiful beach north of Puerto Vallarta. For 15-years, our volunteer/study program has been offering opportunities to guests to learn Spanish and put it to use in rural community volunteer projects, including a medical clinic, an after school program for children, a community kitchen and garden project, ESL classes, and house construction. Guests gain insight into local culture through volunteering. Surrounded by lush jungle with the warm, clear Pacific at our door, they enjoy swimming, surfing, hiking, horseback riding, snorkeling, kayaking, whale-watching, and other excursions. Our calendar of retreats include yoga, meditation among others as well as our teen summer camp.

Dates: Year round. **Costs:** All rates are per person per night and include accommodations and 3 meals daily. Rates start at $60 per person per night for shared accommodations (up to 4 in a room), or $1,200 for 21 day/20 night optional volunteer program. Doubles, singles, suites, master suites, and apartments available. Add 15 percent tax to all rates. Reduced 3-week rates available in May, June, September, October. Children welcome. Optional Spanish classes: $80 per week with minimum of 6-night stay. Group rates available. **Contact:** In Mexico, Tel./fax 011-52-322-21171; Tel. 011-52-322-23524. U.S. mailing address: PMB 078-344, 705 Martens Ct., Laredo, TX 78041-6010; info@mardejade.com, [www.mardejade.com].

Travel/Study Seminars. Learn from Mexicans of diverse backgrounds about their economic, political, and social realities. Emphasis on the views of the poor and oppressed. Programming in Cuernavaca, Mexico City, and Chiapas. Call for a free list of upcoming programs or to learn about organizing your own custom trip.

Dates: Ongoing. **Costs:** $800-$1,900 depending on package, destination, and length of trip. **Contact:** Center for Global Education at Augsburg College, 2211 Riverside Ave., Box 307TR, Minneapolis, MN 55454; 800-299-8889, fax 612-330-1695; globaled@augsburg.edu, [www.augsburg.edu/global].

New Zealand

New Zealand Pedaltours. New Zealand is a cycling paradise with fantastically beautiful scenery. Cycle as much as you wish each day with a comfortable minibus and trailer to carry your luggage and you at any time. Excellent accommodations and great meals. Experienced local guides knowledgeable about local flora and history.

Dates: Nov-Mar. **Costs:** $495-$2,710. **Contact:** Allan Blackman, 522 29th Ave. S., Seattle, WA 98144; 888-696-2080; blackallan@aol.com.

Serious Fun New Zealand. Serious Fun has operated high quality, small-group, locally guided hiking adventure tours of the stunning South Island of New Zealand since 1987. The 14-day Best of the South Island Tour (Oct-Apr) is highlighted by a swim with the dolphins at Kaikoura and a 3-day tramp along the Routeburn Track.

Dates: 2002: Jan 14-27; Feb 4-17; Feb 25-Mar 10, Mar 18-31; Nov 18-Dec 1; Dec 23-Jan 5. 2003: Jan 13-26; Feb 10-23; Mar 10-23. **Costs:** $2,320-$2,950. **Contact:** Stu Wilson, Serious

COSTA RICA ECOCRUISING

SMALL-SHIP TRAVEL TO PROTECTED FORESTS

By Carla Waldemar

I love Costa Rica and hate cruising.

However, after reading the description of Temptress Adventure Cruises' itinerary and philosophy I weakened and signed on. The trip—promoted as offering "all the thrills and inspiration of a rugged adventure" while maintaining a serious commitment to preservation of nature and the local culture—more than fulfilled its pledge.

With a small ship like the 33-cabin Voyager we were able to reach protected forests that the big ships couldn't even wave at and where roads were non-existent.

After nightly briefings, we chose from among the next day's activities—usually a choice of three morning-long hikes of varying difficulty. Each walk was led by a trained naturalist, knowledgeable about the flora and fauna and able to point out many things we'd surely have missed on our own (such as the "logs" that turned out to be crocodiles).

On our return, a lavish picnic lunch awaited us on shore, followed by time for swimming or sunning, snorkeling, scubadiving, or another hike (as well as deep-sea fishing and horseback riding through the jungle at a small extra charge). We could ferry back any time we chose to sip a piña colada on the deck (all drinks as well as exquisitely-served meals and snacks are included in the price).

Travel along the country's west coast was done mostly at night, leaving full days for exploration or relaxing. Cabins, while small, were comfortable, each with a panoramic window that actually opened. With so few cabins and a ration of 3:1 guests to crew, services were never lacking. The friendly crew even provided laundry service twice a week, included in the price.

The temptress bus picks up and drops off passengers in San Jose. Rates for three nights begin at $830, seven nights $1,045, which includes meals and snacks. Visit [www.temptresscruises.com], email info@temptresscruises.com, or call 800-336-8423.

Fun New Zealand, 3103 Whiteway Dr., Austin, TX 78757; 800-411-5724; outland@bga.com, [www.seriousfunnewzealand.com].

Pacific Region

Hawaii's Kalani Oceanside Retreat. Fun, educational and affordable, Kalani Oceanside Retreat is the only coastal lodging facility within Hawaii's largest conservation area. Kalani offers traditional culture, healthful cuisine, wellness programs, and extraordinary natural beauty: thermal springs, a naturist dolphin beach, snorkel pools, kayaking, waterfalls, crater lake, and spectacular Volcanoes National Park. Ongoing offerings in yoga, dance, hula, mythology, and massage. Or participate in an annual week-long event: men's/women's/couples conferences, dance/music/hula festivals, yoga/ meditation/transformation retreats. Applications are also being accepted for our international Volunteer Scholar program.
Dates: Year round. Costs: Lodging $60-$240 per day. Camping $20-$30. $600-$1,542 per week for most programs, including meals and lodging choice. Contact: Richard Koob, Director, Kalani Educational Oceanside Retreat, RR2, Box 4500, Pahoa-Beach Rd., HI 96778-9724; 800-800-6886 or 808-965-7828, fax 808-965-0527; kalani@kalani.com, [www.kalani.com].

Papua New Guinea

Guiye/Waiye Range Environment Project. This is an environment project started by the community to achieve sustainable development at community level. The main aim is to create sustainable ecotourism in the area.
Dates: Aug-Dec. Costs: Contact sponsor. Contact: Peter Gundu, P.O. Box 463, Simbu Province, Papua New Guinea; 011-675-7351103.

Southern Africa

Travel-Study Seminars. Learn from Southern Africans of diverse backgrounds about their economic, political, and social realities. Emphasis on the views of those struggling for justice. Call for details or to organize your own custom trip.
Dates: Summer 2001. Costs: Approx. $3,900 depending on length of stay. Contact: Center for Global Education at Augsburg College, 2211 Riverside Ave., Box 307TR, Minneapolis, MN 55454; 800-299-8889, fax 612-330-1695; globaled@augsburg.edu, [www.augsburg.edu/ global].

Sri Lanka

Peace Work. Samasevaya works for development of Sri Lanka. It focuses on issues of poverty alleviation, environmental protection, women's development, childcare, human rights, and peace education.
Dates: Year round. Costs: $3 per day.
Contact: Samson Jayasinghe, Samasevaya, Anuradhapura Rd., Talawa, Sri Lanka; 011-94-25-76266.

United Kingdom and Ireland

British Studies at Oxford. This program of study in one of the world's most prestigious universities offers undergraduate and graduate credit in art history, business, communication, drama, education, English literature, history, and political science taught by Oxford Univ. professors. The participants live in private rooms tidied daily by the college staff, who also serve 3 bountiful and tasty meals a day in the Great Hall. Field trips are an integral part of each course as well as group trips to the theater in Stratford-upon-Avon and London.
Dates: Summer: Jun 30-Jul 20; Jul 21-Aug 10; or Jun 30-Aug 10. Costs: $3,350 for 3 weeks; $6,050 for 6 weeks. Includes 4 or 8 credits, travel in Britain for course related events, theater, entrance to museums, dinners in country inns, and many field trips. Overseas travel not included. Contact: Dr. M.B. Pigott, Director, British Studies at Oxford, 322 Wilson Hall, Oakland Univ., Rochester, MI 48309-4401; 248-652-3405 or 248-370-4131, fax 248-650-9107; pigott@oakland.edu, [www.oakland.edu/ oxford].

Worldwide

Adventure Travel. The Northwest Passage offers unique adventures from a dogsled/ski expedition to the North Pole, ski expedition to the South Pole, sea kayaking in Crete, Patagonia, Ellemere Island, and Greenland, cycling/rafting/safari in southern Africa, mountaineering in European high Alps and Greenland.
Dates: Vary. Costs: Vary. Contact: Matt Moses, Director, The Northwest Passage, 1130 Greenleaf Ave., Wilmette, IL 60091; 800-732-7328, 847-256-4409, fax 847-256-4476; info@nwpassage.com, [www.nwpassage.com or www.northpole-expeditions.com].

Classic Journeys. Easy-going walking, cultural, and natural history adventures worldwide. Small groups, expert local guides, first class accommodations, and fine cuisine.

ECOTOURISM AND ACTIVISM
IGUANA MAMA LINKS CLIENTS AND LOCAL PEOPLE

By Ed Butts

Ecotourism is really about sustaining local culture," says Patricia Thorndike de Suriel, owner of Iguana Mama Mountain Bike, Hiking, and Cultural Vacations, in Cabarete, the Dominican Republic. "We are a link between our clients and the local people," says de Suriel. We try to be involved in their lives and to help—and we get results."

Patricia came to Cabarete in 1993 on her way to a vacation in Bolivia. She had already hiked and biked her way across 44 countries on six continents and saw the potential for a mountain bike tour operation in the Dominican Republic. In six years she has built Iguana Mama into one of the most responsible and respected tour operators not only in the Caribbean but in the worldwide biking community.

On her tours people learn about the natural history of the island and also meet Dominican people in their homes. Iguana Mama's guides are all local. They are well paid, trained in CPR, first aid, and bike mechanics, and participate in a 4-day "outback" clinic dealing with emergencies.

At least 20 percent of tour fees go to the education of local children, and the Iguana Mama bikeshop is a collection center for clothing and other donated goods. Iguana Mama connects clients interested in scuba diving, horseback riding, rafting, canyoning, whale watching, and jungle river tours in touch with ecoresponsible operators.

Contact: Iguana Mama Mountain Bike, Hiking, and Cultural Vacations, Cabarete, Dominican Republic, c/o Lynx Air, DRNC-Sosua, P.O. Box 407019, Ft. Lauderdale, Fl 33340; 800-849-4720, 809-571-0906, fax 809-571-0734; info@iguanamama.com, [www.iguanamama.com].

Dates: Tours offered throughout the year. **Costs:** Around $2,500 for a week. Airfare not included. **Contact:** Classic Journeys at 800-200-3887; moreinfo@classicjourneys.com, [www.classicjourneys.com].

Cultural Adventures in Russia, Central Asia, and Beyond. Customized trips for individuals and special interest groups are our specialty. Destination specialists offering over 35 sensational "off the beaten path" small group adventures and 50 independent travel itineraries to choose from (Russia, Central Asia, Mongolia, China). On-site offices in Russia, Ukraine, Uzbekistan. Call for a free catalog featuring the legendary Trans-Siberian Railway, the Silk Route, Mongolia, and more.

Dates: Year round for custom and independent programs; scheduled departures for tours. **Costs:** Homestays from $40 a night. Full escorted tours from $1,850. **Contact:** MIR (the Russian word meaning "peace" and "world"), 85 S. Washington St., Suite 210, Seattle, WA 98104; 800-424-7289 or 206-624-7289, fax 206-624-7360; info@mircorp.org, [www.mircorp.com].

ExperiencePlus! Specialty Tours, Inc. Since 1972 ExperiencePlus! has offered quality bicycle and walking tours at affordable prices. Local guides help bring the culture and character of each country to life for participants. Accommodations are clean and comfortable, with a private bath, but are not luxury. Participants range in skill level from beginning to advance and in age from 20s-70s. **Dates:** Year round. **Costs:** $1,675-$3,295. **Contact:** Melissa Groom, Director of Sales, ExperiencePlus! Specialty Tours, Inc., 415 Mason Court, Unit 1, Ft. Collins, CO 80524; 800-685-4565, 970-484-8489, fax 970-493-0377; tours@experienceplus.com, [www.experienceplus.com].

Homestays for Peace. Servas is an international network of hosts and travelers building peace by providing opportunities for mutually arranged individual visits—typically for 2 nights—between people of diverse cultures and backgrounds. Servas encompasses more than 14,000 homes and institutions in more than 130 countries on 6 continents.

Dates: Year round. **Costs:** $65 per adult to travel for 1 year; $25 for international students in the U.S. **Contact:** Carole Wagner, Program Assistant, U.S. Servas, 11 John St., Rm. 505, New York, NY 10038-4009; 212-267-0252, fax 212-267-0292; info@usServas.org, [www.usServas.org].

Sea Kayaking. Explore the natural and cultural history of extraordinary places by sea kayak. San Juan/Canadian Gulf Islands, the Inside Passage, West Coast Vancouver Island, Baja, Hawaii, Virgin Islands. Scheduled and custom group tours. Also (Whale Watch Camping/X-C Ski Tours/Yoga Retreats.)

Dates: Year round. **Costs:** Contact organization for details. **Contact:** Kathleen Grimbly, Blue Moon Explorations, 4658 Blank Rd., Sedro-Woolley, WA 98284; 800-966-8806, Tel./fax 360-856-5622; bluemoon@cww.net, [www.bluemoonexplorations.com].

Voyages with a Vision. MADRE is an international woman's human rights organization that sends delegations to the countries in which it works, including Cuba, Nicaragua, Guatemala, and Palestine. We see firsthand the influence of U.S. foreign policy and visit MADRE's sister organizations that are working at the community level to bring basic needs and human rights to women and families.

Dates: Year round. Call or email for exact dates. Delegations last approx. 1 week. **Costs:** Depends on trip and needs of traveler. **Contact:** Vicki Larson, MADRE, 121 W 27th St., Rm. #301, New York, NY 10001; 212-627-0444, fax 212-675-3704; madre@igc.org, [www.madre.org].

The World Outdoors. Extraordinary biking, hiking, and multisport backcountry adventures since 1988. Experience 50 adventures for all ages and abilities to 25 destinations worldwide. Small groups, local guides, cozy inns, or scenic camps. Specialty trips include singles, seniors, family, custom, charter, and corporate training and development. **Dates:** Year round. **Costs:** From $995 (6 days)-$2,800 (14 days). **Contact:** Brian T. Mullis, The World Outdoors, 2840 Wilderness Pl., #F, Boulder, CO 80301; 800-488-8483 or 303-413-0938, fax 303-413-0926; fun@theworldoutdoors.com, [www.theworldoutdoors.com].

Worldwide Expeditionary Adventures. Zegrahm Expeditions is dedicated to offering an expeditionary adventure to the inquisitive traveler. Our programs are operated with great concern for the environment and sensitivity to fragile wildlife areas and cultures worldwide. Expeditions are accompanied by some of the world's foremost naturalists and expedition leaders.

Dates: Year round. **Costs:** From $3,690-$30,000 per person. **Contact:** Zegrahm Expeditions, 192 Nickerson St., #200, Seattle, WA 98109; 800-628-8747 or 206-285-4000, fax 206-285-5037; zoe@zeco.com, [www.zeco.com].

Youth International. An experiential education program focusing on international travel and intercultural exchange, adventure, community service, and homestays. Teams of 14, aged 18-25, travel together for 1 semester to Asia (including the Philippines, Thailand, India, and Nepal) or Africa (including Kenya, Tanzania, Botswana, and Namibia). Assist refugees, hike the Himalayas, live with and help an African tribe, scuba dive, and much more.

Dates: Every year, early Sep-mid-Dec, and early Feb-late May. **Costs:** $7,500 including airfare. **Contact:** Brad Gillings, Youth International, 1121 Downing St., #2, Denver, CO 80218; 303-839-5877, fax 303-839-5887; director@youthinternational.org, [www.youthinternational.org].

*S*EVEN

HOME & HOSPITALITY EXCHANGES
BEST RESOURCES

Not only are home exchanges and rentals less expensive than staying in hotels, they put you in immediate contact with the people and cultures you come to visit. And because the daily costs are less, you can afford to stay longer. Even if your vacation time is short, you can still immerse yourself in the local culture and meet local people—thanks to the hospitality exchange organizations described below.

Hospitality Exchanges

American International Homestays. 800-876-2048, 303-258-3234, fax 303-258-3264; ash@igc.apc.org, [www.commerce.com/homestays]. Specializes in homestays in Eastern Europe, the former Soviet Union, and China. Full-service homestays start at $99 per night for a private single room, home-cooked breakfast and dinner, 4 hours per day of guiding.

AmeriSpan Unlimited, P.O. Box 40007, Philadelphia, PA 19106; 800-879-6640; info@AmeriSpan.com, [www.AmeriSpan.com]. Family, teen, senior, and adult language programs in 14 countries in Mexico, Spain, Central and South America. Housing with a host family.

Bells' Home Hospitality. An 11-year-old homestay service with a small network of middle class families exemplifying the good nature of the Costa Rican people. The Bells will help you develop your itinerary based on their own and their guests' experiences over the years. Brochure from: Vernon and Marcela Bell, P.O. Box 185, 1000 San Jose, Costa Rica; 011-506-225-4752, fax 011-506-224-5884; homestay@racsa.co.cr, [www.homestay.thebells.org].

FamilyHostel, 6 Garrison Ave., Durham, NH 03824; 800-733-9753; [www.learn.unh.edu]. Ten-day learning and travel programs in foreign countries and the U.S. for families (parents, grandparents, school-age children).

Friends Overseas, 68-04 Dartmouth St., Forest Hills, NY 11375; [www/nordbalt.com/friends]. A Scandinavian-American friendship program run by a retired junior high guidance counselor. Join for $25 and Larry Eisner will send you the names of several Scandinavians interested in meeting and entertaining Americans.

The Hospitality Exchange, P.O. Box 561, Lewistown, MT 59457; 406-538-8770; hospitality@hotmail.com, [www.goldray.com/hospitality]. Annual membership fee ($20) gets you directory of 250 members in 26 countries. Some can offer overnight accommodations; others could hook you up with local families.

Servas. U.S. Servas Committee, Inc., 11 John St., Rm. 505, New York NY 10038; 212-267-0252, fax 212-267-0292;[www.usservas.org]. An international cooperative system of carefully screened hosts and travelers established to help build world peace and understanding.

The World for Free, Box 137, Prince St. Station, New York, NY 10012; fax 212-979-8167; info@worldforfree.com, [www.worldforfree.com]. An international hospitality exchange club started by a touring musician; many musicians and artists are in the group, as well as scores of others.

Women Welcome Women World Wide, 88 Easton St., High Wycombe, Buckinghamshire HP11 1LT, U.K.; [www.womenwelcomewomen.org.uk]. A nonprofit trust to further international friendship by encouraging and facilitating women of different nationalities to visit one another.

WWOOF (Willing Workers on Organic Farms). An exchange group that gives you room and board in return for your help in managing an organic farm or smallholding. Stay for a weekend or a month—whatever you work out with your hosts. Membership is very cheap and there are lots of member groups to choose from. Check out [www.phdcc.com/sites/wwoof/national.html]. WWOOF Australia, Buchan PO, Victoria 3885, Australia; 011-61-3-5155-0218, fax 011-61-3-5155-0342; wwoof@wwoof.com.au, [www.wwoof.com.au]. WWOOF Canada, R.R. 2, S.18, C.9, Nelson, BC, Canada V1L 5P5; 250-354-4417; wwoofcan@uniserve.com. WWOOF Germany, Miriam Wittmann, Postfach 210259, 01263 Dresden, Germany. WWOOF Ireland, Kieran and Rose O'Brien, Harpoonstown, Drinagh, County Wexford, Republic of Ireland. WWOOF UK, Fran Whittle, P.O. Box 2675, Lewes, E. Sussex, BN7 1RB England. U.K. Membership £15 plus IRC. NEWOOF USA, New England Small Farms Institute, P.O. Box 937, Belchertown, MA 01007. Membership $20. Must be a U.S. resident.

Home Exchanges

Home Base Holidays. Lois Sealey, 7 Park Ave., London N13 5PG, England; 011-44 20-8886-8752, fax 011-44-20-8245-9532; homeexchange@btinternet.com, [www.homebase-hols.com]. Exchange in over 40 countries with a particularly large choice of offers throughout Great Britain.

Home Exchange Vacationing: Your Guide to Free Accommodations, by Bill and Mary Barbour (Rutledge Hill Press, 1996, $14.95). The authors have done 40-plus exchanges in the U.S., Europe, and Hong Kong and surveyed 600 swappers worldwide. Good anecdotes, but may not have all the facts you want.

HomeExchange.com is a powerful "open system" for finding home exchange partners. $30 per year.

HomeLink USA/Vacation Exchange Club, P.O. Box 650, Key West, FL 33041; 800-638-3841, fax 305-294-1448; [www.homelink.org]. Join for $98 a year, and get up to five directories and the right to list your own property twice. About 15,000 members around the world, half in Europe.

Intervac U.S., P.O. Box 590504, San Francisco, CA 94159; 415-435-3497, fax 415-435-7440; [www.intervacus.com]. Affiliates covering more than 50 countries; perhaps the largest base of European listings. $50 for web-only membership; $110 for book-web combo that gets you three directories, and access to their online database.

The Invented City. Worldwide Home Exchange, 41 Sutter St., Suite 1090, San Francisco, CA 94104; 415-252-1141, fax 415-252-1171; [www.invented-city.com]. $75 for online access and listing in catalog; $125 to also receive 3 printed catalogs per year; 1,900 listings, about a third in Europe.

Mi Casa Su Casa Gay Home Exchange, P.O. Box 4714, Walnut Creek, CA 94596; 925-944-9776, fax 925-944-9904; mcsc@gayhometrade.com, [www.gayhometrade.com]. International lesbian and gay home and hospitality exchange networks.

Trading Homes International, Box 787, Hermosa Beach, CA 90254; 800-877-8723 or 310-798-3864, fax 310-798-3865; [www.trading-homes.com]. Several thousand members, half in U.S., about 35 percent in Europe. $65 for online access and your listing in the print catalog; $95 gets you 3 annual catalogs, too.

Home Rentals in Europe

Interhome, Inc., 1990 NE 163 St., Suite 110, N. Miami Beach, FL 33162; 800- 882-6864, fax 305-940-2911; [www.interhome.com]. Nearly 20,000 rental homes in 16 European countries, from $400 per week on up. All listings examined, scored, and quality-rated with 1-5 stars. The U.S. reservations office connects to a main office computer in Switzerland for instant, accurate information on availability with guaranteed U.S.-dollar prices.

www.novasol.com. One of Europe's larger rental companies featuring houses for rent in Norway, Sweden, Denmark, Holland, Belgium, Poland, Hungary, Austria and the Czech Republic. Online booking in English.

HOSPITALITY STAYS

IN OVER 100 COUNTRIES LOCAL HOSTS ARE WAITING TO WELCOME YOU

By Kari J. Bodnarchuk

The first time I visited Jakarta, Indonesia—groggy and disoriented after a 15-hour train ride and feeling vulnerable on my own—I was relieved I had prearranged a visit with Margaretha. We explored areas of Jakarta not mentioned in guidebooks, places I never would have discovered on my own.

By the time I left Margaretha's home, three days later, I understood more about Indonesian culture than I had learned during two months of travel in the country. And I'd made a friend for life.

As you plan your next travel adventure—whether it's to study, live, work, or travel—consider joining a hospitality club. As a member, you can stay with local families or individuals and swap ideas, build new friendships, and gain insight into each other's worlds.

In at least 130 countries worldwide local hosts are waiting with open doors to take you into their homes. Some hospitality groups are geared specifically to single travelers or women travelers, while others target senior adventurers or travel groups.

When you join a hospitality club, you typically receive a list of hosts in the country you're visiting, with information on each person's background—address, job, family, interests, hobbies, and languages spoken—as well as a notation on how many people he or she can host and for how long. Stays can range from two nights to a month or more, depending on the arrangements you've made with your host and how well you hit it off.

During an 18-month, around-the-world journey, I spent anywhere from two days to two weeks with different host families including a sheep rancher in New Zealand, students in Indonesia, a doctor in Malaysia, a retired teacher in Thailand, and a social worker in India.

You can organize your stay before you leave home or while you're traveling. Since my plans changed almost daily during my trip, I arranged visits en route through letters, email, or phone calls. Organizing a stay can be the entire focus of your trip, or it can be one aspect of your trip.

You typically pay an annual fee to join a hospitality club and occasionally hosts expect you to chip in for food, but you never pay for a place to sleep (which can range from a luxurious bed to a spot on a floor). These organizations, however, are not free-accommodation clubs; many have a strict screening process to ensure that you're truly interested in cultural exchange and not a cheap crash pad.

For your benefit, hosts are also screened before they're allowed to join, to ensure that they can facilitate hospitality stays. After all, if your aims—and those of your host—are noble, the exchange may be one of the most profound and rewarding travel experiences you'll have, and the friendships you make may last a lifetime.

www.holiday-rentals.com. Not an agency but a catalog that lists over 1500 private homes, most with photos, full details, and prices. Pick the one you like, then contact the owners directly. Prices tend to be low, since you're booking direct and not paying an agency fee.

www.rent-a-holiday.com. A collection of properties from several different agencies. Everything from B and Bs to castles, all over Europe. Great search engine helps you find the features you want at the price you can afford. Offseason rentals for a family of four start as low as $225.

Belgium

Fédération des Gîtes de Wallonie, Avenue Prince de Liège, 5100 Namur (Jambes), Belgium; 011-32-81-311-800, fax 011-32-81-310-200. (Belgium also has gîtes.) Send for booklet with about 450 furnished homes and many more rooms for rent in the French-speaking part of Belgium.

England

British Travel International, P.O. Box 299, Elkton, VA 22827; 800-327-6097. [www.britishtravel.com]. A reliable U.S. agency for British rentals. Ask for their wonderful "English Country Cottages" catalog. Not in the budget range, but they know their stuff. Also handle rentals in France, Spain, and Italy plus airfares and car rentals [www.visitbritain.com]. Log onto the British Tourist Office's outstanding web site and choose "accommodations" and then "self-catering" for an endless list of British and U.S. agencies handling British rentals.

France

Chez Nous, Spring Mill, Earby, Barnoldswick, Lancashire BB9 40AA, England; 011-44-870-444-6600, fax 011-44-1282-445-411; [www.cheznous.co.uk]. Online directory of French rentals owned by Brits. They charge owners only for ads; prices are reasonable ($175 per week plus) since there's no commission. And there's no language gap in making arrangements.

Chez Vous, 1001 Bridgeway, PMB 245, Sausalito, CA 94965; 415-331-2535, fax 415-331-5296; bonjour@chezvous.com, [www.chezvous.com]. Apartments in Paris and London; rental homes and B and Bs throughout the French countryside. Not in the bargain range: prices start at about $900 a week; discounts November-February (except Christmas) and August.

The Gîtes Guide: French Farm and Village Holiday Guide (Hunter Publishing, 1997, $17.95) is an English translation of gîtes guide. Not as current as French guide and contains only a fraction of the properties, but a big help to those whose French is shaky.

Maison des Gîtes de France, 59, rue Saint Lazare, 75439 Paris, Cedex 09, France; 011-33-1-49-70-75-75, fax 011-33-1-42-81-28-53, [www.gites-de-france.fr]. Source for abut 55,000 inexpensive, simple, rural rentals and B and Bs in France.

Germany

Familienferien, Schwarzwald Tourismusverband, Postfach 1660, 79016 Freiburg im Breisgau, Germany; 011-49-761-296-2260, fax 011-49-761-8979-7989. To order guide, fax or email service@tourismus-service.com.

Fränkisches Urlaubskatalog, Tourismusverband Franken, Fürther Str. 21, 90429 Nürnberg, Germany; 011-49-911-26-42-02, fax 011-49-911-27-05-47.

Urlaub auf Bauern- und Winzerhöfen, Rheinland-Pfalz Tourist Office, Schmittpforte 2, 55437 Ober-Hilbersheim, Germany; 011-49-6728-1225, fax 011-49-6728-626.

Ireland

Irish Cottage Holiday Homes, Central Reservations Office, 4 Whitefriars, Aungier Street, Dublin 2, Ireland; 011-353-1-475-1932, fax 011-353-1-475-5321; [www.ichh.ie]. Good variety of listings from £100 to £500 per week.

Irish National Tourist Board [www.irelandvacations.com]. Select "Places to Stay" then "self-catering" for a good selection of listings.

Italy

Agriturist Farm Holidays, CP 84, 58100 Grosseto, Italy; 011-39-564-418051, fax 011-39-564-421828; [www.agriturist.it]. Web site mostly in Italian with token English.

Casa Mia, 011-44-1484-680-865, fax 011-44-1484-680-366; [www.casamia.co.uk]. Directory of Italian, Spanish, and Portuguese rentals owned by Brits. See sister company Chez Nous under "France" above.

The Parker Company, Seaport Landing, 152 Lynnway, Lynn, MA 01902; 800-280-2811, fax 781-596-3125; [www. theparkercompany.com]. Hundreds of villas and apartments, most with

How to Exchange a Home and Live Irish

First, Get Hooked Up With an Organization

By Isabel Bearman Bucher

Email to Ireland from Albuquerque, 7 August:

"Gloom . . . setting the operation into departure mode. Ah well, that's part of vacations . . . if you didn't regret their ending . . . wouldn't have been a great holiday. Dermot."

This message on my computer at Kilkenny, Ireland, home of our Irish exchange family, echoed the way we felt about leaving.

We felt completely comfortable changing homes with the Currans because we'd corresponded for eight months. We left each other's homes better than when we found them. They brought us wonderful Kilkenny pottery, and we left them a New Mexico book and red chili powder. We left each other money for the telephone bills, but simply traded all other expenses like electricity, water, etc.

Because we exchanged houses and cars, we paid just over $100 a day to see the length and breadth of Eire, for over five weeks. Our total expense was under $4,000, including airfare and 13 nights in B and Bs. If you just wanted to stay put, the cost would be less than $50 a day.

Ireland is prosperous and, like most European countries, it's very expensive. You pay 40 percent more than here for everything. Of this, 21 percent is a VAT (value added tax) on all purchases. Gas is $3.20 a gallon.

We became like the locals. Would we do it again? Ach, 'tis a sweet, fair splendid country. You bet we would, in an English minute (which is shorter in the minds of the Irish).

We are planning an Italian house exchange for this year.

If you want to exchange homes, first get hooked up with an organization. Read *Transitions Abroad*'s publications or visit [www.TransitionsAbroad.com]. Or go to any search engine and type in "home or house exchange."

After you've joined an exchange service and found your people, here are some suggestions to make things go smoothly.

Preparing for Guests

• Tape notes to all appliances with directions for use. We made a three-ring binder, with short bullet lists of "do and see" suggestions. Dermot left us an excellent Michelin map of Ireland, with all the routes and towns of interest highlighted, plus excellent historical, hiking, and tour books, which we wore out.

• Try to arrange to meet somewhere along the line. We arranged our ticket so that we could pick up our Irish family at the Albuquerque airport the evening before we left and meet them in Dublin when we were departing. Dermot suggested it so we could "chat, get keys, trade insults, litigation, etc."

• Put some zappable quick foods in the freezer for your exchange family, like pizzas, and buy them some cornflakes, bananas, milk, fruit, and bread. The first few days in any new country are very strange, and jet lag is inevitable.

• Make sure to have your friends call them and check in—after a few days.

Medical, Money, and Insurance

• Know your international bank card emergency phone number and your bank phone number in case of credit card loss. I lost my wallet in the first few days. It was returned, but there were tense moments and I was thankful for a safety net from the home bank.

• In case of medical emergency, know the procedure for treatment, payment, and reimbursement. Check out all auto insurance. Carry a record of all policy numbers and accident and theft procedures with you. The Currans bought a health accident policy before they left which cost them around $90. Check out a similar one in the States to be used in the foreign country. Again, see *Transitions Abroad*.

• No need to carry any traveler's checks or personal checks. Just pop in your bank card at any machine in most cities and out comes the country's money.

• Bring empty duffels for purchases. We brought one, and had to buy another.

• Save every receipt. If you paid VAT taxes on the merchandise, you can claim all of it when you leave the country and get a refund. There's a special desk just for this at the airport. Businesses where you buy items will give you forms to fill out. Fill out the paperwork ahead of time, before you are standing in the line at the airport departure point.

pools. Rentals start at about $550 per week in the off season. Good deals on airfare, cellphones, other travel needs.

RentVillas.com, 1742 Calle Corva, Camarillo, CA 93010; 800-726-6702, fax 805-482-7976; [www.rentvillas.com]. The biggie. More than 2,000 properties, mostly in Tuscany but also elsewhere including apartments in Venice. Starting at $500-$700 in the offseason and running $1,200-$2,500 per week in the high season.

Toscana Agriturismo
[www.toscana.agriturismo.net]. Apartments and houses in Tuscany. Web site in English and Italian. Starting at $250-$400 per week offseason; $475 and up high season.

Tuscany Now, 276 Seven Sisters Rd., London N4, U.K.; 011-44-207-272-5469, fax 011-44-207-272-6184; [www.tuscanynow.com]. About 120 British-owned villas and 100 apartments rented out when the owners aren't there. All with pools. Start at about $450 in the offseason. Many areas of Italy.

Norway

Fjordhytter, Lille Markevei 13, P.O. Box 103, N-5001 Bergen, Norway; 011-47-55-23-20-80, fax 011-47-55-23-24-04. Lovely photo catalog in English with very detailed descriptions. Prices start at $180 off season to $320 high season.

Spain

Casaspain.com. A "go between service" advertising rentals all over Spain. Pick English, then click on the map of Spain to choose an area, then choose "To Let." Once you find a listing you like, you will contact the owners directly. One of the best selections of listings we've seen.

Casas Cantabricas, 31 Arbury Rd., Cambridge CB4 2JB, England; 011-44-1223-328-721, fax 011-44-1223-322-711; [www.casacantab.co.uk]. Rentals in "Green Spain"—Cantabria, Asturias, and Galicia-and in the mountains between Salamanca and Extremadura. Low season starts at about $275, high at about $450.

TurGalicia, Oficina de Información, Carretera Santiago-Noia, km 3, 15896 Santiago de Compostella, Spain; 011-34-981-54-25-27 or 011-34-981-54-25-28, fax 011-34-981-57-15-50; [www.turgalicia.es]. Click on "Where to Stay" and then "Apartments" for listings.

Sweden

Destination Stockholms Skårgård Lillström, S-18497 Ljustero, Sweden; 011-46-8-542-481-00, fax 011-46-8-542-414-00; [www.dess.se]. Cottages in the Stockholm archipelago start at about $250 in the off season and $350 in mid-summer. Book 7-8 months ahead for high season.

Sweden Home Rentals
[www.swedenhomerentals.se]. A great web site covering rentals all over Sweden, starting at about $300 per week.

Switzerland

Holiday-Home [www.holiday-home.ch]. Hundreds of rentals all over Switzerland and many in other countries too. Offseason rentals start as low as $250 per week; high season $375 and up. Schweizer Reisekasse (REKA) [www.reka.ch]. Nonprofit devoted to inexpensive family vacations. Web site in French, German, Italian provides access to 1100 rentals.

Swiss Holiday Farms Assn., Neuengasse 15, 3000 Bern, Switzerland; 011-41-31-329-6633, fax 011-41-31-329-6601; [www.bauernhof-ferien.ch/englisch]. Farm vacations, in cooperation with REKA (above). Some parts of web site in German only.

STUDY ABROAD

*E*IGHT

Whether you're a student looking for an international study program or any traveler who wants to combine the least expense abroad with the most rewards, you'll find what you need in the resources below and in the programs described in the following chapter. Addresses of publishers, when not included in individual listings, begin on page 103.

Key Print Publications

Worldwide Directories

Country and Region directories start on page 97.

Academic Year Abroad Marie O'Sullivan, ed. Annual. $44.95 plus $6 s/h from IIE. Authoritative directory of nearly 2,700 semester and academic year programs offered by U.S. and foreign universities and private organizations. Indexed for internships, practical training, student teaching, adult courses, volunteer work, as well as fields of study. Companion volume to Short Term Study Abroad (below). See also IIE web site at [www.iiepassport.org] for other study abroad information. Can be found in most college libraries and study abroad offices.

Advisory List of International Educational Travel & Exchange Programs. Annual (updated each spring). Council on Standards for International Educational Travel, 212 Henry St., Alexandria, VA 22314; 703-739-9050, fax 703-739-9035; mailboxe@csiet.org, [www.csiet.org]. $17.50 ($22.50 overseas). Lists programs for high school students which adhere to CSIET's standards. The most valuable single resource for prospective exchange students, host families, and schools.

Archaeological Fieldwork Opportunities Bulletin. Annual in January. 120 pp. Archaeological Institute of America. $12.25 for AIA members, $15.25 nonmembers plus $5.25 s/h from Kendall/Hunt Publishing Co., Customer Service, 4050 Westmark Dr., Dubuque, IA 52002; 800-338-8290; [www.kendallhunt.com] (orders can be placed via web site). A comprehensive guide to excavations, field schools, and special programs with openings for volunteers, students, and staff worldwide.

Back in the USA by Dawn Kepets. 2nd ed. 1999. $10 plus $5 s/h from NAFSA. Helps students to put their cross-cultural growth into perspective and prepare for what may be the toughest part of studying abroad: the return home.

Building Bridges: A Manual on Including People with Disabilities in International Exchange Programs. MIUSA; info@miusa.org, [www.miusa]. 2000. $20. Information on accessibility, resource lists to recruit people with disabilities, and checklists and tips to identify specific needs of participants with disabilities. Accompanying video can be purchased for $49. Alternative formats, captions and audio described video available.

CDS International, 871 United Nations Plaza, 15th Fl., New York, NY 10017-1814; 212-497-

3500, fax 212-497-3535; info@cdsintl.org, [www.cdsintl.org]. Paid internship programs in Germany, Switzerland, Singapore, Argentina, and Turkey offered by CDS for college students and young professionals.

Commonwealth Universities Yearbook. Compiled by the Association of Commonwealth Universities. 2000. Two-volume set. $265 plus $15 s/h from Palgrave. Detailed profiles of universities in all 34 of the Commonwealth countries, with comprehensive guide to degree programs and a register of 230,000 academic and administrative staff. Available in major libraries.

Directory of International Internships: A World of Opportunities. Compiled and edited by Charles A. Gliozzo and Vernieka K. Tyson. 4th ed., 1998. Available for $25 postpaid from Michigan State Univ., Attn: International Placement, Career Services & Placement, 113 Student Services Bldg., East Lansing, MI 48824. Based on a wide survey of organizations, this directory describes a variety of experiential educational opportunities—for academic credit, for pay, or simply for experience. Useful indexes. This is the most comprehensive directory to internships entirely located abroad.

Figuring Foreigners Out by Craig Storti (Intercultural Press, $21.95, 1999). This user-friendly workbook provides helpful guidelines for dealing with cultural differences and increasing cross-cultural awareness. A useful training manual for anyone in contact with foreigners, at home or abroad. Other titles by Craig Storti at Intercultural Press: *The Art of Coming Home, Cross Cultural Dialogues, The Art of Crossing Cultures.*

Guide to Architecture Schools Jenifer Doctors, ed. 2001. Biannual. 340+ pp. $32 including shipping from the Association of Collegiate Schools of Architecture, 1735 New York Ave., NW, Washington, DC 20006; 202-785-2324, fax 202-628-0448; [www.acsa-arch.org]. Lists accredited architecture programs in the U.S. and Canada as well as international architecture programs. Available in print and searchable online formats.

A Guide to Educational Systems Around the World Shelley Feagles, ed. 1999. 397 pp. $65 members; $90 nonmembers, plus $5 s/h from NAFSA. Information on the educational systems of more than 156 countries, from Albania to Zimbabwe.

The Insider's Guide to Study Abroad by Ann M. Moore. Peterson's Guides. 2000. 528 pp. $11.96 plus $6.75 s/h. "Covers all the essentials."

InterAct Series. Intercultural Press. InterActs analyze how Americans and nationals of other countries see and do things differently and how these differences affect relationships. Countries/areas covered include Japan, Spain, Mexico, Greece, Israel, Eastern Europe, Brazil, Russia, Australia, China, Thailand, Arab World, Sub-Saharan Africa, Germany, and France.

International Handbook of Universities. 16th ed. 2001. $275 plus $15 s/h. International Association of Universities. Distributed in U.S. and Canada by Palgrave. Entries for more than 5,700 universities and other institutions of higher education in 170 countries and territories.

International Study Telecom Directory. Worldwide Classroom, 2001, 98 pp. $9.95 plus s/h. Worldwide Classroom Publications, Box 1166, Milwaukee, WI 53201; 414-224-3476, fax 414-224-3466; schools@worldwide.edu, [www.worldwide.edu]. Library of listings, both on the Internet and in print, of over 11,000 schools accepting foreign students; includes contact information, program information, as well as country and travel resources.

NAFSA's Guide to Education Abroad for Advisers and Administrators. William Hoffa and John Pearson, eds. NAFSA. 2nd ed., 1997. 494 pp. $45 (nonmembers), $36 (members) plus $5 s/h. An indispensable manual for those working in the field of study abroad advising and administration.

Study Abroad. UNESCO. Vol. 31, 2000-01. $34.95 plus $5 s/h from Bernan Associates, 4611-F Assembly Dr., Lanham, MD 20706; 800-865-3457; [www.bernan.com]. Describes approximately 4,000 international study programs and sources of financial assistance in more than 100 countries.

Study Abroad. Peterson's Guides. Annual. 1,141 pp. $23.96 plus $6.75 s/h. Detailed information on over 2,600 international study programs and sources of financial aid in more than 120 countries.

Study Abroad: A Parent's Guide by William Hoffa. NAFSA, 1998. 112 pp. $15 ($12 members) plus $5 s/h. The first full-length book geared to what parents want and need to know about study abroad.

Studying Abroad/Learning Abroad. by J. Daniel Hess. Intercultural Press, 1997. 159 pp. $14.95 plus $3 s/h. This abridged edition of The Whole World Guide to Culture Learning provides a guide to cross-cultural analysis and adaptation.

Summer Study Abroad 2001. Peterson's Guides. 2000. Annual. 693 pp. $23.96 plus $6.75 s/h.

WHY GO ABROAD?

SUGGESTED TACTICS TO MAKE THE EXPERIENCE SPECIAL

By Kristin Hayes

I missed out on the study abroad experience in college because college itself was simply too much fun. Nothing could tear me away from my four years of independence, not even the promise of an adventure abroad.

To make up for the missed opportunity, I chose to study abroad after college. Like so many other 20-something graduates with a liberal arts degree, I was somewhat lost. In the midst of a discussion on my uncertain future, my college adviser gave me a much-needed boost. "You can do whatever you choose, Miss Hayes. Why, we could even get you into Oxford if we tried."

That was a dare. And so the journey began. But I was still by no means certain that this journey was for me. Four months after Oxford had accepted me into its Comparative and International Education program, I still hadn't committed. The final decision came as I was strolling down a William and Mary brick path, eyes down, and spied one brick stamped with the word OXFORD. Rationally, of course, I realized that Oxford was the name of the brick company. But in my mind it was a sign! Just what I needed after weeks of tottering between staying and going. The point? Any reason for study or travel abroad is a good reason.

Without my expecting it, my year in England turned out to be the most rewarding of my life to date. The following suggestions are in retrospect the tactics that helped make that experience so special.

Suggestion #1: Study up. During my pre-travel preparation, I occasionally hesitated to ask a question for fear of seeming ignorant, but I quickly realized that not asking left me far more ignorant. Ask. If you don't know the language, practice. The more you know about your destination, the easier your transition will be.

Suggestion #2: Once abroad, talk to everyone. Whether you are traveling or studying, you will encounter a diverse range of people. Take advantage of it. When given the chance to interact with the "locals," take it. In my case, my British friendships earned me home-cooked meals, house parties, free stays in London, and delightful days at Wimbledon.

Suggestion #3: Be native. My best Oxford times were the warm spring days by the river, watching the Summer Eights crew races. Take lessons from those who know the country best and enjoy their traditions. You will feel more in tune with your surroundings if you do.

Suggestion #4: Learn what you like and dislike. Time abroad will help you figure out more of what you want and don't want out of life. Follow what your journey teaches you.

Suggestion #5: Enjoy being where you are. Travel broadens your horizons, but take time to enjoy your temporary hometown as well. And when you travel, spend more than just a day in any city. Savor the sounds and sights without too much hurry to move on to the next church or museum. You will feel far more at home.

Suggestion #6: Don't let anyone else dictate your experience. Go your own way, and don't be swayed by co-travelers or classmates from making your own decisions.

Suggestion #7: Be prepared for others' stereotyping of Americans. If only I had known that I would be expected to speak for my whole country! In Oxford's multi-cultural atmosphere my friends and I often represented our nations on issues of foreign policy, entertainment, and other cultural phenomena (like Britney Spears). My word sometimes became American dogma, although against my will. I learned to express things more quietly, with less American slang, and with more sensitivity now that I, for once, was the outsider. Let's face it: Americans are not viewed prettily in many corners of the earth. We are known as spoiled, loud, coarse, and invariably self-centered. Be prepared for these stereotypes, and work to break them down.

Back home, I am still a bit lost. But my time abroad provided several pointers for the future, including the completion of the research which won me my current job.

To return to the path that led me abroad: In the final semester of my senior year I confessed my fears about going to England to a friend who had spent a year in France. "I'm too little to go so far away," I said. And she replied, with a smile, "That's exactly why you should go. It will make you bigger." And so it did.

Guide to over 1,400 credit and noncredit programs overseas.

Survival Kit for Overseas Living: For Americans Planning to Live and Work Abroad by L. Robert Kohls. 4th ed., 2001. $15 plus $3 s/h from Intercultural Press. Practical information and insights into the process of cross-cultural adaptation combined with suggestions for getting the most from overseas experience.

What in the World is Going On? Canada's Guide to International Careers and Studies. 7th ed. 2001. Canadian Bureau for International Education, 220 Laurier Ave. W, Suite 1100, Ottawa, Ontario K1P 5Z9, Canada; 613-237-4820, [www.cbie.ca/world.html]. Includes a lengthy list of study and work abroad possibilities, some restricted to Canadian citizens. Indexed by field.

A World Awaits You (AWAY). National Clearinghouse on Disability and Exchange. 2001. 40 pp. Free. Published by Mobility International USA and Bureau of Educational and Cultural Affairs of the U.S. Department of State. Order from: Mobility International USA, P.O. Box 10767, Eugene, OR 97440; clearinghouse@miusa.org. *Away* is an annual journal with articles and interviews about people with disabilities who have successfully participated in international exchanges and organizations that are creatively including people with disabilities in all aspects of their international programs. Available in alternative formats.

World List of Universities. 22nd ed., 2000. $170 plus $15 s/h from Palgrave. Addresses of over 9,000 institutions of higher education worldwide.

A World of Options: A Guide to International Exchange, Community Service and Travel for Persons with Disabilities by Christa Bucks. Mobility International USA. 3rd ed., 1997. 659 pp. $35 individual, $45 organizations. A guide to international exchange, study, and volunteer opportunities for people with disabilities. Available in alternative formats.

Country and Region Directories

Africa

Guide to Higher Education in Africa. International Association of Universities and Association of African Universities. 1999. $65 plus $15 s/h from Palgrave. Facts and data on 575 African institutions including: name, contact information, faculty listings, historical background, and much more.

Study in Africa: New Opportunities for American Students. 1997. $20 plus $5 s/h from the National Consortium for Study in Africa, c/o African Studies Center, Michigan State Univ., 100 International Ctr., E. Lansing, MI 48824-1035; 517-353-1700, fax 517-432-1209; NCSA@msu.edu, [www.isp.msu.edu/ AfricanStudies]. Outstanding 27-minute video features onsite interviews with Americans studying in several very different countries in Africa. Oriented to parents, students, advisers; promotes Africa as an important site for study abroad. Web site lists study programs in Africa by country.

Asia

Civil Society in Central Asia edited by M. Holt Ruffin and Daniel C. Waugh. 1999. 320 pp. Center for Civil Society International, Central Asia-Caucasus Institute (Washington, DC). Univ. of Washington Press. $19.95 paper plus $4 s/h. Order from CCSI or UW Press, 800-441-4115; [www.washington.edu/uwpress]. Comprehensive guide to U.S. and host-country organizations involved in institutional reform in the former USSR, many of which offer professional, academic, and volunteer exchanges. Includes an excellent guide to online resources.

Australia

Australia: Education Quality Education Excellence. Available from the Australian Education Office, Australian Embassy, 1601 Massachusetts Ave., NW, Washington, DC 20036; 800-245-2575 or 202-332-8285; edu@austudies.org, [www.austudies.org/aeo]. Official information on year, semester, and summer programs; undergraduate, graduate, medical, and law degrees; scholarships and financial aid information (for both U.S. and Canadian citizens); internships, and student visa information. Also available from AEO: *Study Abroad Advisor's Guide, Guide to Australian Short Courses, Beyond the Outback: A Predeparture Guide for North American Students*, and *Federation Scholarship Guide.*

Beyond the Outback: A Pre-Departure Guide for North American Students. Australian Education Office (above), 1999. This well-designed 108-page spiral-bound guide brings together a wealth of practical information for students preparing to study and live in Australia. Available from AEO, contact edu@austudies to order single or multiple copies. Excellent source to be included in predeparture. Bulk orders will be taken.

Graduate to a New World: Australia. Australian Education Office (above). Graduate study information and Federation Scholarship application for Australian universities.

Study Abroad Programs in Australia. A comprehensive admissions service to 32 Australian universities. Full curriculum offered for semester and year abroad. Services include assistance with financial aid, subject selection, credit transfer, visa, predeparture, arrival orientation, housing, travel, and much more. 800-565-9553, 954-680-0453, fax 954-680-0597; auststudy@aol.com, [www.studyabroad.com/australia].

Austria

Austria: Information for Foreign Students; Summer Language Courses for Foreign Students; Summer Courses in Austria; German Language Courses. Annual. Free from the Austrian Cultural Institute, 950 3rd Ave., 20th Fl., New York, NY 10022; 212-759-5165; desk@aci.org, [www.austriaculture.net/ScienceEduc3.html]. Information for foreign students intending to study at an Austrian institution of higher learning.

Canada

Destination Canada: Information for International Students. One copy free from Canadian Bureau for International Education (CBIE), 220 Laurier Ave. W., Suite 1100, Ottawa, ON K1P 5Z9, Canada; 613-237-4820. General information on Canadian education system and tuition fees. This brochure is available at [www.cbie.ca/inter.html].

The Directory of Canadian Universities. 2001 ed. Annual. $39.95 ($5 s/h Canada and taxes; $7 s/h U.S.; $15 row ship). Association of Universities and Colleges of Canada 350 Albert St., Suite 600, Ottawa ON, K1R 1B1, Canada; 613-563-1236, fax 613-563-9745; dseldent@aucc.ca, [www.aucc.ca]. Undergraduate and graduate program listings plus summary information on each university.

China

Living in China: A Guide to Teaching and Studying in China, Including Taiwan & Hong Kong by Rebecca Weiner, Margaret Murphy, and Albert Li. China Books. 1997. 300 pp. $19.95 from China Books and Periodicals, Inc., 2929 24th St., San Francisco, CA 94110; 415-282-2994, fax 415-282-0994; orders@chinabooks.com. Contact: Greg Jones. Contains directories of universities in China and Taiwan that offer study abroad or teaching placement with contact names and particulars. Good for travel planning as well as teaching and studying.

Central and Eastern Europe, Russia, Asia, and the NIS

The Post-Soviet Handbook: A Guide to Grassroots Organizations and Projects in the Newly Independent States by M. Holt Ruffin, et al. 1996. 418 pp. Univ. of Washington Press. $19.95 plus $4 s/h. Order from UW Press, 800-441-4115; [www.washington.edu/uwpress]. Comprehensive guide to U.S. and host-country organizations involved in institutional reform in the former Soviet Union, many of which offer professional, academic, and volunteer exchanges. Includes an excellent guide to online resources.

REESWEB: Russian and East European Studies, Univ. of Pittsburgh (home page). Free on the World Wide Web at [www.ucis.pitt.edu/reesweb]. Tom Twiss; 412-648-7730, fax 412-648-7733. Continuously updated. No hard copy version available. Click on "Academic Programs and Centers" for listings of language and study abroad programs. Links to other REES area studies centers and information.

France

Studies Office, Cultural Services of the French Embassy, 972 5th Ave., New York, NY 10021; 212-439-1463, fax 212-439-1455. Contact Sophie Schiavo@diplomatie.gouv.fr. The office is open Wednesdays and Fridays 2 p.m.-4 p.m. Full information on both formal and informal studies (as well as teaching) in France is on the web site. For questions contact Sophie Schiavo (above) between 9 a.m. and 5:30 p.m. Monday-Friday.

Studying and Working in France: A Student Guide by Russell Cousins, Ron Hallmark, and Ian Pickup. 1994. 314 pp. $17.95 from Manchester Univ. Press (distributed in the U.S. by St. Martin's Press). Useful, detailed information on directly enrolling in French universities and language courses; one brief chapter on working.

Germany

German Academic Exchange Service. The German Academic Exchange Service is the New York office of the Deutscher Akademischer Austauschdienst (DAAD), a German organization with its head office in Bonn. The New York office assists residents of the U.S. or Canada who

Study Abroad: A 10-Step Preparation

By Alia K. Santini

Step #1: Catalog Shopping. You are sitting in front of a heaping pile of travel books and brochures and you have no idea where you want to go. You pick up a catalog of the Univ. of Galway— endless rolling hills and tons of sheep; then a picturebook of Italy—fountains, art, well-dressed Europeans; then a brochure on Africa—a beautiful woman in red jewelry welcomes students to her village. You do not even know what continent you would like to be on, let alone what country. All you know is that you want to go abroad.

Step #2: Customer Service. If your school has a study abroad office, it will also most likely have a handful of individuals to talk to you about their abroad and your opportunities. If your school does not have an abroad office, plenty of national organizations are ready to facilitate your exchange. Before you contact them, think about what you want to get out of your time abroad. Do you want to be in a place where you can easily travel in your free time? Is your trip based on academic goals? Do you have any foreign language skills you wish to exercise? Are the size and location of the university as important as its reputation or course offerings? Do you want to live in a dorm or be part of a homestay? These are just some of the questions you'll want to ask yourself and discuss with a study abroad adviser.

Step #3: Making the Decision. Once you have talked with someone about your possible choices, two or three schools may still seem equally attractive. The next thing to do is research. Besides your study abroad office, the Internet is a fabulous place for information. Take online tours of the places where you wish to go. Look at the cultural life, geography, and demographics of your intended place of study. Ask your study abroad office if anyone at your college has participated in the programs you're interested in. Ask the program organizer for names of past participants from your area. Most anyone who has been abroad for any length of time would love to discuss their adventures with you. By this part of the search, you should be able to narrow your choices down to one school.

Step #4: Applying. Once you've settled on a particular program, don't let the paperwork get you down. Programs abroad want to know who you are and why you want to study there. After all the thinking about it you've already done, you are completely prepared to answer these questions.

Step #5: The Letter of Acceptance. A month ago you didn't know what continent you wanted to visit, and now you are ordering your passport. The best part has just begun. Now it's time to go back to the library to read up on the customs, traditions, and cultures of your destination. Since everything is going to be new to you when you arrive, you will feel a lot better if you at least have a handle on the basics.

Step #6: Prepack Mentally. Do you know the average temperature of the country in the months you'll be there? Are any vaccinations required? Will your hairdryer work there? These are things that you'll want to know before you leave.

This is also a good time to purchase a student-written paperback guide to your country. Although you may have dreams of spontaneous weekend trips to foreign destinations, it never hurts to read about what others have done. Get a feeling for what will be in your surrounding area. If nothing else, student guides can direct you to inexpensive restaurants and hotels and even point out some of the less-touristy treasures of your chosen destination.

Step #7: Packing. *Don't bring more than you need.*

Step #8: Welcome. The fact that you are going on an extended stay in a foreign place and leaving everyone you know and love behind may not fully sink in until you pass through customs and are sitting in the airport. Don't panic! You are about to embark on an adventure that will change the way you view yourself and America.

Step #9: Instructions Not Included. Now you're on your own. *Talk to the natives!* The only way to get to know a country is through the people who live there. You may be surprised to find how many people would love to tell you where to buy the best cheese, or how to get to the nearest theater. Asking questions will help you make friends and keep you busy.

Step #10: Duty Free. The best thing about study abroad memories is that they don't cost anything. Although you are the only person who will ever really know what it was like, your friends will notice that you've changed since the last time they saw you. You're suddenly more open, spontaneous, mature, confident, and cultured. After all, you've seen another part of the world.

are enrolled or employed full-time at an American or Canadian institution of higher education, and would like to study or do research in Germany. For current information on the DAAD programs and scholarships offered to North American students and faculty members, please visit our web site. German Academic Exchange Service (DAAD), 950 3rd Ave., New York, NY 10022; 212-758-3223, fax 212-755-5780; daadny@daad.org, [www.daad.org].

Greece

Athanasopoulos Language Schools, 6 Einstein St., 18757 Keratsini-Piraeus, Greece; 011-30-1-43-14-921; athanasopoulos@acropolis.gr. Eight-month teaching contracts in Greece.

India

Studying in India. Published by Indian Council for Cultural Relations. Free from Indian consulates and embassies. Basic information and advice on studies or research in India's numerous educational and scientific institutions.

Universities Handbook (India). Published biannually. 29th ed. $300 airmail from: Association of Indian Universities, AIU House, 16 Kotla Marg, New Delhi 110002, India. Overview of courses of studies, faculty members, degrees, library, and research facilities.

Israel

Complete Guide to the Israel Experience. Annual. Available from the World Zionist Organization, 633 3rd Ave., 21st Fl., New York, NY 10017; 800-27-ISRAEL, fax 212- 318-6127; usd@jazo.org.il, [www.wzo.org.il]. Information on study and volunteer work opportunities in Israel.

Japan

Directory of Japan Specialists and Japanese Studies Institutions in the U.S. and Canada Patricia G. Steinhoff, ed. The Japan Foundation Library. Association for Asian Studies, 1021 E. Huron St., Ann Arbor, MI 48104; 734-665-2490, fax 734-665-3801; postmaster@aasianst.org, [www.aasianst.org].

Japanese Colleges and Universities. Association of International Education, Japan (AIEJ) and Monbusho, Ministry of Education, Science, Sports, and Culture. 2000. Biennial. 342 pp. Available to institutions from the Association of International Education, Japan, Information Center, 4-5-29 Komaba, Meguro-ku, Tokyo 153-8503, Japan; 011-81-3-5454-5216, fax 011-81-3-5454-5236; nippon@aiej.org.jp, [www.aiej.or.jp]. A directory of degree and short-term programs (latter in English) offered by Japanese institutions and open to foreign students. Produced by AIEJ, a government-sponsored organization that assists with exchanges. Available free from AIEJ: Index of Majors; Scholarships for International Students in Japan; Student Guide to Japan.

Latin America/Caribbean

After Latin American Studies: A Guide to Graduate Study and Employment for Latin Americanists by Shirley A. Kregar and Jorge Nallim. 2000. $15 (check payable to Univ. of Pittsburgh) postpaid from: Center for Latin American Studies, 4E Wesley W Posvar Hall, Univ. of Pittsburgh, Pittsburgh, PA 15260; 412-648-7392, fax 412-648-2199; clas+@pitt.edu, [www.ucis.pitt.edu/clas]. Packed with useful information for anyone with career or scholarly interests in this region, though most listings are not overseas. Extensive bibliography. Also available, free: *A Guide to Financial Assistance for Graduate Study, Dissertation Research and Internships for Students in Latin American Studies*, 1996.

Middle East

Guide to Study Abroad in The Middle East. AMIDEAST. Available free from web site: [www.amideast.org]. Assists with developing cultural and educational exchange programs in Egypt, Jordan, Kuwait, Lebanon, Morocco, Syria, Tunisia, United Arab Emirates, West Bank/Gaza, and Yemen.

Netherlands

Study in the Netherlands. Annual. 100 pp. Free from NUFFIC, P.O. Box 29777, 2502 LT The Hague, Netherlands; fax 011-31-70-426-03-99; mknaapen@nuffic.nl; [www.nuffic.nl]. Official directory of all study abroad and degree courses (most taught in English) open to foreign students in the Netherlands. Also available from NUFFIC: The Education System of the Netherlands and materials on living in Holland.

Scandinavia

Study in Scandinavia. Annual. Free from the American-Scandinavian Foundation, 58 Park Ave., New York, NY 10016; [www.amscan.org]. Summer and academic year programs offered to high school and college students and anyone interested in Scandinavia. Available on web site.

United Kingdom and Ireland

Britain on a Budget. Annual. Free from British Tourist Authority, 551 5th Ave., #701, New York, NY 10176-0799. Information on travel, study, and work in Britain. Call 800-462-2748 and ask for our special "youth" kit.

The BUTEX Guide to Undergraduate Study in the U.K.; The BUTEX Guide to Graduate Study in the U.K. British Universities Transatlantic Exchange Association (BUTEX). Biennial. Each guide approximately 90 pp. Free from BUTEX Secretariat, Int'l. Office, Keele Univ., Keele, Staffordshire ST5 5BG, U.K. Tel./fax 011-44-1782-583404, butex@keele.ac.uk. Guides from a consortium of U.K. universities, with complete contact information.

Study Abroad Advisor's Manual. Education Enquires Officer, The British Council USA, 3100 Massachusetts Ave., NW, Washington, DC 20008; 800-488-2235, 202-588-7830, fax 202-588-7918; studyintheuk@britishcouncil-usa.org, [www.studyintheuk.org]. Web site provides comprehensive information on study in the U.K., funding information, and links to British universities. Access the virtual study abroad advisor and search extensive study abroad database from their web site.

Univ. Courses in Education Open to Students from Overseas 2002-2003. Free, surface mail from Universities Council for the Education of Teachers, 58 Gordon Square, London WC1H 0NT, United Kingdom. Postgraduate courses in education open to foreigners at British universities.

Worldwide Volunteering for Young People by Youth for Britain. £15.95 from How to Books. This directory focuses exclusively on volunteering projects.

Study Abroad Funding Publications

Fellowships in International Affairs: A Guide to Opportunities in the U.S. and Abroad Gale Mattox, ed. Women in International Security. 1994. 195 pp. $10 plus $3.50 s/h from Lynne Rienner Publishers, 1800 30th St., Suite #314, Boulder, CO 80301; 303-444-6684, fax 303-444-0824; [www.rienner.com]. Fellowships and grants for students, scholars, and practitioners (most are for graduate and postdoctoral students or professionals).

Financial Aid for Research and Creative Activities Abroad 2002-2004 by Gail Ann Schlachter and R. David Weber. 2002. 468 pp. $45 plus $5 s/h from: Reference Service Press, 5000 Windplay Dr., Suite 4, El Dorado Hills, CA 95762; 916-939-9620, fax 916-939-9626. Lists over 1,350 funding sources that support research, professional development, teaching assignments, and creative activities (most for graduate students, postdoctorates, professionals).

Financial Aid for Study and Training Abroad 2001-2003 by Gail Ann Schlachter and R. David Weber. 2001. 368 pp. $39.50 plus $5 s/h from Reference Service Press, 5000 Windplay Dr., Suite 4, El Dorado Hills, CA 95762; 916-939-9620, fax 916-939-9626. Lists more than 1,100 financial aid opportunities open to Americans at any level. Very useful indexes.

Financial Aid for the Disabled and Their Families, 2002-2004 by Gail Ann Schlachter and R. David Weber. 484 pp. $40 from: Reference Service Press, 5000 Windplay Dr., Suite 4, El Dorado Hills, CA 95762; 916-939-9620, fax 916-939-9626. Named "best reference book of the year" by *Library Journal*, this comprehensive directory identifies 1,100 scholarships, fellowships, loans, internships, awards, and grants.

Financial Resources for International Study Marie O'Sullivan, ed. 1996. IIE. $39.95 plus $6 s/h from IIE. Lists funding sources available to support undergraduate, graduate, post-doctorate, and professional learning abroad, from study and research to internships and other work experiences. Very useful indexes, including field of study, internships/work abroad.

Rotary Foundation Ambassadorial Scholarships. Information available from The Rotary Foundation of Rotary International, 1 Rotary Center, 1560 Sherman Ave., Evanston, IL 60201-3698; 847-866-3000, fax 847-328-8554; [www.rotary.org]. Information about Rotary scholarships for study abroad, available to undergraduates and graduates who are unrelated to a member of Rotary. Application possible only through local Rotary clubs. Deadlines range between March and July 2001 for 2002-2003 awards (Candidates must apply over a year in advance).

A Student's Guide to Scholarships, Grants, and Funding Publications in International Education and Other Disciplines Vlada Musayelova, John Harrison, and Charles Gliozzo, eds. 1st ed., April 1997. 79 pp. Published by Michigan State Univ. International Studies and Programs in cooperation with the Michigan State Univ. Library. $5 postpaid ($4 each for 10 copies or more) from: Office of the Dean, International Studies and Programs, 209 International Ctr., Michigan State Univ., East Lansing, MI 48824. Attn: Student Guide. An annotated listing of funding sources with directions on where to go for more information, including web sites.

Key Publishers and Organizations

Africa-America Institute, 380 Lexington Ave., Fl. 42, New York, NY 10168; 212-949-5666, fax 212-682-6174; aainy@aaionline.org. Works closely with educational institutions and sustainable development organizations in Africa.

American-Scandinavian Foundation. Exchange Division, 58 Park Ave., New York, NY 10016; 212-879-9779, fax 212-249-3444; asf@amscan.org, [www.amscan.org]. Free publications on study/work in Scandinavia. Offers scholarships and internships in Scandinavia.

AMIDEAST, 1730 M St., NW, Suite 1100, Washington, DC 20036-4505; 202-776-9624, fax 202-776-7024; inquiries@amideast.org, [www.amideast.org]. Assists with developing cultural, and educational exchange programs in Egypt, Jordan, Kuwait, Lebanon, Morocco, Syria, Tunisia, West Bank/Gaza, Yemen, the UAE.

French Cultural Services, 972 5th Ave., New York, NY 10021; 212-439-1400, fax 212-439-1455. Free publications on French higher education and opportunities in France for U.S. students.

German Academic Exchange Service (DAAD), 950 3rd Ave., 19th Fl., New York, NY 10022; 212-758-3223, fax 212-755-5780; daadny@daad.org, [www.daad.org]. Information on studying in Germany, including scholarships.

Groves Dictionaries, 345 Park Ave. S., New York, NY 10010-1707; 800-221-2123 or 212-689-9200, fax 212-689-9711; grove@grovereference.com, [www.grovereference.com]. Publishers of directories of universities worldwide.

Institute of International Education (IIE). IIE Books, Institute of International Education, P.O. Box 371, Annapolis Junction, MD 20701-0371; 800-445-0443, fax 301-206-9789; iiebooks@pmds.com. Publisher of authoritative directories for study abroad and financial aid.

Intercultural Press, P.O. Box 700, Yarmouth, ME 04096; 800-370-2665, 207-846-5168, fax 207-846-5181; books@interculturalpress.com, [www.interculturalpress.com]. Leading publisher of books dealing with cross-cultural issues. Free catalog.

Just Act - Youth Action for Global Justice, 333 Valencia St., Suite 325, San Francisco, CA 94103; 415-431-4204, fax 415-431-5953; info@justact.org, [www.justact.org]. Publishes material on work and internships working for global justice. Formerly Overseas Development Network.

Mobility International USA (MIUSA), P.O. Box 10767, Eugene, OR 97440; 541- 343-1284 (voice and TTY), fax 541-343-6812; info@miusa.org, [www.miusa.org]. Publications and videos on including persons with disabilities in international exchange programs.

NAFSA Publications, P.O. Box 1020, Sewickley, PA 15143; 800- 836-4994, fax 412-741-0609. Free catalog. Publishers of informational materials, geared toward its professional membership, on study, work, and travel abroad opportunities as well as advising and admissions. For more on publications listed in catalog contact Publications Office at NAFSA: 202-737-3699, fax 202-737-2657.

National Clearinghouse on Disability and Exchange. Mobility International USA, P.O. Box 10767, Eugene, OR 97440; 541-343-1284 v/tty; clearinghouse@miusa.org, [www.miusa.org]. A project managed by Mobility International USA and sponsored by the Bureau of Educational and Cultural Affairs of the U.S. Department of State; offers a variety of publications and videos, presents workshops and trainings, and provides consultation, information and referral about international exchange opportunities and disability issues worldwide.

Seven Hills Book Distributors, 1531 Tremont St., Cincinnati, OH 45214; 800-545-2005 (orders only); 513-471-4300, fax 513-471-4311; [www.sevenhillsbooks.com]. Carries a wide range of travel books and maps, living, and working guides, and international education reference guides, from both domestic and international publishers including Vacation Work Publications, Educational International, and Trailblazer Publications.

Superintendent of Documents, U.S. Government Printing Office, Washington, DC 20402; fax 202-512-2250; [www.access.gpo.gov/su_docs]. Publishes a wide range of material, including country "Background Notes" subscription series, $55.

Transitions Abroad Publishing, P.O. Box 1300, Amherst, MA 01004-1300; 413-256-3414, 800-293-0373, fax 413-256-0373; info@TransitionsAbroad.com, [www.TransitionsAbroad.com]. The premier publisher of resources for the learning traveler.

Publishes the bimonthly magazine *Transitions Abroad*, and the books *The Alternative Travel Directory* and *Work Abroad*.

Vacation Work Publications, 9 Park End St., Oxford OX1 1HJ, England; 011-44-1865-241978, fax 011-44-1865-790855; [www.vacationwork.co.uk]. Publisher of books on work abroad and international careers; distributed in the U.S. by Peterson's Guides and Seven Hills (each has different titles).

Key Study Abroad Web Sites

Selected by William Nolting.

Worldwide Databases

The Electronic Embassy [www.embassy.org/embassies/index.html]collects the home pages of all U.S.-based embassies. In addition to essential official information for travel (visas, etc.), many countries provide cultural and educational exchange information on their web sites.

GoAbroad.com [www.goabroad.com]. A comprehensive and up-to-date education abroad web site with excellent search provisions.

Institute of International Education (IIE) publishes the most comprehensive data on study and work abroad programs. **IIE Passport** [www.iiepassport.org] is a user-friendly search engine which lets you find the program characteristics you're interested in, such as location and language of instruction. Includes the entire contents of the IIE books *Academic Year Abroad* and *Vacation Study Abroad*.

Language Course Finder, International Where+How [www.language-learning.net] includes some 6,000 listings of language courses worldwide. Searches possible on a variety of categories, in 20 languages.

Studyabroad.com [www.studyabroad.com] lists study abroad programs as well as special databases for language courses and internships/volunteer programs. Information limited to location and subject.

Transitions Abroad Magazine [www.TransitionsAbroad.com] is unique in its coverage of all education abroad options, from study abroad to educational travel. Subscribers to the magazine have full access to its vast online database of annotated resources and first-hand reports compiled by international education specialists over the past 25 years.

Univ. of California-Irvine, International Opportunities Program. Extensive directories (not databases) of study abroad, summer programs, internships, research, teaching, volunteering and work abroad programs with links to many other education abroad web sites.

Univ. of Michigan, International Center's Overseas Opportunities Office [www.umich.edu/~icenter/overseas] by *Transitions Abroad* Work Abroad Editor William Nolting. Not a database, but a collection of outstanding articles, annotated links, and print resources for study, work, and travel abroad, including in-depth reports on work abroad options.

Univ. of Minnesota, International Study and Travel Center (ISTC) [www.istc.umn.edu] is a comprehensive web site with outstanding search provisions.

Worldwide Classroom [www.worldwide.edu] lists intensive language programs and programs suitable for K-12 students through adults. Includes a "Travel Planner" section offering lots of links. Web version of the International Study Telecom Directory.

World Wide Colleges and Universities [www.usc.edu/globaled/wwcu] links to university and international office web sites. Organized by country.

Yahoo's Worldwide Colleges and Universities [http://dir.yahoo.com/Education/Higher_Education/Colleges_and_Universities] links to university homepages (but not international offices). Organized by country.

Country Databases

Africa

National Consortium for Study in Africa [www.isp.msu.edu/ncsa], hosted by Michigan State University's African Studies Center, includes an extensive list of study abroad programs offered by U.S. institutions, with descriptions, contact information, and links for email and web sites. Excellent video on study in Africa available.

Univ. of Pennsylvania, African Studies [www.sas.upenn.edu/African_Studies/AS.html] has huge number of links to sites for African and African-American studies.

Asia

Association for Asian Studies [www.aasianst.org] is a professional association web site with a section on study abroad. Comprehensive links to other sites on all regions of Asia.

Association of International Education, Japan (AIEJ) [www.aiej.or.jp] provides official information on study abroad and scholarships for Japan.

Freeman Scholarships [http://www.iie.org/pgms/freeman-asia] offers scholarships for undergraduates with financial need to study in Asia. Apply online: Freeman-ASIA@iie.org.

Australia

Australian Education Office (AEO) [www.austudies.org/aeo] is an officially-sponsored web site with listings of study abroad programs (including U.S.-sponsored) at Australian universities. Links to related sites, include Australian Studies Network [www.austudies.org].

Central and Eastern Europe, Russia, and the NIS

American Association of Teachers of Slavic & East European Languages (AATSEEL) [http://clover.slavic.pitt.edu/~aatseel], a professional association web site which includes study abroad internships, scholarships and career information related to Central and East European Studies.

International Research and Exchanges Board (IREX) [www.irex.org] is a nonprofit organization which offers grants for study abroad in this region.

RussNet: The Russian Language Network [www.russnet.org/home.html] is a comprehensive resource for studying and working in Russia.

Why Study Russian [www.russnet.org/why/index.html] introduces the world of Russian studies.

Western Europe

American-Scandinavian Foundation [www.amscan.org/study.htm] includes a comprehensive directory of study, language, and work abroad programs in all Scandinavian countries, including U.S.-sponsored programs.

CDS International [www.cdsintl.org] offers several paid study-internship programs in Germany for students, graduates, and professionals. Web site provides program information and listings of current internship openings plus links for information about Germany.

EduFrance [www.edufrance.fr/en/index.htm]. This official site provides comprehensive information on direct enrollment and French as a foreign language courses in France. See also the *Cultural Services of the French Embassy* site, [http://info-france-usa.org/culture/education/index.html] for additional information on scholarships, teaching assistantships in France, and more.

German Academic Exchange Service (DAAD) [www.daad.org] provides comprehensive official information on direct enrollment, degree study, and scholarships for Germany. Links to German universities and to DAAD's guide to Study and Research in Germany (aka "Surfin' Germany").

Netherlands Organization for International Cooperation in Higher Education (NUFFIC) [www.nuffic.nl/index-en.html] provides official information on direct enrollment in the Netherlands.

United Kingdom

British Council USA - Study in the UK [www.studyintheuk.org] provides comprehensive official information on study, scholarships, internships, and working as a student in the U.K. See also British Information Services [www.britainusa.com/educate/educate.asp].

British Universities Transatlantic Exchange Association (BUTEX) [www.butex.ac.uk/butex] has BUTEX's directories of undergraduate and graduate study programs in the U.K., which include most (but not all) U.K. universities.

Latin America

Univ. of Texas, Latin American Network Information Center (LANIC) [www.lanic.utexas.edu] is an exhaustive source for academic information on Latin America. Countries section provides links to host-country universities, media, country, travel information, and much more.

Middle East

AMIDEAST's Guide to Study Abroad [www.amideast.org/programs/study], the web site of the America-Mideast Educational & Training Services, Inc. (AMIDEAST, includes perhaps the most complete listing of study abroad programs in the Middle East.

World Zionist Organization, Complete Guide to the Israel Experience [www.wzo.org.il] offers directories of study and volunteer opportunities in Israel, along with offices in the U.S. which can provide information and advice

Study Abroad Funding Web Sites

Basic Facts Regarding Financial Aid for Study Abroad [www.secussa.nafsa.org/basicfinancialaid.html] contains overview by an expert, Charles Gliozzo, of how to use financial aid and scholarships for study abroad, with links to web sites for more information.

Council Bowman Scholarship [www.ciee.org/ study/scholarships/bowman.htm]. Undergraduates at CIEE member institutions can receive scholarship funds to cover the cost of airfare for study, work, volunteering, or research in less-traditional countries.

FastWeb [www.fastweb.com] web site provides free customized scholarship search after user fills out profile.

FinAid! (National Association of Financial Aid Administrators) [www.finaid.org]. The web site of the main U.S. professional association for financial aid provides scholarship searches and extensive information about financial aid. Links with FastWeb.

Freeman Scholarships [www.iie.org/pgms/ freeman-asia]. Scholarships for undergraduates with financial need to study in Asia. Apply online: Freeman-ASIA@iie.org.

Fulbright Scholarships [www.iie.org/fulbright] for graduating seniors, graduate students, and alumni; Fulbright Scholar programs for university faculty and international education administrators; Fulbright Teacher Exchange for K-12 and community college teachers.

Gilman Scholarships [www.iie.org/gilman] provides assistance for undergraduates with financial need to use for study abroad. Apply online : gilman@iie.org. *International Education Financial Aid (IEFA)* [www.iefa.org] provides free searches for scholarships for study abroad.

Institute of International Education, Financial Resources for International Study and Funding for United States Study [www.iie.org/ help/search.htm]. IIE's scholarship books online provide free searches.

International Education Finance Corporation (IEFC) [www.iefc.com] is a corporation specializing in loans for study abroad.

Minority International Research Training Grant (MIRT) [www.nih.gov/fic/programs/ mirt.html]. Program of the Fogarty International Center, National Institutes of Health sends minority undergraduates and medical students abroad to do health-related research.

National Security Education Program (NSEP) [www.ndu.edu/nsep/] Information on NSEP scholarships for undergraduate and graduate study in less-traditional regions. Note that NSEP grants have a service obligation.

Reference Service Press [www.rspfunding.com] publishes of some of the best hard-copy directories of scholarships for overseas opportunities.

Rotary Foundation Ambassadorial Scholarships [www.rotary.org/foundation/educational/ amb_scho/rotarian/endowed.html]. The Rotary Foundation provides the largest single U.S. scholarship program for study abroad. Scholarships are available for all levels of study, from high-school, undergraduate, and graduate students to alumni and professionals. Application possible only through local Rotary Clubs.

U.S. Department of Education: Financial Aid for Students [www.ed.gov/offices/OPE/ Students]. The federal government's official guides to financial aid.

U.S. State Department's Bureau of Educational and Cultural Affairs (formerly USIA) [http:// exchanges.state.gov]. Official information about all Fulbright programs (for study, research, and teaching abroad), other official exchange programs, and information about U.S. government regulations concerning international educational exchange

U.S. State Department's Bureau of Educational and Cultural Affairs (formerly USIA) [http:// exchanges.state.gov/education]. Official information about all Fulbright programs (for study, research, and teaching abroad).

Univ. of Minnesota, International Study and Travel Center (ISTC), Scholarships Database [www.istc.umn.edu/study/scholarships.html]. An excellent, free online database of scholarships.

Woodrow Wilson International Fellowship Foundation [www.woodrow.org/public-policy]. Information on several multi-year scholarship programs for students, especially minorities, interested in international careers.

NINE

STUDY ABROAD
BEST PROGRAMS

Whether you're a student looking for an international study program or any traveler who want to combine the least expense abroad with the most awards, you'll find what you want in the programs described below—many of which can be audited for no credit, often at a reduced cost. Contact the program directors to confirm dates, costs, and other details. (Please mention Transitions Abroad!*) Programs based in more than one country are listed under "Worldwide."*

Africa

Full Curriculum and African Studies: Ghana. Located in Accra, the Univ. of Ghana offers courses taught in English in a variety of fields such as agriculture, dance, literature, philosophy, and religion to name a few. Its highly regarded Institute of African Studies researches African languages, history and culture and offers introductory courses to all students, which are perfect for those attending the USAC program. Ghana is one of the most progressive African nations with its civilization government, hospitable people, and a growing tourist industry.

Dates: Fall semester: Aug-Dec; spring semester: Jan-May. **Costs:** Call for cost information. **Contact:** University Studies Abroad Consortium (USAC), Univ. of Nevada, USAC 323, Reno, NV 89557; 775-784-6569, fax 775-784-6010.

Global Education in Namibia. Earn a semester of college credit with "Multicultural Societies in Transition" (fall) or "Nation Building, Globalization, and Decolonizing the Mind" (spring). Includes homestay in rural area, seminar in South Africa, internship option and courses.

Dates: Semesters (Sep-Dec or Feb-May). **Costs:** Contact the Center for current costs.

Contact: Semester Programs Abroad, Center for Global Education, Augsburg College, 2211 Riverside Ave., Box 307TR, Minneapolis, MN 55454; 800-299-8889, fax 612-330-1695; globaled@augsburg.edu, [www.augsburg.edu/global].

Kalamazoo in Africa. Programs combine academics and experiential learning. Course work in a host-country setting (with local students in university courses) gives participants a broad overview of the host country. Instruction in the local language as well as internships or independent projects provide opportunities for greater understanding of the host culture.

Dates: Senegal and Kenya: Sep-Jun. **Costs:** $26,880 (2001-2002). Includes roundtrip international transportation, tuition and fees, room and board, and some excursions. **Contact:** Center for International Programs, Kalamazoo College, 1200 Academy, Kalamazoo, MI 49006; 616-337-7133, fax 616-337-7400; cip@kzoo.edu.

Penn-in-Dar Es Salaam (Tanzania). For students interested in African studies this program affiliated with the Univ. of Dar Es Salaam offers courses in East African history, economics, and politics as well as in African theater and Swahili language and culture. Students stay with host families.

Dates: Jul 9-Aug 10. **Costs:** Tuition $3,390; room and board $600, group travel $1,300. **Contact:** Penn Summer Abroad, College of General Studies, Univ. of Pennsylvania, 3440 Market St., Suite 100, Philadelphia, PA 19104-3335; 215-898-5738, fax 215-573-2053; summerabroad@sas.upenn.edu, [www.sas.upenn.edu/CGS/].

Americas

Educational Homestays. Foreign students or visitors live with host families and may also have optional ESL teaching and/or excursions. Short- or long-term homestays provided for high school or college students in universities, at language schools, or just visiting America or Canada.

Dates: Any time of year. **Costs:** Depends on program and city. Programs includes room, meals, airport or bus transfers, plus use of all household amenities, and local area supervision. **Contact:** Connections, John Shephard, 17324 185th Ave. NE, Woodinville, WA 98072; 425-788-9803, fax 425-788-2785 [www.connections-inc.com].

Argentina

IES La Plata. Features a curriculum focused on Argentina and the Southern Cone as well as broad Latin American studies. Interdisciplinary offerings in environmental studies, Latin American studies, political science/international relations. All IES courses are taught in Spanish and involve field study. Option for courses at Universidad Nacional de La Plata. Housing: homestay, apartments, dormitories.

Dates: Fall: Jul-early Dec; spring: Feb-Jul, 2001; year: Jul. **Costs:** Semester $8,600; year $15,480. Includes tuition, orientation, housing, some meals, selected field trips, and international student ID card. **Contact:** Institute for the International Education of Students (IES), 33 N. LaSalle St., Chicago, IL 60602-2602; 800-995-2300, fax 312-944-1448; info@iesabroad.org, [www.iesabroad.org].

NYU in Buenos Aires. Offers students challenging courses in Spanish language and Latin American culture, the latter in both English and Spanish. Course work is complemented by a series of cultural and social activities, including excursions to Argentina's heartland. Students are housed in apartments near the NYU center, minutes away from the city's "centro."

Dates: Jul 1-Aug 9. **Costs:** 2001: tuition for 8 points $3,920. Housing and activity fees $1,700 (includes a 3-day excursions by plane to the Argentine Northwest). **Contact:** NYU Summer Session, 7 E. 12th St., 6th Fl., New York, NY 10003; 212-998-2292, fax 212- 995-4103; summer.info@nyu.edu, [www.nyu.edu/summer].

Penn-in-Buenos Aires. For students interested in Latin American studies, this program at San Andres Univ. in the bustling and cosmopolitan Buenos Aires will offer courses in Spanish, Latin American culture, and contemporary Argentinean literature. Students will also have the opportunity to live with local families.

Dates: Jul 7-Aug 10. **Costs:** Tuition $3,390; room and board $1,000; activities $200. **Contact:** Penn Summer Abroad, College of General Studies, Univ. of Pennsylvania, 3440 Market St., Suite 100, Philadelphia, PA 19104-3335; 215-898-5738, fax 215-573-2053; summerabroad@sas.upenn.edu, [www.sas.upenn.edu/CGS].

Australia

Environmental Management in Australia. Univ. of Buffalo is pleased to offer the Summer Study Abroad Program in Queensland in conjunction with Griffith Univ. This 3-week program involves 1 week at each of the following sites: the campus of Griffith Univ., Numinbah Valley Environmental Education Center, and the Townsville/Cairns region, the tropical gateway to the Great Barrier Reef.

Dates: Jun 6-30. **Costs:** $2,150 program fee includes tuition for 6 credit hours, all accommodations, a meal stipend, field trips, and administrative costs. Transportation to Australia, health insurance, passport and visa fees, and miscellaneous personal expenses not included. **Contact:** SUNY at Buffalo, Study Abroad Programs, 210 Talbert Hall, Box 601604, Buffalo, NY 14260-1604; 716-645-3912, fax 716-645-6197; studyabroad@acsu.buffalo.edu, [www.buffalo.edu/studyabroad].

Full Curriculum Studies: Melbourne. Victoria offers nearly every discipline in undergraduate/ graduate levels at 5 different university campus sites: Australian studies, art, journalism, performing arts, women's studies, biology, chemistry, math, business, computing, etc. Known as the Garden State, Victoria has some of the country's most spectacular mountain and coastal areas.

Dates: First semester: Jul-Nov; second semester: Feb-Jun. **Costs:** One semester $4,530, both semesters $8,165. **Contact:** University Studies Abroad Consortium (USAC), Univ. of Nevada, USAC 323, Reno, NV 89557; 775-784-6569, fax 775-784-6010; usac@unr.edu, [http:// usac.unr.edu].

IES Adelaide. Direct enrollment at the Univ. of Adelaide offers more than 60 discipline options. Through formal academic study and informal field study students explore the differences between the U.S. and Australia. Past field trips included red center of Australia and Sydney. Housing: dormitories, apartments, or homestay. **Dates:** Fall: Jul-Nov; spring: Feb-Jun 2002; year: Jul-Jun. **Costs:** Semester $10,350; year $18,630. Includes tuition, orientation, housing and meals, health insurance, and some field trips each semeter. Housing and meals not covered during break. **Contact:** Institute for the International Education of Students (IES), 33 N. LaSalle St., Chicago, IL 60602-2602; 800-995-2300, fax 312-944-1448; info@iesabroad.org, [www.iesabroad.org].

IES Melbourne. Direct enrollment at the Univ. of Melbourne offers more than 300 discipline options. Through formal academic study and informal field study, students explore the differences between the U.S. and Australia. Past field trips: Tasmania and the Victorian highlands. Housing: dormitories, apartments, and homestays. **Dates:** Fall: Jul-Dec; spring: Feb-Jul; year: Jul-Jun. **Costs:** Semester $10,800; year $19,440. **Contact:** Institute for the International Education of Students (IES), 33 N. LaSalle St., Chicago, IL 60602-2602; 800-995-2300, fax 312-944-1448; info@IESabroad.org, [www.IESabroad.org].

Marine Ecology of Temperate Australia. A custom-designed short course in marine ecology based around the marine wilderness of the Great Australian Bight. Taught by internationally renowned marine biologists, you will study the region's unique biodiversity which includes southern right whales, fur seals, great white sharks, and thousands of species of invertebrate and algae found nowhere else on earth. **Dates:** January 1-31. **Costs:** Approx. $3,850 includes transport, board, meals, tuition. **Contact:** Study Abroad Officer, Int'l. Office, Flinders Univ., GPO Box 2100, Adelaide, SA 5001, Australia; 011-618-8201-2727 or 800-686-3562; study.abroad@flinders.edu.au, [http://adminwww.flinders.edu.au/IntlOffice/home.html].

Semester in Australia. The Australian International Hotel School in Canberra offers semester-long programs focusing on international hospitality management. Students earn 12-15 credits; courses include Pacific Tourism, Multicultural Management, International Cuisine, Global Hotel Operations, and Resort Development. Students live at AIHS and participate in many travel and cultural activities. AIHS is affiliated with RMIT Univ. (Melbourne). **Dates:** Semester: Feb-May, May-Aug, Sep-Dec. **Costs:** $8,500 includes tuition, room and board, and course-related trips. **Contact:** Prof. Richard H. Penner, AIHS Semester in Australia, Cornell Univ., 182 Statler Hall, Ithaca, NY 14853-6902; 607-255-1842, 800-235-8220, fax 607-255-4179; aihs@cornell.edu, [http://aihs.edu.au].

Study, Work, and Travel! The AEC offers a multitude of affordable options to study, work, and travel in Australia. It provides individualized enrollment services including information, application, credit transfer, subject selection, accommodations, visa, predeparture and on-arrival services. Students receive many benefits such as: ISIC, Australia books, Backpacker Australian membership for travel, insurance, predeparture kit, etc., and an on-arrival Experience Australia 5-day tour program. **Dates:** Semester start dates in Jan, Feb, May, Jul, and Sep. (For Jan, May, and Sep entry, students are restricted to Bond Univ. For Feb and Jul, students have complete choice of 32 Australian universities). Summer: Jul 1-Jul 20; Jul 21-Aug 11. **Costs:** Tuition starts at $3,300 for semester. All-inclusive packages with housing, meals, and airfare also available. **Contact:** Joyce Noronha, Australian Education Connection, 5722 S. Flamingo Rd., #303, Ft. Lauderdale, FL 33330; 800-565-9553, 954-680-0453, fax 954-680-0597; AustStudy@aol.com, [http://studyabroad.com/australia].

Univ. of the Sunshine Coast. Australia's newest university offers students a truly Australian experience. Located 1 hour from Brisbane, on the Sunshine Coast, USC offers courses in a wide range of disciplines, outstanding faculty, small classes, individualized attention, strong program of support services and cultural activities. Internships available with the required prior academic preparation. Student apartments adjacent to campus. **Dates:** Session I: early Feb-end of Jun; Session II: mid-Jul-early Dec. **Costs:** Approx. $4,700 per semester includes orienation in the U.S. and Australia, 20 weeks of housing with food allowance, Australian health insurance, USC tuition, administrative fees. Airfare and SUNY tuition not included. **Contact:** Office of International Programs, P.O. Box 2000, SUNY Cortland, Cortland, NY 13045; 607-753-2209, fax 607-753-5989; koppl@cortland.edu, [www.studyabroad.com/suny/cortland].

Australia/New Zealand

BUNAC's Work Australia and Work New Zealand Programs. Work and travel down under for up to a year (Australia 4 months, New Zealand 12 months). Full support services, job listings, meet and greet, etc. provided in Australia and New Zealand by BUNAC subsidiary, IEP. For U.S. students and young people 18-30 years old.
   Dates: Year round. Call for details. **Costs:** $450/$475 includes visa, admin, arrival package, and on-the-spot support. **Contact:** BUNAC USA, P.O. Box 430, Southbury, CT 06488; 800-GO-BUNAC; info@bunacusa.org, [www.bunac.org].

Semester/Year, Summer, Full Degree. Direct enrollment semester, year of full degrees at 23 accredited Australian and New Zealand universities; all majors and programs. Short-term courses in marine biology, environmental studies, Australian tourism and education. Resident Director. Pre-arranged credit transfer, visa/passport, housing. Scholarships available. Financial aid assistance. Pre-term orientations: Cairns, Australia and Rotorua, New Zealand.
   Dates: Semester/year or full degree: Feb or Jul. Short-term courses: summer. **Costs:** $4,700-$6,500 per semester, depending on university housing and meal plan. Includes tuition, health coverage, orientations, and academic advising services. Short-term courses and full degree: call for details. **Contact:** AustraLearn: North American Center for Australian Universities. CSU Denver Center, 110 16th St., Denver, CO 80202; 800-980-0033, fax 303-446-2214; studyabroad@australearn.org, [www.australearn.org].

Austria

IES Vienna. Extensive liberal arts offerings including all levels of German language, humanities, international business, economics, international relations, and comprehensive music program. English-taught IES curriculum for beginning German students and German-taught courses for advanced German-speaking students. Advanced students may also take courses at the Univ. of Vienna. Housing: apartments.
   Dates: Fall: Aug-Dec; spring: Jan-May 2002; year: Aug-May. (Univ. courses end Jan 26 and Jun 30 for fall and spring semester respectively.) **Costs:** Semester $10,700; year $19,260. Includes tuition, orientation, housing, nonoptional field trips, and international student ID card.
Contact: Institute for the International Education of Students (IES), 33 N. LaSalle St.,

Chicago, IL 60602-2602; 800-995-2300, fax 312-944-1448; info@iesabroad.org, [www.iesabroad.org].

Vienna Master Courses for Music. Master classes (2 weeks) in: singing, opera, lied, piano, violin, cello, guitar, conducting, flute. Diploma for active participation, certificate for listeners, final concerts. Twenty lessons per week. Instructors are leading artists or renowned teachers.
   Dates: Jul 8-Aug 9, Sep 16-28. **Costs:** Registration fee: EURO110; course fee active: EURO380; listen EURO198. **Contact:** Vienna Master Courses, A-1030 Vienna, Reisnerstr. 3, Austria; 011-43-1-714-88-22, fax 011-43-1-714-88-21; wiener-meisterkurse@music.at, [www.wiener-meisterkurse.music.at].

Belize

Internships in Belize. Experience living and working in an English-speaking developing country. Internships are available in most disciplines. Interns live with host families. Following a 1-week orientation, participants work full time with various agencies and organizations. Must be self-starters. Journals and written projects are submitted for assessment at the end of program. Academic credit offered: 15-16 credits per semester. Required: 2.5 cumulative GPA, strong performance in major, maturity, and adaptability. Junior or senior status.
   Dates: Fall and spring, 16-17 weeks each. **Costs:** Estimate: $4,400 includes internship supervision, room and board, health insurance, local transportation, international airfare, full-day orientation prior to departure in Cortland, and 1-week orientation upon arrival in Belize. SUNY tuition not included. **Contact:** Office of International Programs, Box 2000, SUNY Cortland, Cortland, NY 13045; 607-753-2209, fax 607-753-5989; studyabroad@cortland.edu, [www.studyabroad.com/suny/cortland].

Brazil

Brazilian Ecosystems Program. This program is an intensive field study of the tropical and subtropical ecosystems of Brazil. Students learn about current research in ecology, and human impact and resource development from Brazilian scientists. Courses are conducted at program sites in the states of Amazonas, Pará, Mato Grosso, Paraná, and Santa Catarina. Portuguese language and a 4-week internship are integral parts of the program.
   Dates: Sep-Dec. **Costs:** Contact office for details. **Contact:** Antioch Education Abroad, Antioch College, 795 Livermore St., Yellow

Springs, OH 45387; 800-874-7986, fax 937-769-1019; aea@antioch-college.edu, [www.antioch-college.edu/aea].

Canada

Ecole de français, Montréal. For the last 55 years, the Ecole de français has offered courses in French as a second language to students from around the world. The Ecole is continually improving its programs to meet the changing needs of its students. Choose from Oral and Written Communication French (beginner to advanced), Workshop on Teaching French as a Second Language (for teachers), Contemporary Québec Culture (for advanced students), Business French (intermediate to advanced students).

Dates: Spring: May 22-Jun 14; summer 1: Jul 3-20; summer 2: Jul 23-Aug 10; fall: Sep 10-Nov 30; winter 2002: Jan 7-Mar 29. **Costs:** Spring/summer: (3 weeks, 60 hours) CAN$568.75; summer: (3 weeks, 45 hours) CAN$468.75; fall/Winter: (12 weeks, 240 hours) CAN$1,770. Prices subject to change. **Contact:** Nicole Lavergne, Coordinator, Ecole de français, Faculté de l'education permanente, Université de Montréal, C.P. 6128, succursale Centre-ville, Montréal, PQ, H3C 3J7, Canada; 514-343-7492, fax 514-343-5984; infolang@fep.umontreal.ca, [www.fep.umontreal.ca/langues/index.html].

Caribbean

Instituto Internacional Euskalduna. Learn Spanish in Puerto Rico! We offer communicative, learner-centered classes for all language levels. Small groups and private programs, U.S. university credit, weekly cultural activities and homestay programs with or without meals.

Dates: Classes begin every other Monday. **Costs:** Programs starting at $580. **Contact:** NESOL, Inc., Calle Navarro 56, HatoRey, PR 00918; 787-281-8013, fax 787-767-1494; studyabroad@newenglandschool.com, [www.newenglandschool.com].

Central America

Social Justice Internship. The Institute for Central American Development Studies (ICADS) offers a semester internship and research program including coursework, intensive Spanish training, and structured internships in Costa Rica, Nicaragua, Panama, and Cuba in the following areas: Women's Studies, Environment/Ecology, Healthcare, Education. Fall and spring semesters. The program is progressive and aimed at students who wish to work on social justice issues and on behalf of the poor, women, and the oppressed in Central America. Full semester credit.

Dates: Fall and spring terms with academic credit. Summer noncredit program in Costa Rica only. **Costs:** Fall semester $7,600; summer $3,500. **Contact:** ICADS, Dept. 826, P.O. Box 025216, Miami., FL 33102; 011-506-225-0508, fax 011-506-234-1337; icads@netbox.com, [www.icadscr.com].

Sustainable Development and Social Change. Study Spanish while living with families in Guatemala (3 weeks); study the role of the church in social injustice in El Salvador (4 weeks), and examine the theory and practice of economic development and social change movements in Nicaragua (6 weeks).

Dates: Sep-Dec or Feb-May. **Costs:** Call for details. **Contact:** Semester Programs Abroad, Center for Global Education, Augsburg College, 2211 Riverside Ave., Box 307TR, Minneapolis, MN 55454; 800-299-8889, fax 612-330-1695; globaled@augsburg.edu, [www.augsburg.edu/global].

Chile

IES Santiago. IES Courses in humanities and social sciences, environmental studies, archaeology/anthropology taught by native faculty with enrollment options at the Universidad de Chile and the Pontifica Universidad Catholica. Field trips and cultural excursions to destinations such as: Valparaiso, La Serena, Valdiva. Housing in homestays.

Dates: Fall: Jul-Dec 2002; spring: Mar-Jul 2003. **Costs:** Semester $9,000; year $16,200. Includes tuition, orientation, housing, selected field trips, international student card, internship placement. **Contact:** Institute for the International Education of Students (IES), 33 N. LaSalle St., Chicago, IL 60602-2602; 800-995-2300, fax 312-944-1448; info@IESabroad.org, [www.IESabroad.org].

Spanish and Latin American Studies: Santiago. Santiago offers intensive language studies fulfilling up to 2 years of university Spanish requirements in 1 semester, with additional courses in literature, business, teacher ed., history, political science. Week-long, program-oriented field trips to the south and north of Chile, homestays, and many university activities at Chilean university.

Dates: Fall semester Aug-Dec, spring semester Jan-May. **Costs:** One semester $3,980, both semesters $6,650. **Contact:** University Studies Abroad Consortium (USAC), Univ. of Nevada, USAC323, Reno, NV 89557; 775-784-6569, fax

775-784-6010; usac@unr.edu, [http://usac.unr.edu].

Study in Valdivia, Chile. Located approximately 500 miles south of Santiago, in an area with few English-speaking visitors, Vadivia makes an excellent location for students wishing to perfect their Spanish languge skills. Classes are held at La Universidad Austral de Chile. Numerous field trips and excurions included. Twoyears college Spanish or equivalent required. **Dates:** Fall and spring 16-week semesters. **Costs:** $4,300 per term. **Contact:** AHA International, 741 SW Lincoln St., Portland, OR 97201-3178; 800-654-2051; mail@aha-intl.org, [www.aha-intl.org].

China

BCA Dalian Study Center. Earn 16-20 credits per semester at the Dalian Univ. of Foreign Languages in China, with a 1-week orientation period, field trips, and extended study tours through northern or southern China. Advanced Chinese program requires college intermediate level language; beginning program has no language prerequisite. Students from all U.S. colleges and universities accepted. All levels of Chinese language available plus Russian and Japanese, Chinese History, literature, politics, and internships. **Dates:** Sep-Dec or Jan (fall), Feb-Jun or Jul (spring), Sep-Jun or Jul (year). **Costs:** $17,450 academic year; $10,125 semester (1999-2000) includes international transportation, tuition, room and board, insurance, group in-country travel. **Contact:** Program Division, 605 E. College Ave., North Manchester, IN 46962; 219-982-5238, fax 219-982-7755

Beijing Capital Normal Univ. The Beijing Capital Normal Univ. is one of the key institutes of the Beijing municipality. Its 11 departments offer a wide range of courses. The college also has special Institutes of Educational Science, British History, Economic History of Chinese Ancient Society as well as an affiliated campus school. Most study abroad students take intensive Mandarin Chinese language and culture courses. Traditional Chinese painting, instrumental music and business classes are also available. Housing and meals in student residence. One year of Mandarin recommended. Twelve to 15 credits per semester. **Dates:** Fall: late Aug-late Jan; spring: mid-Feb-late Jun; academic: late Aug-late Jun. **Costs:** Fall and spring estimate: $3,000 per semester. Includes full-day orientation before departure, application fee, room and food allowance in residence hall, health and accident insurance,

travel allownace, visa, administrative fees. SUNY tuition not included. **Contact:** Dr. John Ogden, Director, Office of International Programs, Box 2000, SUNY Cortland, Cortland, NY 13045; 607-753-2209, fax 607-753-5989; studyabroad@cortland.edu, [www.studyabroad.com/suny/cortland].

Chinese Studies: Chengdu. The Chinese Studies Program offers intensive language study fulfilling up to 2 years of university language requirements in 1 semester. Additional courses in art history, economics, anthropology, political science, physics, chemistry, literature, history, and calligraphy are taught in English and offer a multidisciplinary approach to understanding the complexities of China and Asia. **Dates:** Summer sessions: Jun and Jul; fall semester: Aug-Dec, spring semester: Jan-May. **Costs:** One semester $4,260; both semesters $6,860; Jun or Jul $1,480; Jun and Jul $2,760. **Contact:** University Studies Abroad Consortium (USAC), Univ. of Nevada, USAC 323, Reno, NV 89557; 775-784-6569, fax 775-784-6010; usac@unr.edu, [http://usac.unr.edu].

Friends World Program (Hangzhou). A semester or year program at Zhejiang Univ. in Hangzhou, including Chinese language instruction, field trips, and an extensive stay in Yunnan Province spring semester. Classes include Chinese culture, customs, Chinese arts or calligraphy. Students also have their own research projects which may include the study of Chinese medicine, gender issues, religion, or environmental issues. Students may earn 12-18 credits per semester. **Dates:** Fall: early Sep to end of Dec; or, for year to mid-May; spring semester is limited to year-long participants. **Costs:** $11,995 per semester in 2000-2001. Includes tuition, travel, room and board, fees, and books. **Contact:** Admissions, Friends World Program, 239 Montauk Highway, Southampton, NY 11968; 631-287-8474; fw@southampton.liunet.edu, [www.southampton.liu.edu/fw].

IES Beijing. Located on the campus of the Beijing Foreign Studies Univ. (Beiwei), IES Beijing offers strong Mandarin Chinese language program with area studies courses taught in English. Students participate in field studies, extensive travel to distant areas of China, and have close interaction with Chinese students. Housing: dormitories. **Dates:** Summer: Jul-Aug 2001; fall: Aug-Dec 2001; spring: Jan-May 2002; year: Aug 2001-May 2002. **Costs:** Summer $3,100; semester $8,800; year $15,840. Includes tuition, orientation, housing, field trips, and interna-

At Home in Dharmasala
On Becoming a World Citizen

By Jennifer Langenbach

As I stepped off the 747 and entered the Delhi airport my senses, dulled by a 24-hour flight, were jolted awake by exhaust fumes, honking cars, and yelping dogs. Lugging an overstuffed pack, I joined a group of American students whose fleece jackets and hiking boots contrasted sharply with the colorful collage of flowing saris that surrounded us.

For four months the 20 of us, enrolled in the School for International Training's Tibetan Studies Program, would travel to India, Nepal, and Bhutan. Our instructors, both Tibetan scholars, designed the program to teach foreign students about Tibet's culture, language, and political situation.

After a day's rest in Delhi, we traveled 12 hours by bus to Dharmasala, the location of His Holiness the Dalai Lama's government in exile. The next morning language classes began. In the afternoon we attended lectures on Tibetan culture and political life. We shared our classroom on the roof of Hotel Tibet with a family of monkeys.

After sunset we were free to roam. As I set out, my instructor's voice rang in my ears: Be approachable and explore alone. Feeling lonely and far from home, I reluctantly complied and sat down for dinner. Within minutes, my fears vanished as Namkala, a 25-year-old Tibetan monk, joined my table. "Will you teach me English?" he asked. I eagerly agreed.

With his help I slowly gained access to the colorful and culturally rich Tibetan exile community. Looking back, I realize how easy it would have been to surround myself with American students and travel like a tourist, seeing the sights but missing the people.

After our 5-day adjustment period, the homestays began. By mentioning only the essentials of decorum necessary to save face, our advisers let us follow our own instincts.

Terry Tempest Williams, the naturalist and writer, defined home as the range of one's instincts, determined by the ability to read people and their landscapes. By venturing into the Tibetan community alone and by living with Tibetan families, our instincts developed in concert with our expanding range.

When I arrived at my new home, a chorus of giggling children greeted me at the door. "Tashi delek Jennyla!" (Hello Jenny!"). I met my omela and pala (mom and dad), momola (grandmother), and my four brothers and sisters. We would live in a 4-room home that included a kitchen, two bedrooms, and my pala's silversmith shop. The public outhouse was four blocks away. During the day we covered our beds with carpets, woven by my omela, to create couches.

Every morning I woke up to my momola's soft prayers and fragrant incense. After a hearty breakfast of eggs, Tibetan bread, and butter tea, I went off to class. When I returned, I played with the children. Not needing words, we wrestled, tickled, and laughed, transcending language and cultural barriers.

For dinner, my omela taught me how to make steamed momos (dumplings) by filling dough with buff (water buffalo meat), spinach, or potatoes. Afterwards, we gathered in front of the TV to enjoy what the single station was broadcasting.

As my life in Dharmasala drew to a close my family insisted on escorting me to the bus. As we entered the crowded town center I was overwhelmed. It appeared as if the entire community was there to bid us farewell. Families, friends, and lepers, who we had befriended, waved goodbye. I cried as I hugged my omela and pala. They presented me with two silky white katas (Tibetan farewell scarves) and urged me to write.

Back at college, I learned that eight of my nine housemates had also been living abroad. Together we covered five of the seven continents. Throughout the year our conversations frequently return to our varied experiences. For most of us, living abroad and gaining perspective on our country, culture, and lifestyle has been the most valuable experience of our lives. We have each called another country "home" and developed the instincts to do so. A world has opened up for each of us through the friends we have made, and we are constantly learning and aware of our world citizenship.

tional student health insurance. **Contact:** Institute for the International Education of Students (IES), 33 N. LaSalle St., Chicago, IL 60602-2602; 800-995-2300, fax 312-944-1448; info@iesabroad.org, [www.iesabroad.org].

Costa Rica

Enjoy Learning Spanish Faster. Techniques developed from our ongoing research enable students to learn more, faster, in a comfortable environment. Classes of 2-4 students plus group learning activities; conversations with middle-class homestay families (1 student or couple per family). Homestays are in a small town near the capital, San José. **Dates:** Year round. Classes begin every Monday at all levels (except Mar 25-29, Dec 14-Jan 5). **Costs:** $345 per week for 26 hours of classes and group activities including Costa Rican dance and cooking classes. Includes tuition, 3 meals per day, 7 days per week, homestay, weekly 3-hour cultural tour, laundry, all materials, and airport transportation. $25 one-time registration fee. **Contact:** Susan Shores, Registrar, Latin American Language Center, PMB 123, Suite 710, 7485 Rush River Dr., Sacramento, CA 95831-5260; 916-447-0938, 916-428-9542; lalc@madre.com, [www.madre.com/~lalc].

Friends World Program (San José). A semester or year in Latin America at Friends World Center in San José, Costa Rica, incorporates seminars, field study, travel, and independent projects. Seminars to introduce students into Latin America and its culture include Central American realities today, intensive Spanish for any level student, ecology and development, women's studies in Latin America. Independent work has included: ecology, community development, peace studies, health and agriculture studies. Students may earn 12-18 credits per semester. **Dates:** Fall: mid-Sep-mid-Dec; spring: mid-Jan-mid-May. **Costs:** $12,605 per semester in 2000-2001. Includes tuition, travel, room and board, fees and books. **Contact:** Admissions, Friends World Program, 239 Montauk Hwy., Southampton, NY 11968; 631-287-8474; FW@southampton.liunet.edu, [www.southampton.liu.edu/fw/].

Learn Spanish While Volunteering. Assist with the training of Costa Rican public school teachers in ESL and computers. Assist local health clinic, social service agencies, and environmental projects. Enjoy learning Spanish in the morning, volunteer work in the afternoon/evening. Spanish classes of 2-4 students

plus group learning activities; conversations with middle class homestay families (1 student or couple per family). Homestays and most volunteer projects are in a small town near the capital, San José. **Dates:** Year round, all levels. Classes begin every Monday (except Mar 25-29 and Dec 14-Jan 5), volunteer program is continuous. **Costs:** $345 per week for 26 hours of classes and group activities including Costa Rican dance and cooking classes. Includes tuition, meals, homestay, laundry, all materials, weekly 3-hour cultural tour, and airport transportation. $25 one-time registration fee. **Contact:** Susan Shores, Registrar, Latin American Language Center, PMB 123, 7485 Rush River Dr., Suite 710, Sacramento, CA 95831-5260; 916-447-0938, fax 916-428-9542; lalc@madre.com, [www.madre.com/~lalc].

Resource Management and Sustainable Development. The Institute for Central American Development Studies (ICADS) offers an interdisciplinary semester program in Costa Rica focusing on development from ecological, socio-economic perspectives. The 14-week semester includes: 1) 4 weeks of intensive Spanish and urban issues, 2) 5 weeks in the field in managed and natural ecosystems learning methodologies of field research in social and natural sciences (banana transnationals, traditional agriculture, community cooperatives, cloud forest and watershed management, 3) 4 weeks of independent research—working in rural communities. References available. **Dates:** Fall and spring terms with academic credit. **Costs:** $7,600. **Contact:** ICADS, Dept. 826, P.O. Box 025216, Miami, FL 33102-5216; icads@netbox.com, [www.icadscr.com].

Spanish and Latin American Studies in Puntarenas. Puntarenas offers intensive language studies which fulfills up to 2-year university Spanish requirements in a semester. Additional courses offered in political science, history, biology, teacher ed., business, literature, etc. Program organized week-long and weekend field trips, homestays, and many local university activities. **Dates:** Fall semester: Aug-Dec; spring semester: Jan-May. **Costs:** One semester $4,980; both semesters $7,980. **Contact:** University Studies Abroad Consortium (USAC), Univ. of Nevada, USAC 323, Reno, NV 89557; 775-784-6569, fax 775-784-6010; usac@unr.edu, [http://usac.unr.edu].

Spanish, Ecology and Latin American Studies in Heredia. Heredia offers intensive language studies which fulfills up to 2-year university

Spanish requirements in a semester or 1 year in the 8-week summer program. Additional courses offered in political science, history, biology, teacher ed., business, literature, etc. Program organized week-long and weekend field trips, homestays, and many local university activities. **Dates:** Fall semester: Aug-Dec, spring semester: Jan-May, summer sessions: Jun, Jul, and Aug. **Costs:** One semester $4,980; both semesters $7,980; Jun or Jul $2,040; Aug $1,660; Jun and Jul $3,790; Jun/Jul, and Aug $3,280; Jun, Jul, and Aug $4,820. **Contact:** University Studies Abroad Consortium (USAC), Univ. of Nevada, USAC 323, Reno, NV 89557-0093; 775-784-6569, fax 775-784-6010; usac@unr.edu, [http://usac.unr.edu].

Universidad de Costa Rica (MLSA). A graduate and undergraduate program at the Universidad de Costa Rica for students interested in studying courses in language, literature, culture and civilization, composition, and history of Costa Rica. All courses are taught by full-time faculty members from the Univ. of Costa Rica. **Dates:** Summer: Jun-Jul; semester: fall and winter. **Costs:** Total cost $1,985 including airfare. **Contact:** Dr. Celestino Ruiz, Modern Language Studies Abroad (MLSA), P.O. Box 548, Frankfort, IL 60423; 815-464-1800, fax 815-464-9458; mlsa@sprintmail.com, [www.mlsa.com].

Cuba

Fall, Winter, and Summer in Havana. Semester and short-term programs taught at the Univ. of Havana by Cuban faculty. English or Spanish instruction. A unique opportunity to experience the blend of cultures—African, European, and American—that form Cuba. Study trips to Pinar del Rio, Matanzas province and Varadero beach, Regla, Ernest Hemingway's home, and other sites. **Dates:** Fall: Aug 31-Dec 20; winter: Dec 28-Jan 20; summer: Jun 8-30. **Costs:** Fall $7,965; winter $2,790; summer $2,790; includes tuition, lodging with 2 meals per day, study/visits and tours, textbooks, health insurance, transcript from The Center for Cross-Cultural Study. **Contact:** Dr. Judith Ortiz, Director U.S., Center for Cross-Cultural Study, 446 Main St., Amherst, MA 01002; 800-377-2621, fax 413-256-1968; lpaulez@cccs.com, [www.studyincuba.org].

NYU in Havana. Students have the opportunity to live and study in the fascinating capital city with distinguished NYU and local faculty. Courses in history, literature and culture, and art and architecture are supplemented by excur-

sions, guest lectures, museum visits and travel to historically important cities. **Dates:** Jul 1-Aug 9. **Costs:** Call for details. **Contact:** NYU Summer Session, 7 E. 12th St., 6th Fl., New York, NY 10003; 212-998-2292, fax 212-995-4103; summer.info@nyu.edu, [www.nyu.edu/summer].

Czech Republic

East/Central European Studies: Prague. This program is ideal for students, teachers, and others who wish to combine academic coursework with the experience of living in an extraordinary medieval city. Students will appreciate the beautiful architecture of the city, its walls, castles, and frescoes. Intensive Czech language courses available. **Dates:** Fall semester Aug-Dec; spring semester Jan-May; summer May-Jul. **Costs:** One semester $3,980; summer $2,480; both semesters $6,650. **Contact:** University Studies Abroad Consortium (USAC), Univ. of Nevada, USAC 323, Reno, NV 89557; 775-784-6569, fax 775-784-6010; usac@unr.edu, [http://usac.unr.edu].

NYU in Prague. NYU in Prague takes students to the crossroads of Europe with a curriculum focusing on the rich history, culture, and language of the region. The NYU Center occupies a 15th century building near the old town square of this famously beautiful city. A modern dormitory houses students near Prague castle. **Dates:** Jul 1-Aug 9. **Costs:** $1,110 housing and activities; $3,920 undergraduate tuition; $633 per point, graduate tuition. (2001 costs). **Contact:** NYU Summer Session, 7 E. 12th St., 6th Fl., New York, NY 10003; 212-998-2292, fax 212-995-4103; summer.info@nyu.edu, [www.nyu.edu/summer].

Penn-in-Prague. For students interested in Czech and central European culture, this program, located amidst the fairy tale beauty of Prague and affiliated with Charles Univ., offers an insight into the rich history and urgent contemporary problems of this important region, as well as an opportunity to learn beginning and intermediate Czech. **Dates:** Jul 9-Aug 17. **Costs:** Tuition $3,390; housing and activities $450. **Contact:** Penn Summer Abroad, College of General Studies, Univ. of Pennsylvania, 3440 Market St., Suite 100, Philadelphia, PA 19104-3335; 215-898-5738, fax 215-573-2053; summerabroad@sas.upenn.edu, [www.sasupenn.edu/CGS].

Denmark

Denmark's International Study. DIS programs: architecture, pre-architecture, interior, furniture, communications, graphic design; international business; humanities and social sciences, including international relations, political science, environmental politics; science programs in Denmark and Iceland; multicultural education; premedicine and public health; field studies, European-wide study tours, and London internships.
Dates: Summer, semester, full year. **Costs:** Call for details. **Contact:** Charlotte Simonsen and Brad Stepan Field Directors, DIS North American Office, 214 Heller Hall, 271 19th Avenue S., Univ. of Minnesota, Minneapolis, MN 55455; 800-247-3477, fax 612-626-8009; dis@tc.umn.edu, [www.disp.dk].

International Business and Economic Studies: Copenhagen. The Copenhagen program combines academic coursework with practical learning. At Copenhagen Business School (CBS), you have the opportunity to study international business and economics, giving you an important academic foundation as well as an opportunity for cultural enrichment and making personal international business contacts.
Dates: Fall semester: Aug-Dec; spring semester: Jan-Jun, summer session: Jun-Aug. **Costs:** One semester $4,530; both semesters $7,880; summer $1,450. **Contact:** University Studies Abroad Consortium (USAC), Univ. of Nevada, USAC 323, Reno, NV 89557; 775-784-6569, fax 775-784-6010; usac@unr.edu, [http://usac.unr.edu].

Ecuador

Academia de Español Quito. Specially designed programs for foreign students. One-on-one instruction up to 7 hours daily. Courses based on conversation, vocabulary, and grammar at all levels. Cultural and social activities provided weekly. The system is self-paced, and it is possible to start at any time. Earn academic credits. Live with an Ecuadorian family, 1 student per family, 2 daily meals (breakfast and dinner).
Dates: Year round. **Costs:** $1,626 for 4 weeks includes tuition, meals, housing, fees, airport transfer. **Contact:** Virginia Villamar M., Director, 0e1-30 Marchena St. and 10 de Agosto Ave., P.O. Box 17-15-0039-C, Quito, Ecuador; 011-593-2-553647/554811, fax 011-593-2-506474/504330; edalvare@pi.pro.ec, [www.academiaquito.com.ec].

Community Development Internship. Credit-bearing internship where volunteers live with a family in rural Ecuador or Mexico, or semi-urban Cuba, while working side by side with community members on grassroots development projects. Project assignments are available in the areas of agriculture, public health, construction, reforestation, animal husbandry, micro-enterprise development, data collection, and other fields. These projects are designed, developed and implemented by the beneficiaries themselves. While project opportunities change as new ones come online and others are completed, every effort is made to match interns' interests with their assignment.
Dates: Year round. Two months advance notice needed for placement in Cuba. Six-week program (3 weeks in Cuba). **Costs:** Six credits: $3,600, no credit: $2,700, 3 credits: $3,400. **Contact:** Ana López, Director, Cuban Studies Institute, Center for Latin American Studies, Tulane Univ., Caroline Richardson Bldg., New Orleans, LA 70118-5698; 504-862-8629 or 504-862-8000 ext. 2601, fax 504-862-8678; lopez@tulane.edu, [http://intern.tulane.edu].

Internships in Latin America. Emphasis on community participation for social change. Students work 3 days a week in an internship, also meet together for core seminar and internship seminar and carry out independent study project. Wide range of internship opportunities in community development, health, environment, youth concerns, women's issues, etc. Family homestay, field trips. Latin American faculty. Full semester's credit, U.S. transcript provided. All majors, 2 years Spanish language required.
Dates: Early Feb-mid-May. **Costs:** $9,450 (spring 2001). Includes tuition, internship placement and supervision, room and board, field trips. **Contact:** Director of Student Services, HECUA, Mail #36, Hamline Univ., 1536 Hewitt Ave., St. Paul, MN 55104-1284; 612-646-8832 or 800-554-1089; info@hecua.org, [www.hecua.org].

Egypt

SUNY Cortland in Cairo. AUC's academic offerings include the Humanities and Social Sciences; Sciences and Engineering; and Business, Economics and Communication. AUC is also renowned for its Arabic language, literature, and culture courses as well as its Egyptology, Islamic Studies, and Middle Eastern Studies programs. Classes taught in English except for Arabic language and literature classes. Housing in dormitories and apartments.

Excellent student support services. Wide range of student organizations and activities.

Dates: Fall: late Aug-late Dec; spring: mid-Jan.-end of May; summer: early Jun.-end of Jul. **Costs:** Fall and spring estimate $7,000; summer estimate $3,300. SUNY tuition not included. **Contact:** Office of International Programs, Box 2000, SUNY Cortland, Cortland, NY 13045; 607-753-2209, fax 607-753-5989; studyabroad@cortland.edu, [www.studyabroad.com/suny/cortland].

The American Univ. in Cairo. Study abroad for a semester, year, or summer with Egyptian and international students from over 50 countries at The American Univ. in Cairo. Directly enroll in liberal arts and professional program courses taught in English at an American-style university.

Dates: Sep-Dec, Jan-Jun, Jun-Aug. **Costs:** Year $11,525; semester $5,845; summer $2,858. **Contact:** Matrans Davidson, The American Univ. in Cairo, 420 5th Ave., 3rd Fl., New York, NY 10018-2729; aucegypt@aucnyo.edu, [www.aucegypt.edu].

Europe

Baroque Art. This course, a general overview of the 16th-18th century art in Malta which focuses on the rich heritage of works in the Cathedral of St. John (Valletta), is primarily aimed at history of art students at both under- and post-graduate levels and others with an informed interest in art history.

Dates: Jul 6-Jul 24. **Costs:** $950 includes accommodations. **Contact:** Jean P. Killick, International Office, Foundation for International Studies, Old Univ. Bldg., St. Paul St., Valletta, Malta; (011) 356-234121/2, fax (011) 356-230538; jkil@cis.um.edu.mt.

BCA in England and Greece. Study abroad in English with BCA. Earn 12-18 credits per semester at Cheltenham and Gloucester College (England) or the Univ. of La Verne Athens (Greece). Orientation and field trips in country. Plus survival Greek language course in Athens. Courses in all majors. No foreign language prerequisite.

Dates: Sep-Dec (fall), Jan-Mar (winter Greece); Feb/Mar-Jun (spring), Sep-Jun (year). **Costs:** $19,500 (academic year), $10,950 (semester). Includes tuition, room and board, orientation, insurance, group study tours in country. **Contact:** Program Division, 605 E. College Ave., North Manchester, IN 46962; 219-982-5238, fax 219-982-7755; inquiry@bcanet.org, [www.bcanet.org].

BCA Spain, France, and Germany. Immerse yourself in Spanish, French or German culture with BCA. Earn 12-18 credits per semester at the Univ. of Barcelona (Spain), Univ. of Nancy (France), Univ. of Strasbourg (France) or Univ. of Marburg (Germany). Includes intensive language training and orientation plus extended study tours. Intermediate college Spanish, French or German required.

Dates: Sep-Dec/Jan (fall), Jan-May/Jun (spring France and Spain), Feb-Jul (spring Germany), Sep-May/Jun (year France and Spain). Sep- Jul (year Germany), Jun-Jul (summer) **Costs:** $19,500 (academic year), $10,950 (semester). Includes tuition, room and board, orientation, insurance, group travel in country. **Contact:** Program Division, 605 E. College Ave., North Manchester, IN 46962; 219-982-5238, fax 219-982-7755; inquiry@bcanet.org, [www.bcanet.org].

BGSU AYA in Salzburg. The Bowling Green State Univ. Academic Year Abroad in Salzburg program, presently in its 32nd year (on the web at [www.bgsu/departments/greal/AYA-Salzburg.html]), is designed to help American students perfect their German skills. Participants gain first-hand knowledge of German-speaking countries while earning credit toward undergraduate and master's degrees in a variety of subjects.

Dates: Oct-Jun, full year program. **Costs:** $13,072 (non-res.) includes program costs, room and board. **Contact:** Bowling Green State Univ., Dept. of German, Russian, and EAL; 419-372-6815, fax 419-372-2571; .; sidors@bgnet.bgsu.edu, [www.bgsu/departments/greal/AYA-Salzburg.htm].

Budapest Semesters in Mathematics. A rigorous mathematics program for students attending colleges and universities in North America majoring in mathematics or computer science. Classes taught in English by eminent Hungarian professors. Unlike any other program you will ever encounter. Mix it all with a world as warm and friendly as Budapest, and it's paradise.

Dates: Spring: Feb-May; fall: Sep-Dec. **Costs:** Tuition: $3,890 plus $300 refundable housing deposit. **Contact:** Dr. Paul D. Humke, Director, Budapest Semesters in Mathematics, St. Olaf College, Northfield, MN 55057; 800-277-0434, 507-646-3114; budapest@stolaf.edu, [www.stolaf.edu/depts/math/budapest].

Center for University Programs Abroad (Paris). Assists American undergraduates with individualized study programs at the universities and a range of institutes in Paris. Semester and year abroad options for highly motivated, linguistically and academically prepared students.

Dates: Deadlines: fall, year: Mar 31; spring: Oct 31. **Costs:** Year $24,000 includes tuition, room and board; semester $14,770 includes tuition, room and board (2001-2002). **Contact:** Mary S. Cattani, Director, CUPA, P.O. Box 9611, N. Amherst, MA 01059.

Europe in Transition: Integration and Post-Industrial Change. An in-depth exploration of contemporary social, economic and political changes across Europe through a semester in Germany, Poland, Hungary, and the Czech Republic. Students examine emerging changes in political economy; growing conflicts over women's rights, and ethnic and racial minorities; and the post Cold-War dynamics of European integration.

Dates: Sep-Dec. **Costs:** Contact office for details. **Contact:** Antioch Education Abroad, Antioch College, 795 Livermore St., Yellow Springs, OH 45387; 800-874-7986, fax 937-769-1019; aea@antioch-college.edu, [www.antioch-college.edu/aea].

Friends World Program. A semester or year program in Europe beginning at Friends World Center in London includes an intensive introduction into European culture and history. The program offers seminars, field study, travel, and independent work anywhere in Europe after the first semester. The center serves as a base to explore all regions and cultures in the European continent. Field studies in literature, politics, arts, history, peace studies, theater, education, and community development are all available. Students may earn 12-18 credits per semester.

Dates: Fall: early Sep-mid-Dec; spring: mid-Jan-mid-May. **Costs:** $14,020 per semester in 2000-2001. Includes tuition, travel, room and board, fees, and books. **Contact:** Admissions, Friends World Program, 239 Montauk Hwy., Southampton, NY 11968; 631-287-8474; fw@southampton.liunet.edu, [www.southampton.liu.edu/fw].

Graduate and Undergraduate. European University offers business administration programs to undergraduate and graduate levels. Specialization is possible in Communication and Public Relations, Information Systems, Leisure and Tourism, Multimedia Management, Sport Management, Human Resources Management.

Dates: Undergraduate programs begin in Oct, Feb, Jun. Graduate programs begin in Oct, Jan, Mar. Executive MBA programs begin in Oct,

Jan, Mar, Jul. Cross MBA courses twice a month during the weekend (on-site courses). **Costs:** Undergraduate $15,500; graduate $20,875; Cross MBA $30,000. **Contact:** Marie-Claire Chabloz, Les Bosquets, CH-1817 Montreux-Fontanivent, Switzerland; 011-41-21-964-84-64, fax 011-41-21-964-84-68; euruni01@urbanet.ch, [www.euruni.edu].

NYU Arts and Science Study Abroad. NYU's Faculty of Arts and Science offers undergraduate and graduate programs in Athens, Berlin, Buenos Aires, Dublin, Florence, London, Madrid, Nanjing, Paris, and Prague. Led by distinguished faculty, courses on the art, architecture, culture, civilization, politics of the program.

Dates: Jun-Aug. **Costs:** Call for details. **Contact:** NYU Summer Session, 7 E. 12th St., 6th Fl., New York, NY 10003; 212-998-2292, fax 212-995-4642; summer.info@nyu.edu, [www.nyu.edu/2001summer].

Summer Intensive in European Affairs. Business program on the European market and the EU, graduate or undergraduate. Includes meetings with entreprenuers, politicians, high-ranking civil servants, field trips. In English: emphasis on business opportunities in Europe for U.S. business.

Dates: Summer. **Costs:** $2,500. **Contact:** Dr. Heyndrickx, IEBA, St. Piekeishieuwstzaat 202, 9000 Gent, Belgium; 011-32-9223-44-36, fax 011-32-236-1221.

France

Center for University Programs Abroad (Paris). CUPA assists American undergraduates with individualized study programs at the universities and a range of institutes in Paris. Semester and year abroad options for highly motivated, linguistically and academically prepared students.

Dates: Deadlines: fall, year: Mar 31; spring: Oct 31. **Costs:** Year $24,000 includes tuition, room and board; semester $14,770 includes tuition, room and board (2001-2002). **Contact:** Mary S. Cattani, Director, C.U.P.A., P.O. Box 9611, N. Amherst, MA 01059.; cupausa@aol.com, [www.cupa-paris.org].

Davidson in Tours. Academic year at Univ. of Tours or semester at the Institute of Touraine in Tours. Earn 8 course credits for the year or 4 per semester. Live with families in Tours. A 2- to 4-week stay in Paris as well as numerous group activities and excursions is included. A Davidson faculty member serves as resident director and teaches one course each semester.

Dates: Sep-Jun (may attend for semester or year). **Costs:** $14,500 per semester includes all academic expenses, room, board, international airfare, excursions, international student identity card. **Contact:** Carolyn Ortmayer, Office of Study Abroad, Davidson College, P.O. Box 1719, Davidson, NC 28036; 704-892-2250, fax 704-892-2120; abroad@davidson.edu, [www.davidson.edu/administrative/study_abroad/abroad.html].

Francis-Tous Niveaux. Programme pour etudients et pour formation continue. Civilisation, littérature, grammaire, conversation.
Dates: Tous les debuts de mois au tous lundis (débutant), après un test de niveau. **Costs:** Vingt heuers par semaine FF2,800/ 4 semaine. **Contact:** Alain Bois, Directeur, Institut de Langue Française, 3, av Bertie Albrecht, 75008 Paris, France; 011-33-1-45-63-24-00, fax 011-33-1-45-63-07-09; ilf@inst-langue-fr.com, [www.inst-langue-fr.com].

French Studies: Pau and Bayonne. Pau offers intensive language studies—up to 4 semesters of university language courses in 1 semester, 1 year in the 8-week summer program—in addition to art, political science, history, literature, second language teaching methods, etc. Week-long field trips to Paris, homestay or student residence, and many activities at the French university.
Dates: Summer terms: Jun, Jul, and Aug (taught in Bayonne); fall semester: Sep-Dec; spring semester: Jan-Apr. **Costs:** One semester $4,590; both semesters $7,690; Jun $2,040; Jul $2,040; Aug $1,660; Jun and Jul $3,790; Jun and Aug $3,280; Jul and Aug $3,280; Jun, Jul, and Aug $4,820. **Contact:** University Studies Abroad Consortium (USAC), Univ. of Nevada, USAC 323, Reno, NV 89557; 775-784-6569, fax 775-784-6010; usac@unr.edu, [http://usac.unr.edu].

IES Dijon. A unique opportunity for business and economics majors to study European business management and international economics at IES Dijon and the l'Ecole Supeierure de Commerce de Dijon (ESCD). IES courses in French and ESCD in both French and English. Field trips and cultural excursions. Housing: homestays or dormitories.
Dates: Fall: Sep-Dec 2001; spring: Jan-May 2002; year: Sep-May. **Costs:** Semester $9,900; year $17,820. Includes tuition, orientation, housing, some meals, selected field trips, international student card. **Contact:** Institute for the International Education of Students (IES), 33 N. LaSalle St., Chicago, IL 60602-2602; 800-995-2300, fax 312-944-1448; info@iesabroad.org, [www.iesabroad.org].

IES Nantes. Program focuses on improving students' written and verbal French proficiency through language and area studies courses. IES courses in French by native faculty. Options for courses at the Université de Nantes, Conservatoire National de Musique, École regionale des Beaux-Arts de Nantes, and École Superieure de Commerce Nantes Atlantique. Housing: homestay.
Dates: Fall: Sep 2001-Jan 2002; spring: Jan-May 2002; year: Sep-May. **Costs:** Semester $9,400; year $16,920. Includes tuition, orientation, housing, some meals, selected field trips, and international student ID card. **Contact:** Institute for the International Education of Students (IES), 33 N. LaSalle St., Chicago, IL 60602-2602; 800-995-2300, fax 312-944-1448; info@iesabroad.org, [www.iesabroad.org].

IES Paris. Combine language study with courses in humanities, social sciences, and business/economics. Option for courses at a number of leading French universities including Université de Paris-Sorbonne, L'Institute Catholique, École Normal de Musique. All IES courses taught exclusively in French by native faculty. Field trips and cultural excursions. Housing: homestay.
Dates: Summer: Jun-Jul 2001; fall: Sep-Dec 2001; spring: Jan-May 2001; year: Sep-May. **Costs:** Summer $3,800; semester $10,500; year $18,900. Includes tuition, orientation, housing, some meals, selected field trips, and international student ID card. **Contact:** Institute for the International Education of Students (IES), 33 N. LaSalle St., Chicago, IL 60602-2602; 800-995-2300, fax 312-944-1448; info@iesabroad.org, [www.iesabroad.org].

Immersion Course in French. Intensive 2-4 week course for professional adults in Villefranche (next to Nice) overlooking the French Riviera's most beautiful bay; 8 hours a day with 2 meals. Audiovisual classes, language lab, practice sessions, discussion-lunch. Evening film showings, evening outings with teachers, excursions to cultural landmarks. Accommodations in comfortable private apartments.
Dates: Courses start Jan, Feb, Mar, May, Jun, Aug, Sep, Oct, Nov, Dec. **Costs:** Tuition fees: Dec-Apr EURO 200/4 weeks; May-Nov EURO 2,650/4 weeks. Accommodations: Dec-Apr EURO 300-EURO 800/4 week; May-Nov EURO 350-900/4 weeks. **Contact:** Frédéric Latty, Institut de Francais, 23, avenue General Leclerc, 06230 Villefranche Sur Mer, France;

Practice Teaching Abroad

ELTAP Matches College Students with Overseas Schools

By Brian Johnson

At the end of my junior year, my need to travel somewhere coincided with a time when I had almost no money—a condition shared with many college students. I had to find something that would give me full-time student status, fulfill upper division requirements, and get me somewhere other than Western Europe.

My searching led me to ELTAP (English Language Teaching Assistant Program). Under the Univ. of Minnesota Morris system, ELTAP matches college students with high school and elementary schools all over the world. With my airfare, tuition, and housing fee combined, the price was almost identical to living expenses and full-time tuition at my public university. Although ELTAP has assignments in Western Europe, the emphasis is on countries in Asia and Eastern Europe as well as Africa. I was assigned a position in Cameroon.

The goal of ELTAP is to "development of cross-cultural understanding" by assigning students as assistant teachers in local schools. Being an education major is not required. Cultural immersion is 24 hours a day. There was also time for travel around the country.

Expect some culture shock. Things often did not always happen when and the way I thought they should, and sometimes they didn't happen at all. One can fight it or go with the flow and count it all an adventure.

More information and applications are on [www.mrs.umn.edu/cerp/eltap].

011-33-493-01-88-44, fax 011-33-493-76-92-17; instfran@aol.com, [www.institutdefrancais.com].

MA in French Cultural Studies. This MA program critically examines the many ways in which French society represents itself and the many voices that engage in discourse to produce what we call French society. A variety of required and elective courses allows students to concentrate in specific areas. Study of the francophone diaspora puts French studies in an international context. Under the direction of a faculty associate, each student writes an MA essay (in French or English) on one particular aspect of modern France. Students study in Paris, 2 semesters of residency plus a summer term at Reid Hall and at French institutions of higher learning.

Dates: Sep-Aug. **Costs:** $19,750 includes tuition and fees (2000). **Contact:** Beatrice Terrien, Associate Dean, Graduate School of Arts and Sciences, Columbia Univ., 109 Low Memorial Library, 535 W. 116th St., MC 4306, New York, NY 10027; 212-854-5052, fax 212-854-4912; bt3@columbia.edu, [www.columbia.edu/cu/gsas].

Penn-in-Bordeaux. For students interested in anthropology, archaeology, and the origins of humankind. This program is located near Lascaux and Cro-Magnon, areas where anthropologists have unearthed much of our knowledge about the beginnings of modern humankind. It will center on the issue of what makes us human and how this quality evolved. Lectures will be augmented with the examination of artifacts and fossils as well as visits to important sites.

Dates: Jun 25-Jul 12. **Costs:** Tuition $1,695; housing and excursions $450. **Contact:** Penn Summer Abroad, College of General Studies, Univ. of Pennsylvania, 3440 Market St., Suite 100, Philadelphia, PA 19104-3335; 215-898-5738, fax 215-573-2053; summerabroad@sas.upenn.edu, [www.sas.upenn.edu/CGS].

Penn-in-Compiègne. For students with some proficiency in French who are interested in international relations, sociology, economics, or business. The program, affiliated with The Université de Technologie de Compiègne, also offers a 2-week internship in a French enterprise. Students live with local families.

Dates: May 28-Jul 5; with internship: May 28-Jul 20. **Costs:** Tuition $3,390; room and board, and activities $900 (study only) or $1,200 (full program). **Contact:** Penn Summer Abroad,

College of General Studies, Univ. of Pennsylvania, 3440 Market St., Suite 100, Philadelphia, PA 19104-3335; 215-898-5738, fax 215-573-2053; summerabroad@sas.upenn.edu, [www.sas.upenn.edu/CGS].

Penn-in-Tours. For students interested in French language, literature, art, and civilization. Penn-in-Tours also offers various cultural opportunities and excursions in the beautiful Loire Valley. Students live with local families.

Dates: May 28-Jul 11. **Costs:** Tuition $3,390; family lodging $1,250; excursion and activity fee $200. **Contact:** Penn Summer Abroad, College of General Studies, Univ. of Pennsylvania, 3440 Market St., Suite 100, Philadelphia, PA 19104-3335; 215-898-5738, fax 215-573-2053; summerabroad@sas.upenn.edu, [www.sas.upenn.edu/CGS].

Germany

Antioch in Germany Program. This program is the closest experience to living and studying as German students do. Orientation and intensive language study precede enrollment in Eberhard-Karls-Universität in Tübingen. Language of instruction is primarily German; 2 years of college-level German is recommended.

Dates: Fall, spring, year. **Costs:** Contact office for details. **Contact:** Antioch Education Abroad, Antioch College, 795 Livermore St., Yellow Springs, OH 45387; 800-874-7986, fax 937-769-1019; aea@antioch-college.edu, [www.antioch-college.edu/aea].

Davidson in Würzburg. This program starts with a month-long family stay in northern Germany followed by an intensive language course in Würzburg after which students enroll at the university. Students earn 8 course credits for the year. A Davidson faculty member serves as resident director and teaches 1 course in the fall. Students live in dormitories. Numerous group activities and excursions are included.

Dates: Sep 1-late Jul. **Costs:** $25,500 includes all academic expenses, room, international airfare, insurance, excursions. **Contact:** Carolyn Ortmayer, Office of Study Abroad, Davidson College, P.O. Box 1719, Davidson, NC 28036; 704-892-2250, fax 704-892-2120; abroad@davidson.edu, [www.davidson.edu/administrative/study_abroad/abroad.html].

German Studies: Lüneburg. Intensive language study—up to 2 years of university language requirements in 1 semester. Additional courses in history, political science, culture, literature, etc. Program-organized field trips and housing. Beautiful city only 30 minutes from Hamburg.

Dates: Summer terms: Jun and Jul; fall semester: Aug-Dec; spring semester: Jan-May. **Costs:** One semester $3,980; both semesters $6,650; summer term $2,040 per session, $3,790 both sessions. **Contact:** University Studies Abroad Consortium (USAC), Univ. of Nevada, USAC 323, Reno, NV 89557; 775-784-6569, fax 775-784-6010; usac@unr.edu, [http://usac.unr.edu].

IES Berlin. IES Berlin offers the strength of IES courses in humanities, social sciences, business and economics taught in German by native faculty along with access to courses at Humboldt Univ. intensive German language instruction for all levels. Field trips have included Dresden, Vienna, Cracow/Warsaw, Moscow/St. Petersburg. Housing: apartments.

Dates: Fall: Aug-Dec 2001; spring: Jan-Jun 2002; year: Aug-Jun. **Costs:** Semester $9,900; year $17,820. Includes tuition, orientation, housing, nonoptional field trips, and international student ID card. **Contact:** Institute for the International Education of Students (IES), 33 N. LaSalle St., Chicago, IL 60602-2602; 800-995-2300, fax 312-944-1448; info@iesabroad.org, [www.iesabroad.org].

IES European Union (Freiburg). Semester program designed for economics, political science, international relations, and business majors to study development of the EU and its policies and relations with outside nations. All courses taught in English except German language course. Past field trips included Geneva, Strasbourg, and other destinations. Housing in German residence halls.

Dates: Fall: Sep-Dec 2001; spring: Jan-May 2002. **Costs:** Semester $9,600. Includes tuition, orientation, housing, field trips, and international student card. **Contact:** Institute for the International Education of Students (IES), 33 N. LaSalle St., Chicago, IL 60602-2602; 800-995-2300, fax 312-944-1448; info@iesabroad.org, [www.iesabroad.org].

IES Freiburg. Liberal arts program with focus on German language, economics, humanities and social sciences. All IES area studies courses taught in Germany by native faculty with opportunity to enroll in courses at Albert-Ludwigs-Universität. Past field trips include Berlin, East Germany, Frankfurt, and Bonn. Housing: German residence halls.

Dates: Fall: Aug-Dec; spring: Jan-Jun; year: Aug-Jun. **Costs:** Semester $9,100; year $16,380. Includes tuition, orientation, housing, and international student ID card. **Contact:** Institute for the International Education of Students (IES), 33 N. LaSalle St., Chicago, IL 60602-2602; 800-995-2300, fax 312-944-1448; info@iesabroad.org, [www.iesabroad.org].

International Univ. at Heidelberg. Schiller Univ. is an American-style university with all courses except language classes taught in English. Schiller's particular strengths are in international business and international relations but it offers courses in the humanities and social sciences as well. Students may take German at Schiller or intensive German at the Collegium Palatinum, a specialized language division. One semester college German or equivalent is recommended. Housing in residence halls, with families, or in student apartments.

Dates: Fall: late Aug-mid-Dec; spring: mid-Jan-mid-May. **Costs:** Fall or spring estimate: $6,000 per semester (prices somewhat higher for Collegium students staying in homes). Includes overseas instructional costs, pre- and post-departure orientation, room and food allowance, health and accident insurance, German Residence Permit, administrative fees. SUNY tuition, airfare, incidental expenses not included. **Contact:** Dr. John Ogden, Director, Office of International Programs, Box 2000, SUNY Cortland, Cortland, NY 13045; 607-753-2209, fax 607-753-5989; studyabroad@cortland.edu, [www.studyabroad.com/suny/cortland].

Junior Year in Munich. Founded in 1953, the Junior Year in Munich (JYM) is America's oldest academic year abroad program in Germany with 3,400 alumni from 500 colleges and universities across the U.S. JYM enjoys unique status in Germany as an institute at the Ludwig Maximilian Univ. (LMU) of Munich. Students live in German student housing, have the entire LMU curriculum available to them, and receive a Wayne State Univ. transcript for all coursework completed in Munich. Internships available. JYM distributes approximately $30,000 in scholarships each year. All instruction is in German. Full year and semester options are available.

Dates: Full year: Sep 9, 2002-Jul 19, 2003; second semester only: Apr 3, 2003-Jul 19, 2003. **Costs:** $8,300 for tuition and fees. Scholarships and financial aid available. **Contact:** Junior Year in Germany, Wayne State Univ., Detroit, MI 48202; 313-577-4605; jym@wayne.edu, [www.worldbridge.wayne.edu/jym].

Kalamazoo in Erlangen. This university-integrated program begins with a 5- to 6-week intensive German course. Participants then enroll in regular courses at the Univ. of Erlangen-Nürnberg. All participants complete an individualized cultural research project or internship of personal interest under the guidance of a local mentor. Minimum of 2 years of college German required.

Dates: Late Sep-late Jul (academic year); late Sep-late Feb (fall). **Costs:** Academic year (2001-2002): $26,880; 1 semester $17,920 includes roundtrip international transportation, tuition and fees, room and board, and some excursions. **Contact:** Center for International Programs, Kalamazoo College, 1200 Academy St., Kalamazoo, MI 49006; 616-337-7133, fax 616-337-7400; cip@kzoo.edu, [www.kzoo.edu/cip].

NYU in Berlin. NYU in Berlin, a 6-week program affiliated with Humboldt Univ., offers German language courses as well as content courses focusing on the extraordinary culture and history of Germany's restored capital. Includes excursions and cultural activities in around the city and Germany.

Dates: Jun-Aug. **Costs:** $1,500 housing and activities, $3,608 undergraduate tuition (2001). **Contact:** NYU Summer Session, 7 E. 12th St., 6th Fl., New York, NY 10003; 212-998-2292, fax 212-995-4642; summer.info@nyu.edu, [www.nyu.edu/summer].

Penn-in-Freiburg. For students interested in coursework in intensive intermediate German, cultural exploration of Freiburg and the Black Forest as well as the role of Germany in the European Union. Numerous field trips will complement class instruction.

Dates: Jul 24-Aug 31. **Costs:** Tuition $3,390; housing and activities $700. **Contact:** Penn Summer Abroad, College of General Studies, Univ. of Pennsylvania, 3440 Market St., Suite 100, Philadelphia, PA 19104-3335; 215-898-5738, fax 215-573-2053; summerabroad@sas.upenn.edu, [www.sas.upenn.edu/CGS].

Univ. of Maryland Univ. College-Schwäbisch Gmünd. This is a 4-year residential campus located 33 miles east of Stuttgart in scenic southwestern Germany. Through classes taught in English, individualized attention, and an international student body, UMUC-SG provides an ideal environment for academic achievement and cultural enrichment. Applications are invited from potential freshman, transfer, and study abroad students.

Dates: Fall semester: Aug-Dec; spring semester: Jan-May. **Costs:** Tuition and fees $17,500 (Maryland residents $14,200) per year. Includes tuition, fees, double-residence room, and room and board. **Contact:** Schwäbisch Gmünd Admissions, 3501 University Blvd., E, Adelphi, MD 20783; 800-955-4458, fax 301-985-6450; sginfo@umuc.edu, [www.aiug.de].

Greece

Classic Theatre Study. Three weeks on a Greek island with morning workshops in voice, movement, acting, and drama and evening rehearsals of a classic tragedy or comedy. Then a week of touring sites, seeing a play at Epidauros, and performing in amphitheaters. Admission by audition.

Dates: Mid-Jun to mid-Jul. **Costs:** $4,300 includes food, housing, travel, and courses/6 hours credit additional $1,000. **Contact:** Dr. Arthur J. Beer, Theatre Company, Univ. of Detroit Mercy, P.O. Box 19900, Detroit, MI 48219-0900; beeraj@udmercy.edu, [http://libarts.udmercy.edu/dep/greece.html].

NYU in Athens. NYU in Athens, in the historical center of the city, combines classroom study of the language, history, and culture of Greece with extracurricular activities to introduce students to modern Hellenic culture. Includes visits to monuments, museums, dramatic and musical performances, and a half-day trip to Attica's beautiful coastline.

Dates: Jun 25-Aug 3. **Costs:** $1,730 housing and activities; $3,920 undergraduate tuition; $633 per point, graduate tuition. **Contact:** NYU Summer Session, 7 E. 12th St., 6th Fl., New York, NY 10003; 212-998-2292, fax 212- 995-4642; summer.info@nyu.edu, [www.nyu.edu/summer].

Odyssey in Athens. A semester or full year program for mature and resourceful college-age students eager to explore the rich cultural and historical landscape of Greece. Sponsored by the Univ. of Indianapolis at Athens, we offer courses in language, culture, art, business, and international affairs. Accredited by the Midwest Association of Schools and Colleges. Summer program offers art, archaeology, and anthropology.

Dates: Fall semester mid-Sep-mid-Dec, spring semester Feb 11-Jun 7, summer term Jun 17-Jul 17. **Costs:** $7,600 for 1 semester, $14,330 for full year. Includes tuition, fees, housing, and excursions. Summer term $2,000 includes tuition, housing, excursions, and museum admissions. **Contact:** Barbara Tsairis, U.S. Director, P.O. Box 5666, Portsmouth, NH 03802-5666; odyssey@star.net, [www.star.net/People/~odyssey].

Study in Athens. Program held in the heart of the city, within walking distance of main shopping areas, archaeological sites, and museums. Numerous field trips and excursions included. No language prerequisite. Classes held at The Athens Centre. "Athens was a wonderful learning experience in culture, academics, and myself." - Traci Clarke, Western Washington Univ.

Dates: Fall and spring 12-week terms. **Costs:** $6,172 per term. **Contact:** AHA International, 741 SW Lincoln St., Portland, OR 97201-3178; 800-654-2051; mail@aha-intl.org, [www.aha-intl.org].

Guatemala

Environment, Economy, and Community in Latin America. Intensive, hands-on learning experience among Mayan peoples, exploring the impact of global development on the local culture and enviornment. Discover the implications of diverse worldviews through seminars, homestays, field projects, language study, and independent research. Understand local perceptions of sustainability and implications for the U.S. and global community. Based in Guatemala with comparative field study in Cuba. Latin American faculty. Full semester's credit, U.S. transcript provided. All majors, 2 years Spanish language required.

Dates: Early Feb-mid-May. **Costs:** $10,100 (spring 2001). Includes tuition, room and board, field trips. **Contact:** Director of Student Services, HECUA, Mail #36, Hamline Univ., 1536 Hewitt Ave., St. Paul, MN 55104-1284; 651-646-8832 or 800-554-1089, fax 651-659-9421; info@hecua.org, [www.hecua.org].

South American Urban Semester. Innovative approach combines classroom experience with extensive field work. Courses include introduction to Latin America, urbanization and development in Latin America, Spanish language, and independent study. Based in Guatemala with 2 weeks field study in Ecuador. Family homestay. Latin American faculty. Full semester's credit, U.S. transcript provided. All majors, 2 years Spanish language required.

Dates: Late Aug-early Dec. **Costs:** $9,250 (spring 2001). Includes tuition, room and board, field trips. **Contact:** HECUA, Mail #36, Hamline Univ., 1536 Hewitt Ave., St. Paul, MN 55104-1284; 651-646-8832 or 800-554-1089, fax 651-659-9421; info@hecua.org, [www.hecua.org].

Hong Kong

Cantonese and Putonghua. Intensive Cantonese and Putonghua courses from beginning through advanced levels for foreigners, optimum 15 classroom hours per week. At advanced levels, part-time or private tutorials available. Students at any level may register for admission to any term. Center study recognized by major international universities for degree credit.

Dates: Fall term (Sep); spring term (Jan); summer term (Jun). **Costs:** HK$23,700 (fall); HK$23,700 (spring); HK$17,325 (summer). **Contact:** Admission Coordinator, New Asia—Yale-in-China Chinese Language Ctr., The Chinese Univ. of Hong Kong, Shatin, NT, Hong Kong; 011- 852-2609-6727, fax 011-852-2603-5004; chilangctr@cuhk.edu.hk, [www.cuhk.edu.hk/lac].

India

BCA Cochin Study Center. India TITLE: BCA Cochin Study Center DESCRIPTION: Earn 16-18 credits per semester at the Cochin Univ. of Science and Technology, with an orientation period, field trips, and extended study tour. Students from all U.S. colleges and universities accepted. No foreign language prerequisite; all classes in English. Liberal arts curriculum including Hindi, Gandhian Studies, and international relations. Science curriculum including environemental science and marine biology.

Dates: Sep-Dec, Jan-Apr or Sep-May. **Costs:** $19,500 (year), $10,950 (semester). Includes tuition, room and board, insurance, group travel in country, on-site director. **Contact:** Program Division, 605 E. College Ave., North Manchester, IN 46962; 219-982-5238, fax 219-982-7755; inquiry@manchester.edu, [www.studyabroad.com/bca/bcahome.html].

Buddhist Studies Program in India. Living and studying in Bodh Gaya, an international pilgrimage center, provides students with an opportunity to examine Buddhism and its impact on several Asian cultures. Course offerings include: history, philosophy, anthropology, a meditation practicum, Hindi, Tibetan, and an independent research component.

Dates: Sep-Dec. **Costs:** Contact office for details. **Contact:** Antioch Education Abroad, Antioch College, 795 Livermore St., Yellow Springs, OH 45387; 800-874-7986, fax 937-769-1019; aea@antioch-college.edu, [www.antioch-college.edu/aea].

Friends World Program (Bangalore). A semester or year program in India at the Friends World Center in Bangalore includes orientation, intensive seminars, field studies, travel, and independent work. The core curriculum serves as an introduction to India's complex cultures. Independent study sample topics include: Gandhian studies, sustainable development, Buddhist studies in Nepal, dance, women's studies, philosophy, and traditional medicine. Students may earn 12-18 credits per semester.

Dates: Fall: early Sep-mid-Dec; spring: mid-Jan-mid-May. **Costs:** $13,045 per semester in 2000-2001. Includes tuition, travel, room and board, fees, and books. **Contact:** Admissions, Friends World Program, 239 Montauk Hwy., Southampton, NY 11968; 631-287-8474; fw@southampton.liunet.edu, [www.southampton.liu.edu/fw].

Geo Communities Semester. A Living Routes program in ecological awareness, cooperative community, and mindful living. Participants spend three months at Auroville, an international community of 1,200 people working towards sustainability and "human unity," two weeks traveling India, and one week at Plum Village, a buddhist community in France. College credit available.

Dates: Fall semester approx. Sep 3-Dec 17; spring semseter approx. Jan 20-May 5. **Costs:** $11,500. Includes tuition, predeparture orientation, international airfare from Boston, lodging, meals, and local transportation. Financial Aid accepted. Some scholarships available. **Contact:** Vanessa Long, Director of Programs, Living Routes, 85 Baker Rd., Shutesbury, MA 01072; 888-515-7333, 413-259-0025, fax 413-259-1256; Programs@LivingRoutes.org, [www.LivingRoutes.org].

Penn-in-India. For students interested in South Asian studies, performing arts, religion, and traditional medicine, PSA's newest program offers students a survey of both India's rich cultural history and its burgeoning industrial life. The program is located in Pune, a cosmopolitan city of 4,000,000 which is a thriving arts center, a hub of scholarship, and a growing economic presence. Students will live with Indian families in the area and be involved in community projects.

Dates: Jun 5-Jul 20. **Costs:** Tuition $3,390; program cost $1,790. **Contact:** Penn Summer Abroad, College of General Studies, Univ. of Pennsylvania, 3440 Market St., Suite 100, Philadelphia, PA 19104-3335; 215-898-5738, fax 215-573-2053; summerabroad@sas.upenn.edu, [www.sas.upenn.edu/CGS].

Summer Program in Kerala. This 10-week program in the capital city of Thiruvanantha-puram, Kerala, allows you to immerse yourself in study of a variety of Indian performing arts—dance, drama, and vocal music, as well as Indian martial or meditational arts. Academic program includes a mandatory basic Malayalam language course. In addition, a local resident coordinator helps to arrange study with master teachers in Indian arts. Application deadline 1st Friday in Feb. Late applications considered on a space available basis.

Dates: Late May-mid-Aug. **Costs:** Call for current information. **Contact:** Office of International Studies and Programs, 261 Bascom Hall, Univ. of Wisconsin, 500 Lincoln Dr., Madison, WI 53706; 608-265-6329, fax 608-265-6329; peeradvisor@bascom.wisc.edu, [www.wisc.edu/studyabroad].

Wisconsin College Year in India. The program provides integrated language training, tutorial instruction, and independent fieldwork projects, beginning with summer language classes in the U.S. The 3 program sites are in Varanasi (for Hindu-Urdu students); in Hyderabad (for Telugu students), and in Madurai (for Tamil students).

Dates: Summer in Madison: early Jun-mid-Aug; academic program abroad: late Aug-Apr. **Costs:** Call for current information. Summer school and related expenses additional. **Contact:** Office of International Studies and Programs, 261 Bascom Hall, 500 Lincoln Dr., Madison, WI 53706; 608-262-2851, fax 608-262-6998; peeradvisor@bascom.wisc.edu, [www.wisc.edu/studyabroad].

Israel

Boston Univ.-Hebrew Univ. of Jerusalem Pre-Medical Program. Receive a Boston Univ. transcript for studying pre-medicine at the Hebrew Univ. of Jerusalem. Program consists of either an autumn semester or full year at the Rothberg Int'l. School. Students enroll in intensive Hebrew language program during the summer and take a minimum of 4 courses per semester, 3 of which are pre-medical sciences courses. Electives include: Hebrew language, Jewish and Israel studies.

Dates: Jul-Jan or Jul-Jun. **Costs:** $16,575 (autumn semester) and $29,500 (full year). Fees include tuition, room and board, medical insurance, excursions, and roundtrip airfare from New York. **Contact:** Hebrew Univ. of Jerusalem/Rothberg Int'l. School, Office of Academic Affairs, 11 E 69th St., New York, NY 10021; 800-404-8622; hebrewu@hebrewu.com, [http://overseas.huji.ac.il].

Freshman Year Program. One-year study abroad for credit at an American college or university. Visiting freshman program includes: Hebrew/Language Instruction, courses in Jewish, Israel, and Middle East studies, and introductory

THE U.K. VIA BUNAC

WORK PROGRAM PROVIDES ASSURANCE AND INCENTIVE FOR THE MOVE

By Luke S. White

In a spontaneous move, I decided to head to Europe in the autumn off-season and work through the winter to avoid the summer crowds. After landing a student fare from the West Coast to London and back via Dublin for $330, I also found out through *Transitions Abroad* about BUNAC, the reciprocal work exchange which lines up 6-month visas for Americans who want to do short-term work in the U.K. The program costs $225 and is open to currently enrolled students and those still within a semester of having graduated.

Slightly taken aback by the greyness and impersonal grandeur of London, I made my way up to Edinburgh in hopes of a more welcoming small-city atmosphere. The first week I landed in a grungy hostel that turned out to be a virtual refugee camp for Australians doing service jobs, mostly through temp agencies. Then I landed both a job and a room on the same day.

Opting to live with locals rather than get a place with other BUNACers made the search a little harder, but it was worthwhile in the long run. I worked for a temp agency the first month, mostly at a bank doing data entry. Not much fun, but I managed to save enough to fly to Sweden and spend a lovely white Christmas with a new friend's family on the island of Gotland. Then, determined to do something other than office work, I found a job with a courier company as a bike messenger. (On international flights most airlines allow for a boxed bicycle as one piece of baggage at no extra charge. So I'd brought mine for inexpensive transportation and as a pleasant way to see the countryside.)

Edinburgh is a beautiful city. The job gave me freedom to ride all day, on radio call, through downtown and around the lovely old castle and all the spectacular monuments of weathered stone. It was often exhausting and the pay wasn't great, but I was on my own and could take lunch in the park or sit and read in bookstores on slow days.

By keeping on a shoestring budget, I managed to save enough to travel through Italy, France, Germany, and Ireland before heading back stateside in mid-spring. Miraculously, I made it home with most of the funds I had left with intact.

I found my room and jobs in other ways than through the BUNAC office, and I was rarely asked to show my visa for inspection. However, the program provided me the assurance and incentive to go ahead and make the move. It served as a base if I needed it and as a resource to fall back on (and it made me legal). Plus the biweekly pub meets provide a decent way to meet other working travelers. All of this is well worth the $225.

Contact BUNAC USA at 800-GO-BUNAC or 203-264-0901; wib@bunacusa. org, [www.bunac.org].

courses in the Social Sciences. Exciting array of internship/volunteer opportunities. Trips and cultural activities throughout the country.

Dates: Fall: Jul-Jan; spring: Jan-Jun; full year: Jul-Jun. **Costs:** Year $11,000 plus board and transportation. Semester $8,000 plus board and transportation. **Contact:** Hebrew Univ. of Jerusalem/Rothberg Int'l. School, Office of Academic Affairs, 11 E. 69th St., New York, NY 10021; 800-404-8622; hebrewu@hebrewu.com, [http://overseas.huji.ac.il].

Friends World Program (Jerusalem). A semester or year program in the Middle East at Friends World Center in Jerusalem consists of intensive seminars that introduce students to the culture of the Middle East. Field work, travel, and independent research are also offered. Sample topics include: desert agriculture, archaeology, anthropology, journalism, public health, conflict resolution, religious studies. Fieldwork can be conducted in Israel, Jordan, and other countries and may earn 12-18 credits per semester.

Dates: Fall: early-Sep-mid-Dec; spring: mid-Jan-mid-May. **Costs:** $13,840 per semester 2000-2001. Includes tuition, travel, room and board, fees and books. **Contact:** Admissions, Friends World Program, 239 Montauk Hwy., Southampton, NY 11968; 631-287-8474; fw@southampton.liunet.edu, [www.southampton.liu.edu/fw].

Israeli and Middle Eastern Studies: Beer Sheva. The program in Beer Sheva offers students the opportunity to enroll in a wide range of courses at the Ben-Gurion Univ. in a variety of disciplines. You may take courses in anthropology, archaeology, biology, engineering, environmental studies, Hebrew, history, political science, social sciences, etc. Taught in English. Intensive Hebrew language courses available.

Dates: Aug-Dec, Jan-Jun. **Costs:** One semester $7,510; both semesters $11,065. Includes housing. **Contact:** University Studies Abroad Consortium (USAC), Univ. of Nevada, USAC 323, Reno, NV 89557; 775-784-6569, fax 775-784-6010; usac@unr.edu, [http://usac.unr.edu].

MA in English. Six 2-year MA programs in English: Jewish Education, Israeli Studies, Jewish Civilization, Religious Studies, Bible Studies, and Middle Eastern Studies. Learn under the tutelage of Hebrew Univ.'s renowned professors. Take advantage of opportunities for private tutorials and intensive language study. Students with sufficient command of Hebrew may take graduate courses taught in Hebrew in the faculties of humanities and social sciences.

Research at the Jewish National Univ. library. Trips and cultural activities throughout the country available.

Dates: Jul-Jun each academic year. **Costs:** Approx. $11,000 plus board and transportation per year. **Contact:** Hebrew Univ. of Jerusalem/Rothberg Int'l. School., Office of Academic Affairs, 11 E. 69th St., New York, NY 10021; 800-404-8622; hebrewu@hebrewu.com, [http://overseas.huji.ac.il].

One Year/Semester Program. Receive credit at an American college or university for 1-year study in Israel. Courses range from Israeli studies to Jewish studies to business and economics, art, archaeology, women's studies, and more. Exciting array of internship/volunteer opportunities. Trips and cultural activities throughout the country.

Dates: Fall: Aug-Jan; spring: Jan-Jun; full year: Aug-Jun. **Costs:** Year $11,000 plus board and transportation. Semester $8,000 plus board and transportation. **Contact:** Hebrew University of Jerusalem/Rothberg Int'l. School, 11 E 69th St., New York, NY 10021; 800-404-8622; hebrewu@hebrewu.com, [http://overseas.huji.ac.il].

Summer Courses. Three-, 4-, or 6-week academic courses at Hebrew Univ.'s Mount Scopus campus. Courses include Hebrew, Yiddish, and Arabic languages, archaeology, historical geography, Jewish studies, Israel studies, Middle East studies, law, international relations, arts and literature, and more.

Dates: Jun, Jul, Jun-Jul language sessions. **Costs:** Approx. $1,500 includes tuition and housing. **Contact:** Hebrew Univ., of Jerusalem/Rothberg Int'l. School, Office of Academic Affairs, 11 E. 69th St., New York, NY 10021; 800-404-8622; hebrewu@hebrewu.com, [http://overseas.huji.ac.il].

Visiting Graduate Programs. One-year study in Israel, for credit at an American college or university. Graduate division offers seminars and tutorials in Jewish and Biblical Studies, Jewish Education, Politics and Society of Israel, the Middle East, and Comparative Religion. Hebrew language instruction available at all levels, as are courses in Arabic, Yiddish, Greek, Akkadian, and German. Take advantage of Hebrew Univ. academic advisers, intensive seminars, private tutorials, and resources of the Jewish National Univ. Library.

Dates: Fall: Jul-Jan; spring: Jan-Jun; full year: Jul-Jun. **Costs:** Year $11,000 plus board and transportation. Semester $8,000 plus board and transportation. **Contact:** Hebrew Univ. of

Jerusalem/Rothenberg Int'l. School, Office of Academic Affairs, 11 E. 69th St., New York, NY 10021; 800-404-8622; hebrewu@hebrewu.com, [http://overseas.huji.ac.il].

Italy

Accademia Italiana (Florence). The Accademia Italiana is one of the most qualified European institutes of art, design, fashion, Italian language. The prestigious headquarters of the Accademia Italiana is located in Piazza Pitti, one of the most beautiful Italian squares.

Dates: Summer term: Jun-Jul-Aug; fall semester: Sep-Dec; spring semester: Jan-May. **Costs:** Vary. **Contact:** Accademia Italiana, Piazza Pitti n. 15, 50125 Florence, Italy; 011-390-55-284616/211619, fax 011-390-55-284486; modaita@tin.it, [www.accademic.italiana.com].

American Univ. of Rome. Programs for students of Communications, Italian Language and Culture, Art History, International Relations and Business Studies. Credits fully transferable through affiliations with U.S. institutions. Housing in studio apartments. All courses (except language classes) in English. All programs are designed to provide students with studies of immediate relevance in a highly competitive job market.

Dates: Fall semester begins the end of Aug; spring semester begins the end of Jan; summer program in Jun and Jul. **Costs:** $1,228 per course (3 credits). **Contact:** Mara Nisdeo, American Univ. of Rome, Via Pietro Roselli 4, Rome 00153, Italy; 011-390-6-58330919, fax 011-390-6-58330992.; a.sirocchi@aur.edu, [www.aur.edu].

Art Studio Fuji School of Jewelry Making and Textile Design. Beginning, intermediate, advanced courses in jewelry making, jewelry design with computer, stonesetting, engraving, casting, gemology, textile design, screenprinting, serigraphy printmaking, batik, silk printing, weaving, textile sculpture, quilting, sewing, tailoring—all taught in English.

Dates: One month, semester, 1- year, 2-year courses from Sep-end of Jul. **Costs:** From $350 for 1 month course, 1 student. **Contact:** Kathleen Knippel, Director, Art Studio Fuji School of Jewelry Making and Textile Design, Via Guelfa 79A, Florence 50129, Italy; 011-390-55-216877, fax 011-390-55-214500; info@artfuji.it, [www.artfuji.it].

Art Under One Roof. One of Europe's most complete art studio programs. Over 15 areas of study, academic term or year abroad. Studies include Euro programs. Academic studies include jewelry making, interior and boutique design, furniture and industrial design, painting restoration, painting and drawing, figurative sculpture, mural and fresco painting, wood decoration, and many more.

Dates: Academic studies: Jan, May, Sep. Many courses offered monthly. Deadlines: Jun, Nov, Mar. **Costs:** Academic term studies $2,500; summer studies $800. **Contact:** Arte Sotto un Tetto Admissions, Florence Programs, Via Pandolfini, 46/R 50122 Florence, Italy; Tel./fax 011-39-055-247-8867; arte2@arteurope.it, [www.arteuropa.org].

IES Milan. Italian language program with strong options in humanities, fine arts, and music. The intensive beginning/intermediate Italian program offers language study with area studies courses taught in English. Advanced program for those proficient in Italian offers all courses in Italian and the option to take courses at a local university. Housing: apartments.

Dates: Summer: Jun-Jul; fall: Aug-Dec; spring: Jan-May; year: Aug-May. **Costs:** Summer: $3,700; semester $10,500; year $18,900. Includes tuition, orientation, housing, field trips, and international student ID card. **Contact:** Institute for the International Education of Students (IES), 33 N. LaSalle St., Chicago, IL 60602-2602; 800-995-2300, fax 312-944-1448; info@iesabroad.org, [www.iesabroad.org].

International Business, Art and Architecture, Italian Studies: Turin. Turin offers a diversified curriculum in business, economics, art, and architecture plus intensive courses in Italian language and culture, literature, etc., at the foot of the majestic Alps. Program-organized housing and field trips and many Italian university activities.

Dates: Summer term: May-Jul and Jun-Aug; fall semester: Sep-Dec; spring semester: Jan-May. **Costs:** Summer term $2,040 per session $3,790 both sessions; one semester $4,590; both semesters $7,690. **Contact:** University Studies Abroad Consortium (USAC), Univ. of Nevada, USAC 323, Reno, NV 89557; 775-784-6569, fax 775-784-6010; usac@unr.edu, [http://usac.unr.edu].

Italian Language Courses. DILIT-IH has been teaching Italian as a foreign language since 1974. Group and individual courses start every 2 weeks from level 1 (beginner) to level 9 (advanced). Minimum period 2 weeks. Social activities, accommodations can be arranged: host family, flat.

Dates: Year round, every 2 weeks. **Costs:** Enrollment fee LIT75,000; intensive course 2 weeks a.m. LIT610,000 for 40 hours, p.m.

LIT470,000 for 30 hours. **Contact:** DILIT International House, Via Marghera 22, I-00815 Rome, Italy; 011-39-06-4462592, fax 011-39-06-4440888; info@dilit.it, [www.dilit.it].

Italian Studies in Florence. For students interested in intensive beginning and intermediate language courses and cultural studies in literature, cinema, and art history taught in one of the world's most beautiful cities. Numerous cultural opportunities and field trips offer a valuable supplement to class work.
Dates: Jun 4-Jul 13. **Costs:** Tuition $3,390; housing $1,935; travel $850. **Contact:** Penn Summer Abroad, College of General Studies, Univ. of Pennsylvania, 3440 Market St., Suite 100, Philadelphia, PA 19104-3335; 215-898-5738, fax 215-573-2053; summerabroad@sas.upenn.edu, [www.sas.upenn.edu/CGS].

Studio Art Centers International. SACI is a complete program in Florence for students seeking excellence in studio art and liberal arts instruction at the U.S. university level. SACI offers courses in 31 different studio and academic disciplines at all levels. Centrally located, SACI offers the opportunity to fully immerse oneself in Italian culture.
Dates: Sep-Dec; Jan-Apr; May-Jun; Jun-Jul. **Costs:** Fall/spring tuition $8,250 per term; late spring/summer $3,300. **Contact:** SACI, The Institute of International Education, 809 UN Plaza, New York, NY 10017-3580; 212-984-5548, fax 212-984-5325; saci@iie.org, [www.saci-florence.org].

Studio Camnitzer Printmaking Residency Program. The studio is available to mature artists on a weekly basis (2 weeks minimum) for printmaking and painting. Fully equipped workshop with technical assistance. Lodging included in price. Situated near Lucca in farmhouse surrounded by 8 acres.
Dates: May 15- Oct 15. **Costs:** $380 per week with double occupancy, single $50 extra. **Contact:** Studio Camnitzer, 124 Susquehanna Ave., Great Neck, NY 11021; 516-466-6975, fax 516-487-8244; camnitzer1@aol.com, [www.studio-camnitzer.com].

Study in Italy. Semester and summer programs in Florence and Perugia. Courses are taught in English in the following areas: fashion, art and design, illustration, politics, literature, cinema, internships, photography, history, and business. All students will study the Italian language at the appropriate level. Full range of program services including onsite orientation, housing, academic advising and personal support while overseas. Scholarships and financial aid available.

Dates: Academic year, fall, spring, and summer options. **Costs:** Call for current fees. **Contact:** Barbara Dennig, Center for Education Abroad, Beaver College, 450 S. Easton Rd., Glenside, PA 19038; 888-232-8379, fax 215-572-2174

Study in Macerata. Nestled in the hills above the Adriatic sea. Numerous field trips and excursions included. Language classes held at the Univ. of Macerata. Studio art classes held at The Macerata Academy of Art. No Italian language prerequisite. "An ideal setting for a superb study abroad program!" - Erin Schueler, Western Washington Univ.
Dates: Fall and winter semesters. **Costs:** Fall (12 weeks) $6,695; winter (14 weeks) $7,140. **Contact:** AHA International, 741 SW Lincoln St., Portland, OR 97201-3178; 800-654-2051; mail@aha-intl.org, [www.aha-intl.org].

Temple Univ. Rome. Temple Univ. in Rome, established in 1966, offers a semester or academic year and a 6-week summer program of full-time study designed primarily for 3rd year undergraduate students. The semester program is comprised of 4 academic components: Architecture, Liberal Arts and Italian Studies, Visual Arts, and International Business. Except for courses in Italian language and literature, all instruction is in English. The academic program is enriched by course field trips and a broad range of extracurricular activities.
Dates: Please contact organization for details. **Costs:** (1999-2000) 1 semester: approx. $8,000-$12,000, depending on state residency. Includes tuition and fees, housing, meals. **Contact:** Mike Dever, Temple Univ., International Programs, 200 Tuttleman Learning Center, Philadelphia, PA 19122; 215-204-0720, fax 215-204-0729; intlprog@vm.temple.edu, [www.temple.edu/intlprog].

UGA Studies Abroad Program-Cortona. Primarily a studio art program which includes art history in a small Tuscan hilltown. Three semester hours of university credit for each course taken. Spring and fall terms last about 13 weeks and summer term lasts about 9 weeks. Classes can be taken at the undergraduate and graduate level.
Dates: Feb 1-May 2 (spring semester), Jun 5-Aug 7 (summer), Aug 23-Nov 21 (fall semester). **Costs:** $7,900 spring and fall, $6,200 summer. Airfare not included. **Contact:** R.G. Brown, III, Director, Univ. of Georgia, Studies Abroad Program, Lamar Dodd School of Art, Athens, GA 30602; cortona@arches.uga.edu, [www.visart.uga.edu/cortona, www.visart.uga.edu/cortona].

Japan

BCA Sapporo Study Center. Earn 15-18 credits per semester at Hokusei Gakuen Univ. in Sapporo, with a 1-week orientation, homestay with Japanese families, field trips, and extended study tour through Honshu. Extensive extracurricular activities. Students accepted from all U.S. colleges and universities. No foreign language prerequisite. All levels of Japanese language study available.

Dates: Aug-Dec (fall), Mar-Jul (spring), Aug-Jul or Mar-Dec (year). **Costs:** $19,900 (academic year); $11,500 (semester). Includes international transportation, room and board, tuition, insurance, group travel in country. **Contact:** Program Division, 605 E. College Ave., North Manchester, IN 46962; 219-982-5238, fax 219-982-7755

Buddhist Studies Program in Japan. Study and experience Zen, Pure Land, and Shingon Buddhist traditions in Kyoto. Course offerings include: philosophy and historical development of Buddhism in Japan, Japanese Buddhist culture, meditation traditions, Japanese language, and an independent research component. Participants live in a series of 3 monasteries; previous Japanese language study is not required.

Dates: Sep-Dec. **Costs:** Contact office for details. **Contact:** Antioch Education Abroad, Antioch College, 795 Livermore St., Yellow Springs, OH 45387; 800-874-7986, fax 937-769-1019; aea@antioch-college.edu, [www.antioch-college.edu/aea].

College of Business and Communication, Kawasaki. Beginners to advanced in Japanese. Study the language, life, and culture of Japan.

Dates: Apr and Oct entrance. **Costs:** ¥796,000. **Contact:** Ms. Mutsumi Harada, College of Business and Communication, Kawasaki 20-7 Ekimae-honcho, Kawasaki-ku, Kawasaki-shi, Kanagawa-ken 210-0007, Japan; 011-81-44-244-3959, fax 011-81-44-244-2499; jpn@cbc.ac.jp, [www.cbc.ac.jp].

Friends World Program (Kyoto). A semester or year program at the Friends World Center in Kyoto includes intensive seminars focused on Japanese culture, language, and the arts. Writing workshops are also offered. Students design internships and independent research projects. Sample topics include: traditional medicine, education, Buddhism, gender studies, peace movements, and environmental policy. Student may earn 12-18 credits per semester.

Dates: Fall: early-Sep-mid-Dec; spring: mid-Jan-mid-May. **Costs:** $14,070 per semester 2000-2001. Includes tuition, travel, room and board, fees, and books. **Contact:** Admissions, Friends World Program, 239 Montauk Hwy., Southampton, NY 11968; 631-287-8474; fw@southampton.liunet.edu, [www.southampton.liu.edu/fw].

IES Kasugai-Chubu. Students enroll in Chubu Univ.'s Japanese Language and Culture programs with an intensive curriculum of Japanese language and area studies. IES students can enroll in customized tutorials, taught in English, in the fields of Engineering, Science, Business, and International Studies. Field trips and cultural excursions. Housing: student residence halls.

Dates: Fall: Aug-Dec; spring: Mar-Jul; year: Aug-Jul. **Costs:** Semester $11,300; year $20,340. Includes tuition, housing, orientation, some meals, field trips, international student card. **Contact:** Institute for the International Education of Students (IES), 33 N. LaSalle St., Chicago, IL 60602-2602; 800-995-2300, fax 312-944-1448; info@IESabroad.org, [www.IESabroad.org].

IES Nagoya. Students enroll in either Nanzan Univ.'s Center for Japanese Studies taking Japanese culture course taught in English and intensive Japanese language or at Chubu Univ. with curriculum of intensive Japanese language, area studies taught in English, and tutorials in the areas of engineering, physical sciences, business, communications or international studies.

Dates: Fall: Aug-Dec; spring: Jan-May; year: Aug-May. **Costs:** Semester $11,600; year $20,880. Includes tuition, orientation, housing, some meals, field trips, and international student card. **Contact:** Institute for the International Education of Students (IES), 33 N. LaSalle St., Chicago, IL 60602-2602; 800-995-2300, fax 312-944-1448; info@iesabroad.org, [www.iesabroad.org].

IES Toyko. IES Tokyo offers students the unique opportunity to supplement Japanese organization with insightful field study. All students complete a field experience as a participant observer in a Japanese organization. In addition all IES area studies courses include a field study component. Field trips and cultural excursions. Housing: homestay, dormitories.

Dates: Summer: Jun-Jul 2001; fall: Aug-Dec 2001; spring: Mar-Jul 2002. **Costs:** Summer $3,850; semester $12,500; year $22,500.

Includes tuition, orientation, housing, some meals for homestay, field trips, international student card. **Contact:** Institute for the International Education of Students (IES), 33 N. LaSalle St., Chicago, IL 60602-2602; 800-995-2300, fax 312-944-1448; info@iesabroad.org, [www.iesabroad.org].

Intensive Language and Culture. Japan is one of the most dynamic countries in the world, with the world's second largest economy. The Western Washington Univ., Univ. of Idaho, Lincoln Univ., and KCP offer a unique opportunity to learn more about this country and its language, people, and culture. Programs are open to all English speaking students in good class standing as well as recent college graduates. Our carefully integrated language and culture program offers the student a unique opportunity to develop Japanese language proficiency while gaining an understanding of the Japanese culture and modern society.

Dates: Jan-Mar; Apr-Jun; Jul-Sep; Jul-Aug; Oct-Dec. **Costs:** $5,150 for dorm option and $5,500 for homestay option. Includes registration fee's at sponsor university, tuition, textbooks, local transportation in Tokyo, numerous excursions in and around Tokyo, homestay or private dormitory. Summer short-term is $3,950 and includes all above. **Contact:** Mike Anderson, KCP International, P.O. Box 28028-0028, Bellingham, WA 98228-0028; 888-KCP-7020 or 360-647-0072, fax 360-647-0736; kcp@kcp-usa.com, [www.kcp-usa.com].

Kyoto: An Ancient Window into Contemporary Japan. Based in Kyoto, the Antioch in Japan program focuses on history, art, literature, language, legend, and contemporary changes in this 1,200-year-old city.

Dates: May-Jun. **Costs:** Contact office for details. **Contact:** Antioch Education Abroad, Antioch College, 795 Livermore St., Yellow Springs, OH 45387; 800-874-7986, fax 937-769-1019; aea@antioch-college.edu, [www.antioch-college.edu/aea].

Teaching English in Japan. Two-year program to maximize linguistic and cultural integration of participants who work as teachers' assistants. Placements twice yearly in Apr. and Aug. Most positions are in junior high schools in urban and rural areas. Bachelor's degree and willingness to learn Japanese required.

Dates: Hiring for positions every Apr and Aug. Applications accepted year round. Potential applicants are encouraged to submit applications between Oct-Feb. **Costs:** No application fees. **Contact:** Institute for Education in Japan, Earlham College, 801 National Rd. West, D-202,

Richmond, IN 47374; 888-685-2726, fax 765-983-1553; sebener@earlham.edu, [www.earlham/edu~aet].

Temple Univ. Japan. U.S. undergraduate students can study in the heart of Tokyo for a semester, academic year, or summer alongside bilingual Japanese students. The academic program is comprised of an extensive liberal arts curriculum that includes Japanese language at all levels and upper level Asian studies courses. With the exception of Japanese language courses, all courses are conducted in English.

Dates: Fall: Aug 29-Dec 10, application deadline May 1; summer: May 18-Jul 29, application deadline Mar 1; spring: Jan 4-Apr 15, 2001, application deadline Oct 6, 2000. **Costs:** Costs (2001-2002) $9,540 per semester; $7,100 for the summer. Includes tuition, housing in shared accommodation, refundable housing deposit, and activity fee. **Contact:** Mike Dever, Temple Univ., International Programs, 200 Tuttleman Learning Center, Philadelphia, PA 19122; 215-204-0720, fax 215-204-0729; intlprog@vm.temple.edu, [www.temple.edu/intlprog].

Korea

Penn-in-Seoul. For students interested in East Asia, Korea, international relations and other business disciplines. This program, offered in conjunction with Kyung Hee Univ., includes courses in the area of international relations as well as internships with multinational corporations, government agencies, and think tanks. Field trips exploring Korean history and culture are integral to the program.

Dates: Jun 8-Aug 13. **Costs:** Tuition $3,390; housing and partial board $1,465. **Contact:** Penn Summer Abroad, College of General Studies, Univ. of Pennsylvania, 3440 Market St., Suite 100, Philadelphia, PA 19104-3335; 215-898-5738, fax 215-573-2053; summerabroad@sas.upenn.edu, [www.sas.upenn.edu/CGS].

Latin America

BCA Quito and BCA Xalapa. Choose from 2 linguisitic and cultural immersion programs: Quito, Ecuador or Xalapa, Mexico. Earn 13-18 credits per semester at Universidad San Francisco de Quito or the Universidad Veracruzana with a 3-4-week intensive language and orientation, homestay with families, field trips, extended study tours. Internships, practica, and volunteer work available.

Dates: Aug-Dec (fall), Jan-May (spring Quito), Feb-Jun (spring Xalapa), Aug-May/Jun (year).

Choosing an Overseas Program

The Big City or Belize? The Options Are Nearly Limitless

By Sara Cooley

The options for studying abroad continue to multiply. Want to trek in Tibet or excavate a Turkish burial ground? Paint in Provence or investigate coral reefs in Australia? The possibilities are nearly limitless, and most likely you never again will have the opportunity to spend three months to a year undisturbed in a far-off land. So don't let the daunting task of finding the perfect program overwhelm you.

Make a list of what you want in a study abroad program and then go search for it. The combined reference, *Academic Year Abroad* and *Vacation Study Abroad*, both published by the Institute for International Education, is an ideal starting point for your research. Basic information about every study abroad program and is indexed by location, field of study, and cost. Compare the list you've made to the descriptions in the book. When you find a match, note the program's web site. (Both books are also available on a completely searchable database, [www.iiepassport. org].

I was torn between the attractions of big city life in London and the natural wonders of Belize. After calling the sponsoring organizations and contacting alumni of both the programs I was interested in, I decided to do a semester in each. The contrast added a whole other dimension to my time abroad.

Not only does reading up and learning about the region that will be your temporary home enhance your excitement, it also prepares you for the changes you will encounter.

Guidebooks are incredibly helpful on the hot spots and highlights of the area, but they are designed for tourists. Look for travel accounts and ethnographies that give you a glimpse into everyday life in your future home.

Study abroad is about self discovery and the adventures of cultural immersion, but that discovery will be more intense when you go prepared and have picked the program that contains the features you've selected for yourself based upon your own criteria.

Costs: $19,500 (academic year); $10,950 (semester). Includes tuition, room and board, orientation, insurance, group travel in country. **Contact:** Program Division, Brethren College, 605 E. College Ave., North Manchester, IN 46962; 219-982-5238, fax 219-982-7755; mail@bcanet.org, [www.bcanet.org].

Malta

Full Curriculum Studies: Msida. The Malta program offers students the opportunity to enroll in a wide range of courses at the Univ. of Malta in a variety of disciplines such as art, architecture, engineering, education, sciences, etc. The Univ. is located in Msida about 4 miles outside of Valletta, the capital city of Malta in the center of the Mediterranean.

Dates: Fall semester: Sep-Jan; spring semester: Jan-Jun. **Costs:** One semester $2,390, both semesters $4,290. **Contact:** University Studies Abroad Consortium (USAC), Univ. of Nevada, Reno #323, Reno, NV 89557-0093; 775-784-6569, fax 775-784-6010; usac@unr.edu, [http://usac.unr.edu].

Mexico

Center for Bilingual Multicultural Studies. Intensive semester or intensive Spanish language programs for executives, bilingual teachers, healthcare professionals, seniors, nurses, high school students. Group-5 system, 40 class hours per week include Spanish class, Latin American courses and lectures, housing with Mexican host family or guest residence; excursions to historical and archaeological sites. Students enrolled may attend the university courses at no additional cost.

Dates: Year round starting every Monday. **Costs:** Registration fee $100; tuition $200 per week; lodging $168 per week, Plan A. **Contact:** Javier Espinosa, President, San Jeronimo #304, Col. Tlaltenango, Cuernavaca, Mor. 62179, Mexico; 011-527-317-10-87, fax 011-527-3-17-05-33; U.S. 800-932-20-68.; admission@bilingual-center.com.mx, [www.bilingual-center.com].

Gender Issues in Cuernavaca. Study "Crossing Borders: Gender and Social Change" or "Social and Environmental Justice" in a semester-long program in Cuernavaca with travel to Central America. Program includes homestay, Spanish, political science, internship option and courses. **Dates:** Sep-Dec or Feb-May. **Costs:** Call for details. **Contact:** Semester Programs Abroad, Center for Global Education, Augsburg College, 2211 Riverside Ave., Box 307TR, Minneapolis, MN 55454; 800-299-8889, fax 612-330-1695; globaled@augsburg.edu, [www.augsburg.edu/global].

Guadalajara Summer School. For the 50th year, the Univ. of Arizona Guadalajara Summer School will offer intensive Spanish in the 6-week session, intensive Spanish in the 3-week session, and upper-division Spanish and Mexico-related courses in the 5-week session. Courses may be taken for credit or audit.

Dates: Jul 1-Aug 16. **Costs:** $1,200-$2,302 includes tuition and host family housing with meals. **Contact:** Dr. Macario Saldate IV, Director, Guadalajara Summer School, The Univ. of Arizona, P.O. Box 40966, Tucson, AZ 85717; 520-621-5137; gss@u.arizona.edu, [www.coh.arizona.edu/gss].

Winter Session in Cuernavaca. Spend winter session studying Spanish Language and Culture with SUNY Cortland's program at SLI, Spanish Language Institute, in Cuernavaca, Mexico, the City of the Eternal Spring. Grammar classes with no more than 5 students, homestays, excursions to Mexico City and Teotihuacán included. All levels from basic to proficient. Three undergraduate credits. Faculty director accompanies group.

Dates: Dec 28-Jan 18. **Costs:** Approx. $975 (does not include SUNY tuition, airfare, insurance or spending money) **Contact:** SUNY Cortland International Programs, P.O. Box 2000, SUNY Cortland, Cortland, NY 13045; 607-753-2209, fax 607-753-5989; studyabroad@cortland.edu, [www.studyabroad.com/suny/cortland].

Middle East

American Univ. in Dubai. AIU's Dubai campus offers an American curriculum in a multicultural learning environment. Study abroad students take courses in International Business, Middle Eastern Studies, Arabic, Fashion Design/Marketing, Interior Design, and Visual Communication. Program features a full campus setting with dorms and recreation facilities, student activities, and scholarships and financial aid.

Dates: Five regular academic quarters: fall (Oct-Dec); winter (Jan-Mar); spring (Mar-May); summer I (Jun-Jul); summer II (Aug-Sep). **Costs:** Three classes and housing $4,835. **Contact:** American InterContinental Univ., Study Abroad Programs, 6600 Peachtree-Dunwoody Rd., 500 Embassy Row, Atlanta, GA 30328; 800-255-6839, fax 404-965-8006; studyabroad@aiuniv.edu, [www.studyabroad.aiuniv.edu].

Nepal

Volunteer Nepal!. This program is designed to meet the needs of participants who desire more than typical tourist experience. It provides volunteer service opportunities for people who are genuinely interested in learning about a new and different community and culture while contributing their time and skills to benefit worthwhile community service throughout Nepal.
Dates: Feb, Apr, Aug, and Oct. Other dates can be arranged. **Costs:** $650 (for whole program) includes pre-service training, language instruction, homestay, hiking, lectures on different topics, meditation, cultural orientation tour, transportation from airport and within the country, trekking, whitewater rafting, jungle safari, volunteering, food and accommodations, etc. **Contact:** Rajesh Shrestha, Director, Cultural Destination Nepal, GPO Box #11535, Kathmandu, Nepal; 011-977-1-426996, fax 011-977-1-426996; cdnnepal@wlink.com.np, [www.volunteernepal.org.np].

Wisconsin Year in Nepal. The program provides integrated language training, tutorial instruction, and independent fieldwork projects. Participants attend summer school in U.S. prior to the term abroad for intensive language study and orientation to South Asian life and cultures. The first semester begins with a homestay period in a 1-month village-study tour. The entire second semester is devoted to fieldwork projects.
Dates: Summer school in Madison: early Jun-mid-Aug; academic program abroad: late Aug-Apr. **Costs:** Summer school and related expenses additional. Call for current information. **Contact:** Office of International Studies and Programs, 261 Bascom Hall, Univ. of Wisconsin, 500 Lincoln Dr., Madison, WI 53706; 608-262-2851, fax 608-262-6998; peeradvisor@bascom.wisc.edu, [www.wisc.edu/studyabroad].

New Zealand

Full Curriculum Studies: Hamilton. Located in the City of Hamilton at the Univ. of Waikato, students are able to take a variety of courses in several disciplines. The courses concerning New Zealand/Pacific Society and Culture are especially popular with international students. Students are able to enjoy excellent study facilities and participate in organized university activities.
Dates: Semester 1: Jul-Nov; semester 2: Feb-Jun. **Costs:** One semester $4,530; both semesters $8,165. **Contact:** University Studies Abroad Consortium (USAC), Univ. of Nevada, Reno #323, Reno, NV 89557-0093; 775-784-6569, fax 775-784-6010; usac@unr.edu, [http://usac.unr.edu].

Norway

Ambassadors for the Environment Program. Summer program for students ages 15 and up, focusing on global environmental issues, ecology, and culture. Hands-on exploration of the various landscapes in Norway including mountains and fjords. Topics include wildlife management, biological diversity, climate change, sustainable agriculture, forestry, geography as well as cultural development issues. Activities include hiking, boating, camping, traditional crafts, and food preparation, swimming and family visits.
Dates: Jul 8-25. **Costs:** $2,300. Includes program fee, room and board, field trips, and transportation while in Norway. **Contact:** Scandinavian Seminar-Student Programs, 24 Dickinson St., Amherst, MA 01002; 413-253-9736, fax 413-253-5282; students@scandinavianseminar.com.

Camp Norway. Camp Norway is an innovative summer program combining fast-paced learning with the direct experience of living in Norway. Camp Norway takes place in Skogn, about a 1-hour drive north of Trondheim on the beautiful Trondheimsfjord. Camp Norway provides top-notch language instructon, as well as field trips exploring the spectacular scenery of the area, visits to historic sights and opportunities to develop international friendships. College and high school credit are available.
Dates: Jun 20-Jul 17 (optional post-program tour Jul 17-22). **Costs:** $2,650 for Sons of Norway members, $2,750 for nonmembers. Cost includes room and board, books, field trips, activities, and transportation from Trondheim to Skogn. (Prices subject to change if significant fluctuations in the exchange rate occur.) **Contact:** Sons of Norway, 1455 W. Lake St., Minneapolis, MN 55408; 612-827-3611 or 800-945-8851; fratenal@sofn.com.

Oslo International Summer School. The International Summer School of the Univ. of Oslo in Norway welcomes qualified participants from all parts of the world from late Jun-early Aug. The ISS is a center for learning in an international context, offering courses in the humanities, social sciences, and environmental protection to more than 500 students from over 80 nations every summer.
Dates: Jun 23-Aug 3. **Costs:** Approx. $2,400 (basic fees, room and board). **Contact:** Torild Homstad, Administrator, Univ. of Oslo,

International Summer School, North American Admissions-A, St. Olaf College, 1520 St. Olaf Ave., Northfield, MN 55057-1098; 800-639-0058 or 507-646-3269, fax 507-646-3732; iss@stolaf.edu, [www.uio.no/iss/iss.html].

Poland

Penn-in-Warsaw. For students interested in Polish history and culture, as well as international relations, economics, and other business disciplines. Taught in English, this program will acquaint students with the political and economic changes occurring in Poland and provide insight into the conditions for doing business in a changing economy. Short-term internships with Polish or joint-venture institutions will complement class instruction. **Dates:** Jun 23-Jul 31. **Costs:** Tuition $3,390; housing $350. **Contact:** Penn Summer Abroad, College of General Studies, Univ. of Pennsylvania, 3440 Market St., Suite 100, Philadelphia, PA 19104-3335; 215-898-5738, fax 215-573-2053; summerabroad@sas.upenn.edu, [www.sas.upenn.edu/CGS].

Semester in East Central Europe. Polish History, Art and Culture program at the Jagiellonian Univ. (1364); Krakow with entry tour through Germany, the Czech and Slovak Republics, Hungary, Austria; field trips in Poland. Witness history in the making as the history of the 20th century is now being rewritten in these countries. International student dorm living. Classes taught in English in humanities, social sciences. Polish language at all levels (8-credit intensive option). **Dates:** Sep 1-Dec 15. **Costs:** Approx. $5,350-$5,650 (for Wisconsin residents; tuition surcharge for out-of-staters), room and board, group travel, airfare, etc. **Contact:** International Programs, Univ. of Wisconsin-Stevens Point, 2100 Main St., Stevens Point, WI 54481; 715-346-2717, fax 715-346-3591; intlprog@uwsp.edu, [www.uwsp.edu/studyabroad].

Russia and the NIS

Moscow Institute for Advanced Studies. A comprehensive program in Russian language, culture, and politics. Russian language instruction at all levels and/or electives in politics, international affairs, literature, history. Offered in Russian or English, lecture series featuring prominent Russian figures, excursions, internships, financial aid, research stays. **Dates:** 2001: Jan 27-May 11; Jun 9-Aug 3; Aug 24-Dec 7. **Costs:** Intensive Language Program $6,700 (fall and spring), $4,400

(summer). **Contact:** Louise White, 152 W. 57th St., 48th Fl., New York, NY 10019; 212-245-0461, fax 212-489-4829; info@mifas.org, [www.studyabroad.com/moscow].

Penn-in-Moscow. For students interested in Russian language as well as in contemporary Russia, this program, housed at the Lomonosov Moscow State Univ., offers an in-depth introduction to the social and economic changes, cultural developments, and political movements that have emerged in the last years. The non-language courses will be taught in English. **Dates:** Jun 1-Jul 7. **Costs:** Tuition $3,390; housing $150; activites $100; travel $800. **Contact:** Penn Summer Abroad, College of General Studies, Univ. of Pennsylvania, 3440 Market St., Suite 100, Philadelphia, PA 19104-3335; 215-898-5738, fax 215-573-2053; summerabroad@sas.upenn.edu, [www.sas.upenn.edu/CGS].

Scandinavia

Semester or Year Abroad in Folk School. Students are individually matched with school that meets their needs in Denmark, Finland, Norway, or Sweden. Subjects such as outdoor life, weaving, textile arts, music, boat building as well as others are offered. **Dates:** End of Aug-Jan, Jan-end of May. **Costs:** Varies. Orientation session available for fall semester students. Open to students 17 and older. **Contact:** Leslie Evans, Scandinavian Seminar, 24 Dickinson St., Amherst, MA 01002; 800-316-9833 or 413-253-9736, fax 413-253-5282; students@scandinavianseminar.com.

Scotland

Findhorn Community Semester. A Living Routes program where students participate in academic study and community life while witnessing first hand an integrated spiritual and ecological model for living in the 21st century. Through experiential learning in a group context, the program focuses on community, ecology, sustainability, spirituality, creativity, and Scottish culture and history. **Dates:** Fall semester approx. Sep 1-Dec 15; spring semester approx. **Costs:** $10,200 includes tuition, airfare, room and board. **Contact:** Vanessa Long, Director of Programs, Living Routes, 85 Baker Rd., Shutesbury, MA 01072; 888-515-7333, 413-259-0025, fax 413-259-1256; Programs@LivingRoutes.org, [www.LivingRoutes.org].

Senegal

Kalamazoo in Senegal. Program combines academics with experiential learning. Course work at Universite Cheikh Anta Diop in Dakar and excursions give participants a broad overview of Senegal. Instruction in Wolof as well as a field study project provides opportunity for greater understanding of host culture. All courses taught in French. Minimum 2 years of French required.

Dates: Sep-Jun. **Costs:** Academic year: (2001-2002) $26,880. Includes roundtrip international transportation, tuition and fees, room and board, and some excursions. **Contact:** Center for International Programs, Kalamazoo College, 1200 Academy St., Kalamazoo, MI 49006; 616-337-7133, fax 616-337-7400; cip@kzoo.edu, [www.kzoo.edu/cip].

Univ. of Wisconsin in Senegal. Study abroad in Francophone Africa at the Université Gaston Berger in Saint Louis, Senegal. Students experience a blend of African, French, and Muslim traditions while they live in dorms with Senegalese roommates. Classes are taught in French in a variety of humanities and social sciences. Includes a year-long course in Wolof and an independent fieldwork project. Orientation includes several days in Madison and 3 weeks in Dakar, Senegal. Four semesters of French or equivalent required. Application deadline: first Friday in Feb. Late applications considered on a space-available basis.

Dates: Mid-Sep-mid-Jun. **Costs:** Call for current information. **Contact:** Office of International Studies and Programs, 261 Bascom Hall, Univ. of Wisconsin, 500 Lincoln Dr., Madison, WI 53706; 608-262-2851, fax 608-262-6998; peeradvisor@bascom.wisc.edu, [www.wisc.edu/studyabroad].

South America

Spanish for Foreigners. Intensive Courses 2 hours a day. Based on Eso Es and Barron's. Regular courses also available.

Dates: Contact organization for details. **Costs:** Two hours a day $100 per week, group (2-4) $50 per week. **Contact:** Adriana N. Crom, Rodriguez Peña 2061-5°B CP1021, Buenos Aires, Argentina; 01154-114-814-0792; mort_@hotmail.com.

Spain

IES Barcelona. Choice of courses taught at the ICE Center in English by native faculty in Art History, Business, Communications, Environmental Studies, History, Spanish Language and Literature and Political Science. Students enjoy the opportunity to enroll in courses at the Universitat de Pompeu Fabra in Business and Economics and at the Universitat de Barcelona in Spanish Studies. Field trips and cultural excursions. Housing: homestays, student residences or apartments.

Dates: Fall: Sep-Dec; spring: Jan-Jun; year: Sep-Jun. **Costs:** Semester $11,100; year $19,980. (NB. Estimated costs). Includes tuition, housing, orientation, some meals, field trips, international student card. **Contact:** Institute for the International Education of Students (IES), 33 N. LaSalle St., Chicago, IL 60602-2602; 800-995-2300, fax 312-944-1448; info@IESabroad.org, [www.IESabroad.org].

IES Madrid. Wide range of courses taught at the IES Center in Spanish by native faculty as well as courses at the Universidad Complutense de Madrid. This program focuses on development of oral and written Spanish skills and has a special curriculum for Spanish bilinguals. Field trips and cultural excursions. Housing: homestay.

Dates: Summer: Jun-Jul; fall: Sep-Dec; spring: Jan-May; year: Sep-May. (Univ. courses end early Oct and Jun for fall and spring respectively). **Costs:** Summer programs $3,600; semester $10,600; year $19,080. Includes tuition, orientation, housing, some meals, field trips, and international student ID card. **Contact:** Institute for the International Education of Students (IES), 33 N. LaSalle St., Chicago, IL 60602-2602; 800-995-2300, fax 312-944-1448; info@iesabroad.org, [www.iesabroad.org].

IES Salamanca. IES courses focus on Spanish language and Iberian culture, comparative studies of the Mediterranean basin, and comparative studies of Spain and Latin America. All taught in Spanish by faculty from the Universidad de Salamanca. Option also to enroll in university courses. Field trips and cultural excursions. Housing: homestay.

Dates: Summer: Jun-Jul, and Jul-Aug; fall: Aug-Dec; spring: Jan-May; year: Aug-May. (Univ. courses end early Feb and early Jun for fall and spring semester respectively.) **Costs:** Summer $2,700; semester $10,100; year $18,180. Includes tuition, orientation, housing, some meals, selected field trips, international, and student card. **Contact:** Institute for the International Education of Students (IES), 33 N. LaSalle St., Chicago, IL 60602-2602; 800-995-2300, fax 312-944-1448; info@iesabroad.org, [www.iesabroad.org].

Intensive Spanish Courses, Seville. CLIC IH, one of Spain's leading language schools, is located in the heart of Seville, the vibrant capital of Andalusia, and boasts a beautifully renovated Sevillian mansion as its center. Year-round intensive Spanish language courses, business Spanish, and official exam preparation are taught by highly qualified and motivated native teachers. CLIC IH combines professionalism with a friendly atmosphere. Academic credits available. Accommodations are carefully selected and we offer a varied cultural program as well as exchanges with local students.

Dates: Year round. **Costs:** Approx. $859 for a 4-week Spanish course and homestay, individual room, 2 meals per day. **Contact:** Bernhard Roters, CLIC IH Seville, C/ Albareda 19, 41001 Sevilla, Spain; 011-34-95-450-2131, fax 011-34-95-456-1696; clic@clic.es, [www.clic.org].

ISIS Barcelona Program. ISIS is an independent institution specializing in the social sciences taught within an international and cross-cultural context. Spanish language is offered at all levels and elective classes are taught in English. Transcripting is provided by Portland State Univ. Programs offered fall, winter, spring, summer.

Dates: Sep-Dec; Jan-Mar; Apr-Jul. **Costs:** Fall winter, spring tuition and fees $4,950; homestay and meals $1,950; summer tuition and fees $2,600, homestay and meals $750. **Contact:** Richard L. Browning, Institute for Social and Int'l. Studies (ISIS), Portland State Univ., Int'l. Education Services, P.O. Box 751, Portland, Or 97207-0751; isis@pdx.edu, [www.isis.pdx.edu].

Penn-in-Alicante. For students interested in the language, literature, and culture of Spain, this program combines classroom instruction with visits to points of cultural and historical interest, including Madrid and Toledo. Students live with local families.

Dates: Jun 25-Jul 30. **Costs:** Tuition $3,390; room and board $1,450. **Contact:** Penn Summer Abroad, College of General Studies, Univ. of Pennsylvania, 3440 Market St., Suite 100, Philadelphia, PA 19104-3335; 215-898-5738, fax 215-573-2053; summerabroad@sas.upenn.edu, [www.sas.upenn.edu/CGS].

Semester in Spain. Semester, year, summer, and January terms for high school graduates, college students, and adult learners. Beginning, intermediate, and advanced Spanish language studies along with Spanish literature, culture, history, and art. All courses taught in Spanish by native Spaniards. Four courses per semester, 1 course per short term, 4 credits per class. Homestays are arranged for all students.

Dates: Winter: Jan; spring semester: Feb-May; summer terms: Jun and/or Jul; fall semester:

Sep-Dec. **Costs:** Fall or spring semester $8,100; year approx. $15,600; summer terms and Jan term approx. $2,000 each term. Includes tuition, books, full room and board. **Contact:** Debra Veenstra, U.S. Coordinator, Semester in Spain, 6601 W. College Dr., Palos Heights, IL 60463; 800- 748-0087, fax 708-239-3986.; spain@trnty.edu, [www.semesterinspain.org].

Spanish and Basque Studies: San Sebastián. San Sebastián offers intensive language (Spanish or Basque) that fulfills up to 2 years of university language requirements in 1 semester, plus courses in history, literature, political science, economics, art, teacher education, etc. Program organized field trips to Madrid and other exciting locations, housing, and many local university activities at this beautiful seaside resort.

Dates: Summer terms: Jun, Jul, Aug; fall semester: Aug-Dec, spring semester: Jan-May. **Costs:** One semester $7,470; both semesters $11,980; Jun or Jul session $2,340; Aug session $1,990; Jun and Jul sessions $4,290; Jun and Aug sessions $3,920; Jul and Aug sessions $3,920; Jun, Jul and Aug sessions $5,660. **Contact:** University Studies Abroad Consortium (USAC), Univ. of Nevada, USAC 323, Reno, NV 89557; 775-784-6569, fax 775-784-6010; usac@unr.edu, [http://usac.unr.edu].

Spanish Studies: Alicante. Alicante offers intensive Spanish language studies that fulfille up to 2 years of university language requirements. Additional courses available in Spanish studies. Alicante is a seaside year round resort built around a natural habor.

Dates: Summer: Jun, Jul, and Aug. Fall: Aug-Dec. Spring semester: Jan-May. **Costs:** Jun or Jul session $2,340; Aug $1,990; Jun and Jul sessions $4,290; Jun and Aug 1 semestre $6,680, both semester $9,980. Jul and Aug $3,920; Jun, Jul, and Aug sessions $5,660. **Contact:** University Studies Abroad Consortium (USAC), Univ. of Nevada, USAC 323, Reno, NV 89557; 775-784-6569, fax 775-784-6010; usac@unr.edu, [http://usac.unr.edu].

Spanish Studies: Madrid. The Madrid program offers intensive language study—up to 2 years of university language requirements may be met in 1 semester. This program opens a window on the Spanish people, introducing you to the rich diversity of Spain and offering a truly, multicultural experience.

Dates: Fall semester: Sep-Dec; spring semester: Jan-May. Summer: Jun and Jul. **Costs:** One semester $7,180; both semesters $11,556. Summer 1 semester $2,340 or both $4,290. **Contact:** University Studies Abroad Consortium

(USAC), Univ. of Nevada, USAC 323, Reno, NV 89557; 775-784-6569, fax 775-784-6010; usac@unr.edu, [http://usac.unr.edu].

Spanish, International Business and/or Basque Studies: Getxo-Bilbao. The Getxo-Bilbao area offers intensive language studies (Spanish or Basque) that fulfill up to 2 years of university language requirements in 1 semester, plus courses in history, political science, art, culture, economics, teacher education, literature, etc. Program organized field trips, housing, and many local university activities at this seaside city.
Dates: Fall semester: Aug-Dec; spring semester: Jan-May. **Costs:** One semester $4,620; both semesters $7,600. **Contact:** University Studies Abroad Consortium (USAC), Univ. of Nevada, USAC 323, Reno, NV 89557; 775-784-6569, fax 775-784-6010; usac@unr.edu, [http://usac.unr.edu].

Study in Segovia. Program held in one of the most picturesque and charming cities in Spain. Numerous field trips and excursions included. Students live with homestay families. Two years of college-level Spanish required. "The program was well-run, the classes excellent, the overall experience was invaluable." - Sarah Potter, Central Michigan Univ.
Dates: Fall and winter semesters, summer session. **Costs:** Fall and winter (14 weeks) $6,990; summer (6 weeks) $3,030. **Contact:** AHA International, 741 SW Lincoln St., Portland, OR 97201-3178; 800-654-2051; mail@aha-intl.org, [www.aha-intl.org].

Study in Seville. Semester, academic year, January, and summer terms in Seville. Intensive immersion. Classes taught in Spanish by Spanish faculty. Intermediate and advanced-level courses are offered during Jan and semester. Resident director, homestays, 35-room mansion, library, computer lab, email; includes study/tours, "intercambios" with Spaniards, scholarships, internships, credits transferable, free video.
Dates: Jan term: Jan 1-Jan 25; spring: Jan 22-May 30; summer I: Jun 3-Jun 28; summer II: Jul 1-Jul 25. Fall: Aug 28-Dec 21. **Costs:** Semester $7,995, Jan term $2,145, summer terms $1,935-$3,585. Includes tuition, double occupancy room and full board, laundry, study visits, orientation, health insurance, enrollment, activity and computer fees including email account. **Contact:** Dr. Judith Ortiz, Director U.S., Center for Cross-Cultural Study, 446 Main St., Amherst, MA 01002; 800-377-2621, fax 413-256-1968; ta@cccs.com, [www.studyinspain.org].

Univ. of Salamanca. Founded in the early 13th century, the Univ. of Salamanca is one of the most distinguished centers of learning in Europe. SUNY Cortland is celebrating the 34th consecutive year in this "City of the Golden Stones." Fields of study include Spanish language (7 levels) and literature, humanities, social sciences. Specially contracted course on the Arab influence in Spain (concluding with excursion to Andalucía) is offered in the spring in addition to traditional classes. Homestays. Excursions. Resident Director.
Dates: Fall: early Sep-mid-Dec; spring-option 1: early Jan-end of Mar; option 2: early Jan-mid-May. **Costs:** Fall estimate: $3,850, spring Jan-Mar $2,200; Jan-May $4,500. Includes pre and post departure orientation programs, Spanish insurance, overseas instructional costs, room and board with a family, transportation from Madrid airport if arriving with group flight, excursions, administrative fees. SUNY tuition and airfare not included. **Contact:** Liz Kopp, Assistant Director, Office of International Programs, Box 2000, SUNY Cortland, Cortland, NY 13045; 607-753-2209, fax 607-753-5989; studyabroad@cortland.edu, [www.studyabroad.com/suny/cortland].

Universidad Complutense de Madrid (MLSA). A graduate and undergraduate program at the Universidad (Complutense) de Madrid for students interested in studying courses in language, literature, culture and civilization, composition, art history, philosophy of Spain. Students are taught by full-time faculty members from the Universidad (Complutense) de Madrid.
Dates: Summer program: Jul; semester: fall, winter, spring. **Costs:** Summer: total cost from $1,985 including airfare; year: $10,250 total cost including airfare. **Contact:** Dr. Celestino Ruiz, Modern Language Studies Abroad (MLSA), P.O. Box 548, Frankford, IL 60423; 815-464-1800, fax 815-464-9458; mlsa@sprintmail.com, [www.mlsa.com].

UVA Hispanic Studies Program. Summer, year, and semester programs at the Univ. of Valencia, in collaboration with the Univ. of Virginia. A wide range of courses in language, literature, art history, and culture. Participants from over 100 colleges and universities. Live with families a short distance from the university.
Dates: Summer: May-Jul; fall: Sep-Dec; spring: Jan-May. **Costs:** Summer: $3,560; fall $6,240; spring $7,405; year $11,495. **Contact:** Liz Wellbeloved-Stone, Hispanic Studies, Univ. of Virginia, P.O. Box 400776, Charlottesville, VA

22904-4776; 804-924-7155, fax 804-924-4025; hispanicstudies@virginia.edu, [www.virginia.edu/~spitpo/spanish/valencia].

Sweden

Uppsala Int'l. Summer Session. Sweden's oldest academic summer program focuses on learning the Swedish language. All levels from beginners to advanced. Additional courses in Swedish history, social institutions, arts in Sweden, Swedish pop music, Swedish film. Excursions every Friday. Extensive evening program includes both lectures and entertainment. Single rooms in dormitories. Apartments at extra cost. Open to both students and adults, who have university eligibility. Credit possible.

Dates: Jun 23-Aug 16; Jun 23-Jul 19; Jul 21-Aug 16, Jul 7-Aug 16. **Costs:** SEK24,400 (approx. $2,300) for the 8-week session, SEK13,200 (approx. $1,250) for the 4-week session. Includes room, some meals, all classes, evening and excursion program. **Contact:** Dr. Nelleke van Oevelen-Dorrestijn, Uppsala Int'l. Summer Session, Box 1972, 751 49 Uppsala, Sweden; 011-31-13-521-23-88 or 011-46-18-10-23-70, fax 011-31-13-521-2389; nelleke.vanoevelen@uiss.org, [www.uiss.org].

Switzerland

Caux Scholars Program (CSP). The CSP, held in Caux, Switzerland, is a month-long academic program in conflict transformation with an internship component. It is open to college and graduate students from around the world who are interested in learning about the moral and spiritual dimensions of peacemaking and the relationship between individual transformation and change in the world.

Dates: Mid-Jul to mid-Aug every year. **Costs:** $2,000 includes tuition, room and board. **Contact:** Program Director, 1156 15th St., NW, #910, Washington, DC 20005; 202-872-9077, fax 202-872-9137; cauxsp@aol.com, [www.cauxscholars.org].

Univ. of Geneva Summer Courses. Three-week French language and civilization at all levels, beginners to advanced. All instructors have a university diploma. Excursions and visits to Geneva and its surroundings. Class of 15-20 students. Minimum age 17.

Dates: Jul, Aug, Sep. **Costs:** SFR500 for 3 weeks (tuition). **Contact:** Mr. G. Benz, Univ. of Geneva, Summer Courses, rue de Candolle 3, CH-1211 Geneva 4, Switzerland; 011-41-22-705-74-34, fax 011-41-22-705-74-39; elcfete@unige.ch, [www.unige.ch/lettres/elcf/coursete/cournet.html].

Univ. of Lausanne Summer Courses. Courses are taught in French in 4 series of 3 weeks each for elementary level to advanced. We also offer 2 courses for beginners that last at least 6 weeks. One or more series may be attended. Classes are constituted according to the students' test.

Dates: Series I: Jul 8-26; Series II: Jul 29-Aug 16; Series III: Aug 19-Sep 6; Series IV: Sep 9-27. **Costs:** CHF500 for 3 weeks; CHF1,100 for 6 weeks (2002). **Contact:** Univ. of Lausanne, Cours de Vacances, BFSH2, CH-1015 Lausanne, Switzerland; 011-41-21-692-30-90, fax 011-41-21-692-30-85; CoursDeVacances@cvac.unil.ch, [www.unil.ch/cvac].

Thailand

Business and Southeast Asian Studies: Bangkok. Diverse courses in culture, language, economics, business, society, and religions provide a fascinating, well-balanced approach to Southeast Asia. Program-organized field trips, student residence halls, and many university activities at one of Thailand's most modern universities.

Dates: Summer session: May-Aug; fall semester: Sep-Dec, spring semester: Dec-Apr. **Costs:** One semester $2,680; both semesters $4,380; summer term $2,680, both semesters and summer $5,880. **Contact:** University Studies Abroad Consortium (USAC), Univ. of Nevada, USAC 323, Reno, NV 89557-0093; 775-784-6569, fax 775-784-6010; usac@unr.edu, [http://usac.unr.edu].

Globalization and Development. Program combines academics with experiential education. Specially arranged course work at the Univ. of Chiang Mai and field study excursions give students overview of problems and processes of globalization and development in Northern Thailand. Field study project with local NGO provides intensive opportunity for understanding host culture.

Dates: Sep-Jan. **Costs:** Academic year: (2001-2002) $17,920. **Contact:** Center for International Programs, Kalamazoo College, 1200 Academy St., Kalamazoo, MI 49006; 616-337-7133, fax 616-337-7400; cip@kzoo.edu, [www.kzoo.edu/cip].

GlobalQuest. GlobalQuest offers 12-week fall and spring semester study programs in Thailand for high school seniors, students deferring college for a semester or a year, and for college students. Each cluster is for 12 students and 3 teachers. Study takes place throughout Thailand and includes an individual research project, Thai language, natural history and environmental issues, culture, a homestay, and service.

Dates: Mid-Feb-mid-May; mid-Sep-mid-Dec. **Costs:** $12,000. **Contact:** Tim Ellis, Executive Director, GlobalQuest, 195 Montsweag Rd., Woolwich, ME 04579; 207-443-5451, fax 207-443-2551; tellis@wiscasset.net, www.gquest.org].

Wisconsin College Year in Thailand. The program at Chiang Mai Univ. features Thai language study, subject tutorials, and a fieldwork project. Students attend summer school in Madison before the term abroad for intensive Thai language study as well as cultural and academic orientation. Application deadline: second Friday in Feb. Late applications are considered on a space-available basis.

Dates: Summer school in Madison Jun-mid-Aug; academic year abroad late Aug-May. Also fall semester option late Aug-mid Dec. **Costs:** Call for current information. Summer school and related expenses additional. **Contact:** Office of International Studies and Programs, 261 Bascom Hall, Univ. of Wisconsin, 500 Lincoln Dr., Madison, WI 53706; 608-262-2851, fax 608-262-6998; peeradvisor@bascom.wisc.edu, www.wisc.edu/studyabroad].

United Kingdom and Ireland

AIU London Study and Internship Program. AIU's central London campus offers a U.S.-accredited curriculum and a multicultural population. Study abroad students take courses in International Business, Communication, Liberal Arts, Fashion Design/Marketing, Interior Design, Visual Communication, and Media Production. Program features include comprehensive student services, activities/travel, furnished apartment accommodations, and scholarships and financial aid.

Dates: Five regular academic quarters: fall (Oct-Dec); winter (Jan-Mar); spring (Mar-May); summer I (Jun-Jul); summer II (Aug-Sep). Special 4-week summer sessions as well. **Costs:** Three classes $4,900; 4 classes $5,700; 2 classes and internship $4,900. **Contact:** American InterContinental Univ., 6600 Peachtree-Dunwoody Rd., 500 Embassy Row, Atlanta, GA 30328; 800-255-6839, fax 404-965-8006; studyabroad@aiuniv.edu, [http://studyabroad.aiuniv.edu].

Annual Readers Theatre Workshop. A 2-week program that covers all aspects of Readers Theatre and related fields with a large faculty, morning classes, out-of-class activities. Up to 12 credits available from the Univ. of Southern Maine. No previous experience required for this unique hands-on study.

Dates: Jul. **Costs:** $1,495 (2002). **Contact:** Dr. Bill Adams, Director, P.O. Box 17193, San Diego, CA 92177; 619-276-1948, fax 858-576-7369; [www.readers-theatre.com].

British Studies at Oxford. This program of study in one of the world's most prestigious universities offers undergraduate and graduate credit in art history, business, communication, drama, education, English literature, history, and political science taught by Oxford Univ. professors. The participants live in private rooms tidied daily by the college staff, who also serve 3 bountiful and tasty meals a day in the Great Hall. Field trips are an integral part of each course as well as group trips to the theater in Stratford-upon-Avon and London.

Dates: Summer: Jun 30-Jul 20; Jul 21-Aug 10; or Jun 30-Aug 10. **Costs:** $3,350 for 3 weeks; $6,050 for 6 weeks. Includes 4 or 8 credits, travel in Britain for course related events, theater, entrance to museums, dinners in country inns, and many field trips. Overseas travel not included. **Contact:** Dr. M.B. Pigott, Director, British Studies at Oxford, 322 Wilson Hall, Oakland Univ., Rochester, MI 48309-4401; 248-652-3405 or 248-370-4131, fax 248-650-9107; pigott@oakland.edu, [www.oakland.edu/oxford].

BUNAC's Work in Britain Program. Allows full-time U.S. university or college students and recent graduates to work for up to 6 months, in any job, any time of year in England, Scotland, Wales, or Northern Ireland. Job and accommodations listings and general support from BUNAC in London and Edinburgh offices.

Dates: Year round. **Costs:** $250 work permit, admin., U.K. support. **Contact:** BUNAC USA, P.O. Box 430, Southbury, CT 06488; 800-GO-BUNAC; 203-264-0901; info@bunacusa.org, [www.bunac.org].

CCIS Study Abroad Programs in England. CCIS offers 3 programs in England: Kingston Univ. and Thames Valley Univ., London; and Edge Hill College, Lancashire. CCIS programs in England allow for full integration in the host college/university. You'll be in classes with local students, share facilities, and live as they do. Students receive U.S. transcript upon completion of program.

Dates: Fall: Sep-Dec; spring: Jan-Jun; summer: TVU: Jun-Jul, KU: Jul-Aug. **Costs:** Contact organization for cost information or check out web site. **Contact:** Penny Schouten, SUNY Rockland, 145 College Rd., Suffern, NY 10901; 845-574-4205, fax 845-574-4423; studyabroad@sunyrockland.edu, [www.studyabroad.com/suny/rockland].

Central Saint Martins Short Courses. Short practical courses in all aspects of art and design suitable for professional and student artists and designers. Includes fashion, graphics, fine art, theater design, textiles, product design, computer graphics, and multimedia. All courses held in heart of London in the U.K.'s largest college of art and design.
Dates: Courses run year round in evenings and weekends. Intensive week long courses in summer, Christmas, and Easter. **Costs:** Costs from £150 ($250) per week for tuition. Accommodations from £23 ($35) per night. **Contact:** Developments at Central Saint Martins, Southampton Row, London WC1B 4AP, U.K.; 011-44-207-514-7015, fax 011-44-207-514-7016; shortcourse@csm.linst.ac.uk, [www.csm.linst.ac.uk].

Exchange Program in Limerick. Students attend class at Mary Immaculate College, located in the heart of Limerick and part of the Univ. of Limerick system. A faculty member from FSU accompanies the group and teaches 3 FSU courses. Accommodations are located within a 5-minute walk of campus.
Dates: Spring semester only: early Feb-early Jun. **Costs:** Students pay FSU tuition: $1,671 in-state, $4,246 out-of-state, Limerick hostel costs, food, airline ticket, passport, ISIC, personal costs (approx. total $4,500). **Contact:** Dr. Amy C. Simes, Director, Ctr. for Int'l. Education, Frostburg State Univ., 101 Braddock Rd., Frostburg, MD 21532; 301-687-3091; asimes@frostburg.edu.

Full Curriculum Studies: Brighton. Brighton offers courses in many disciplines: art, business, sports science, engineering, computing, geography, design, education, math, etc. Organized field trips, housing in student residence halls. Only 45 minutes from London.
Dates: Fall semester: Sep-Feb; spring semester: Jan-Jun. **Costs:** One semester $4,180; both semesters $7,260. **Contact:** University Studies Abroad Consortium (USAC), Univ. of Nevada, USAC 323, Reno, NV 89557; 775-784-6569, fax 775-784-6010; usac@unr.edu, [http://usac.unr.edu].

Full Curriculum Studies: Bristol. The program at the Univ. of Bristol offers students the opportunity to enroll in a wide range of courses in a variety of disciplines. A few of the choices are: archaeology, drama, geographical sciences, economics and accounting, engineering. Students are able to participate in the full range of university activities.
Dates: Fall semester: Sep-Jan; year: Sep-Jun. **Costs:** Fall semester only $5,260; year $9,880.

Contact: University Studies Abroad Consortium (USAC), Univ. of Nevada, USAC 323, Reno, NV 89557; 775-784-6569, fax 775-784-6010; usac@unr.edu, [http://usac.unr.edu].

Full Curriculum Studies: Cork. The program at the Univ. College Cork offers students the opportunity to study in a variety of disciplines such as: archaeology, Celtic civilization, Irish studies, sciences, and law. Students also can participate in university clubs, societies, and sporting activities.
Dates: Fall early semester: Aug-Dec; fall semester: Sep-Dec; spring semester: Jan-May. **Costs:** One semester $5,190; both semesters $9,680. **Contact:** University Studies Abroad Consortium (USAC), Univ. of Nevada, USAC 323, Reno, NV 89557; 775-784-6569, fax 775-784-6010; usac@unr.edu, [http://usac.unr.edu].

Full Curriculum Studies: St Andrews, Scotland. The program at the Univ. of St Andrews offers students the opportunity to enroll in a wide range of courses such as International Relations, Scottish History, Management, Economics, Environmental Sciences, etc. St Andrews is a beautiful town situated in its own sheltered bay on the Fife coast, 45 miles north of Edinburgh.
Dates: Fall semester: Sep-Jan; spring semester: Feb-May. **Costs:** One semester $7,280; both semesters $12,280. **Contact:** University Studies Abroad Consortium (USAC), Univ. of Nevada, USAC 323, Reno, NV 89557; 775-784-6569, fax 775-784-6010; usac@unr.edu, [http://usac.unr.edu].

Harlaxton College. Harlaxton College is owned and operated by the Univ. of Evansville in Indiana. Therefore, all courses are U.S. accredited and usually transfer easily. Students live and study in a magnificent 19th-century Victorian manor house in the English Midlands. Assistance is available with air arrangements and airport pickup; optional field trips are available throughout England, Ireland, Scotland, Wales, and the Continent. Harlaxton is a full-service study abroad program with help every step of the way.
Dates: Fall: Aug 30-Dec 12; summer: May 13-Jun 13; spring 2002: Jan 10-Apr 24. **Costs:** $11,122 per semester. Includes tuition, room and board (2000-2001). **Contact:** Suzy Lantz, Harlaxton Coordinator, Univ. of Evansville, 1800 Lincoln Ave., Evansville, IN 47722; 800-UKMANOR or 812-488-1040; sl5@evansville.edu, [www.ueharlax.ac.uk].

IES Dublin. IES courses in humanities and social sciences taught by native faculty with enrollment options at Newman School of Irish

By Autumn Tallman

CETLALIC, the Tlahuica Center for Language and Cultural Exchange, offers year-round Spanish language instruction and cultural immersion programs in Cuernavaca, Mexico. Each June CETLALIC also offers two concurrent 3-week programs: In/Visibility: Lesbian Lives in Mexico and Coming Out: The Gay Men's Experience in Mexico. Both programs include Spanish study, programming that fosters cultural immersion, and homestays with gay- and lesbian-friendly families.

CETLALIC is one of the very few education abroad programs to directly address gay and lesbian issues. Most overseas programs do not consider the needs of gay and lesbian participants and most programs in locations with organized gay and lesbian communities do not tap into local resources to offer a gay and lesbian homestay option or referrals to local support groups. Furthermore, advisers often lack the knowledge necessary to effectively advise students about local attitudes toward gay men and lesbians in a given country and about safety issues that any gay or lesbian student must address in deciding where to study or travel.

The lack of reliable information is a major deterrent to international travel for gay men and lesbians. They, along with their international education advisers, often overestimate or underestimate the risk involved for gay men and lesbians traveling to another country.

Bob Barrett, a participant in the CETLALIC gay men's program, said, "My expectations were centered around my anxiety about the risk I perceived myself to be taking. Those anxieties faded and everything was wonderful."

Conversely, it is possible to underestimate the risks involved. At the age of 15, having recently come out of the closet, I participated in a high school program in Israel. Being far from family and friends without a support system was a lonely experience at best. When I confided in my program director that I was having trouble adjusting because I felt I had to hide my gayness from other program participants for fear of rejection, he gave me a sermon on the immorality of homosexuality. Had I considered the implications of being gay in another country and received advising prior to departure, I might have looked for a program more responsive to my needs, a country more receptive to gay men and lesbians, or at least have known how to contact local gay and lesbian organizations for support. As it was, I didn't know that such organizations existed in Israel until after I came back home, having left the program early, dejected and convinced that international education was not for gay people.

Over 10 years later, I found myself in Cuernavaca, in a gay- and lesbian-friendly homestay. Finally, I was able to focus my attention and energy on an international experience without being preoccupied with my identity. The experience led to my mastery of Spanish, years of working in Mexico, and ultimately my decision to make international education a career.

In addition to offering gay and lesbian programs each June. CETLALIC periodically offers 3-week thematic programs, including Women and Social Change in Mexico and Multicultural Mexican Reality in the Third Millennium. Gay and lesbian homestays are available throughout the year. For more information contact CETLALIC [www. giga.com/~cetlalic].

Other gay and lesbian themed programs include one in The Netherlands: Sexuality Gender and Identity, sponsored by College Semester Abroad, School for International Training, a semester program offering academic credit to undergraduates. The program includes a gay and lesbian friendly homestay option, field study, independent study, Dutch language study, and a thematic seminar. For more information, see College Semester Abroad's web site [www.sit.edu/studyabroad].

Direct enrollment can be an option for students of gay and lesbian studies interested in a semester or year abroad. Many universities abroad have gender studies departments or course offerings. Check directly with the university where you are interested in studying to see if courses or programs are available.

Studies at Univ. College Dublin. Full integration options at Trinity College in EU honors program and natural science honors program. Field trips and cultural excursions. Housing: homestays, apartments.

Dates: Summer: Jun-Jul 2001; fall: Aug-Dec 2001; spring: Jan-May 2002; year: Aug-May. (Trinity options end Jun 15 for spring and full year.) **Costs:** Summer: $4,150; semester $10,800; year $19,440. Includes tuition, orientation, housing, and international student ID card. **Contact:** Institute for the International Education of Students (IES), 33 N. LaSalle St., Chicago, IL 60602-2602; 800-995-2300, fax 312-944-1448; info@iesabroad.org, [www.iesabroad.org].

IES London. Broad curriculum including concentrations in international business, British literature, international studies, and the creative and performing arts. University course options at City Univ., The Courtauld Institute of Art, LAMDA, Queen Mary and Westfield, SOAS, and the Slade School of Art. Field trips and cultural excursions. Housing: flats, homestay.

Dates: Summer: Jun-Jul 2001; fall: Aug-Dec 2001; spring: Jan-May 2002; year: Aug 2001-May 2002. **Costs:** Summer: $3,950; semester $11,770; year $21,186. Includes tuition, orientation, housing, and international student ID. **Contact:** Institute for the Int'l. Education of Students (IES), 33 N. LaSalle St., Chicago, IL 60602-2602; 800-005-2300, fax 312-944-1448; info@iesabroad.org, [www.iesabroad.org].

Irish Way Program. The Irish Way is a 5-week travel-study program for American high school students. Participants take classes in Irish culture, history, dance, sports, Gaelic, go on field trips and stay with an Irish host family for 1 week. The Irish Way has sent over 2,800 students to Ireland since 1976.

Dates: Jul (5 weeks). **Costs:** $2,995 includes roundtrip, transatlantic airfare. **Contact:** Anne-Marie Crowell, Irish American Cultural Institute, 1 Lackawanna Pl., Morristown, NJ 07960; 973-605-1991, fax 973-605-8875; irishwaynj@aol.com, [www.irishaci.org].

MA Continental Philosophy. Taught MA with substantial independent research component. Modules selected from a list including phenomenology, existentialism, deconstruction, feminism, post-modernism, etc. Lively but intimate and friendly department at the center of the U.K. Entry requirement: good first degree involving significant study of philosophy; cognate study considered.

Dates: Sep-Aug (12 months); apply by June. **Costs:** Approx. $10,000 tuition for full year.

Area has low living costs. **Contact:** Dr. Douglas Burnham, Staffordshire Univ., Stoke-on-Trent, ST4 2XW, U.K.; 011-44-1782-294415, fax 011-44-1782-294760; h.d.burnham@staffs.ac.uk.

Modern Britain and British Literature/Theater: Reading. Reading offers courses in nearly every academic disciplines: art, business, literature, performing arts, engineering, computing, geography, education, agriculture, etc. Housing in student residence halls. Only 25 minutes from London.

Dates: Fall session: Sep-Dec; winter session: Jan-Mar; spring session: Apr-Jul, summer session: Jul-Aug. **Costs:** One term $4,580; two terms $7,680; year long $10,680, summer $3,180. **Contact:** University Studies Abroad Consortium (USAC), Univ. of Nevada, USAC 323, Reno, NV 89557; 775-784-6569, fax 775-784-6010; usac@unr.edu, [http://usac.unr.edu].

NYU in Dublin. NYU in Dublin is located at beautiful Trinity College, Ireland's oldest university. Along with a lively review of contemporary Irish culture through courses in literature, history, politics, cinema and language. Students also attend theater, poetry readings, traditional music sessions, and film screenings and visit Belfast, Donegal, and other significant sites.

Dates: Jul 25 -Aug 3. **Costs:** $1,962 housing and activities; $3,920 undergraduate tuition; $633 per point, graduate tuition. **Contact:** NYU Summer Session, 7 E. 12th St., 6th Fl., New York, NY 10003; 212-998-2292, fax 212- 995-4642; summer.info@nyu.edu, [www.nyu.edu/summer].

NYU in London. Offers a wide selection of courses, including British literature and modern drama, art and architecture, the Renaissance, Shakespeare, and contemporary political science. Students also enjoy a range of introductions to British life, including city tours of London, performances of Shakespeare's plays in Stratford-upon-Avon and at the Globe Theatre in London, and visits to Stonehenge, Salisbury, and Wilton House. Students live in the NYU dormitory, and classes are held at the NYU Center, a short walk away, in the historic Bloomsbury section of the city.

Dates: Jul 1-Aug 9. **Costs:** 2001: Undergraduate tuition (8 points) $3,920; graduate tuition (per point) $633; theater fee (required for Shakespeare and Modern Drama courses) $180; housing and activities $1,750. **Contact:** NYU Summer Session, 7 E. 12th St., 6th Fl., New York, NY 10003; 212-998-2292, fax 212- 995-4103; summer.info@nyu.edu, [www.nyu.edu/summer].

Oxford Advanced Studies Program. An academic summer course at Magdalen College, Oxford, for high school sophomores, juniors, and seniors. Classes are complemented by a full calendar of visits and activities, including London, Stratford, Stonehenge, and Warwick Castle. Teaching includes a weekly individual tutorial [www.oxtutor.co.uk].
Dates: Jul 1-26. **Costs:** $5,750 (plus $300 registration fee). **Contact:** Joan Ives, The Oxford Edge, P.O. Box 2043, Darien, CT 06820; 203-966-2886 or 203-972-3083; oxedge@inetmau.att.net.

Penn-in-London. For students interested in theater and literature, this program offers first-hand opportunities to experience the best in traditional and contemporary British theater, from page to footlights.
Dates: Jul 1-Aug 3. **Costs:** Tuition $3,390; theater tickets $525; housing $950. **Contact:** Penn Summer Abroad, College of General Studies, Univ. of Pennsylvania, 3440 Market St., Suite 100, Philadelphia, PA 19104-3335; 215-898-5738, fax 215-573-2053; summerabroad@sas.upenn.edu, [www.sas.upenn.edu/CGS].

Study Abroad in Ireland and U.K. Study at Ulster Univ., Queens Univ., National Univ. of Ireland at Dublin, Cork and Galway, Univ. of Limerick, Trinity College Dublin for Summer, semester or full year. Study abroad at English, Welsh, and Scottish universities.
Dates: Semester: Jan 2002; fall: late Sep 2002; summer: Jul 2002. **Costs:** Summer approx. $3,000-$3,500; semester $8,000-$9,000; full year $17,000. **Contact:** North American Institute for Study Abroad (NAISA), 129 Mill St., Danville, PA 17821; 570-275-5099, fax 570-275-1644.

Study/Work with Drexel in London. The Drexel in London program offers students the opportunity to study and work in London, England. Students can select from courses in Business and Administration, Design and Merchandising, Hotel and Restaurant Management. Students may choose to study only or pair their studies with a 3-month internship.
Dates: Fall: Sep-Dec, winter: Jan-Mar, spring Mar-Jun, summer: Jun-Sep. **Costs:** $8,500 for 3 months, $12,750 for 6 months (2001-2002). **Contact:** Daniela Ascarelli, Drexel Univ., 3141 Chestnut St., Philadelphia, PA 19104; 215-895-1704, fax 215-895-6184; studyabroad@drexel.edu.

Summer Teachers Institute London. Earn 6 graduate credits in Education in a 4-week program at the Univ. of North London,

sponsored by the State Univ. of New York College at Cortland. Curricular options in arts, British history or urban education are appropriate for both elementary and secondary teachers.
Dates: Fall: mid-Sep-mid-Dec:, spring: end-Jan-mid-May. **Costs:** Approx. $4,000. Estimates include full-day orientation in the U.S., application fee, accommodations, meals, commuter ticket on underground and buses, excursions, insurance, roundtrip airfare from NYC, transportation from airport to London upon arrival with group flight, books and supplies, various cultural activities, administrative fees and 6 graduate credits of SUNY tuition. **Contact:** Dr. Del Janik, Program Coordinator, Office of International Programs, Box 2000, SUNY Cortland, Cortland, NY 13045; 607-753-2209, fax 607-753-5989; studyabroad@cortland.edu, [www.studyabroad.com/suny/cortland].

The Univ. of Ulster. The Univ. of Ulster is now the largest university on the island of Ireland. We have such a wide variety of courses on our 4 main campuses that you are sure to find modules to match your needs. The University is modern and informal yet retains the highest standards of expertise in teaching and research.
Dates: Semester 1: Sep-Jan; semester 2: Jan-Jun. **Costs:** Semester: £2,515; 2 semesters: £4,615. **Contact:** Joan Reilly, International Office, Univ. of Ulster at Jordanstown, Co. Antrim, BT37 OQB Ireland; 011-44-2890-368220; ej.reilly@ulst.ac.uk, [www.ulst.ac.uk].

Three Pre-Session Programs. "This Scepter 'd Isle" introduces important general aspects of British history and culture. "Changing Places: Lancaster and the Lake District" focuses on historical, geographical and cultural perspectives on Northern England. "The World About Us" looks at history of science, physics for non-mathematicians, ecology, and geology.
Dates: Aug 15-Sep 14. **Costs:** £1,120 includes orientation, accommodations, teaching, assessment, field trips. **Contact:** Paula Foster, Lancaster Summer Univ., Dept. of Continuing Education, Lancaster Univ., LA1 4YN U.K.; 011-44-1524-592567, fax 011-44-1524-592448; summer.university@lancaster.ac.uk, [www.lancs.ac.uk/users/conted/pre_sess.htm].

Univ. College Cork. First opened in 1849, the Univ. College Cork (UCC) is 1 of 5 constituent colleges of the National Univ. of Ireland. Eight faculties comprise the educational offerings of UCC: arts, Celtic studies, commerce, law, science, food science and technology, engineering, and medicine. Direct Enrollment in regular UCC classes with Irish students. Cortland's program specializes in language, history, and culture, but other courses may be available. Housing arranged prior to departure from U.S. in apartments near campus. Fall, spring, summer, academic year.

Dates: Fall: Early Sep-mid-Dec:, spring: mid-Jan-early Jun; summer: early Jul-end of Jul. **Costs:** Fall and spring estimate: $6,000; summer: $2,000; academic year: $12,000. Estimates include orientation, application fee, apartment rental (including utilities), food allowance, health and accident insurance. SUNY tuition, airfare, incidental expenses not included. **Contact:** Office of International Programs, Box 2000, SUNY Cortland, Cortland, NY 13045; 607-753-2209, fax 607-753-5989; studyabroad@cortland.edu, [www.studyabroad.com/suny/cortland].

Univ. of Cambridge Summer Schools. Intensive study in Cambridge as part of an international community. Plenary lectures and special subject courses are offered, together with evening activities and excursions. Both multi-disciplinary and specialist-subject programs are available.

Dates: Jul and Aug. **Costs:** Tuition from £510-£740, accommodations from £285-£1,040 (2001 prices, 2002 TBA). **Contact:** International Division, Univ. of Cambridge, Madingley Hall, Cambridge CB3 8AQ, U.K.; 011-44-1954-280398, fax 011-44-1954-280200; intenq@cam.ac.uk, [www.cont-ed.cam.ac.uk/IntSummer].

Univ. of North London. SUNY Cortland celebrates its 29th consecutive year at UNL. Over 400 courses are offered. Fields of study include education, natural sciences, humanities, communications, social sciences, business, health, theater arts, fine arts, and others. Direct enrollment with British students. Credits per semester: 12-16. Pre-arranged housing in flats in the Bayswater district. Full- and part-time internships available.

Dates: Fall: late-Sep-mid Dec; spring: end of Jan-mid-May. **Costs:** Estimates: $7,800 per semester; academic year: $13,000. Estimates include full-day orientation in the U.S., application fee, pre-arranged apartment rental, meals, commuter ticket on underground, London tour and Thames cruise, insurance, roundtrip airfare from N.Y., transportation from airport to downtown London upon arrival, passport, books and supplies, various cultural activities, administrative fees. SUNY tuition and spending money not included. **Contact:** Office of International Programs, Box 2000, SUNY Cortland, Cortland, NY 13045; 607-753-2209, fax 607-753-5989; studyabroad@cortland.edu,

[www.studyabroad.com/suny/cortland].

Visiting Students Program. The opportunity to study alongside British undergraduates in a traditional university environment and gain credit to transfer back to your home institution. You may study for a 3-, 6-, 9-, or 12-month period. We guarantee single accommodations for all visiting students.

Dates: Jan-Mar, Apr-Jun, Jul-Sep, Oct-Dec **Costs:** £2,499 per term for tuition plus accommodations (2000). **Contact:** Michael J. McCrostie, Univ. of Buckingham, Hunter St., Buckingham MK18 1EG, England; 011-44-1280-820117, fax 011-44-1280-820151; mjm@buckingham.ac.uk, [www.buck.ac.uk].

Work in Britain. Santa Rosa Junior College offers college credits (up to 8 semester units) for students working in London for a semester. Students obtain their work permit through BUNAC, attend an in-person or on-line orientation through Santa Rosa Junior College, and work and live in London independently while remaining in contact with college faculty.

Dates: Spring and fall 2002. **Costs:** Approx. $3,500. **Contact:** Kathleen Simmons, Program Coordiantor, Work and Earn College Credit in Britain, Work Experience Dept., Santa Rosa Junior College,1501 Mendocino Ave., Santa Rosa, CA 95401; ksimmons@santarosa.edu, [www.santarosa.edu/workexp/wib].

United States

Cambridge CELTA (Certificate in English Language Teaching to Adults). Four-week intensive courses leading to the prestigious, internationally-recognized Cambridge CELTA qualification, taught by a highly experienced and qualified team of trainers. Graduate credit recommendation of 6 hours (MA TESOL) and lifelong expert job guidance and assistance.

Dates: Four-week courses begin Oct 15, Nov 26, 2001; Jan 7, Feb 11, Mar 11, 2002. **Costs:** $2,695. **Contact:** Carrie Priestley, St Giles Language Teaching Center, 1 Hallidie Plaza, 3rd Fl., San Francisco, CA 94102; (415) 788-3552; (415) 788-1923.; sfsgile@slip.net, [www.stgiles-usa.com].

Masters for International and Intercultural Management and Study Abroad. The School for International Training (SIT) offers academic curriculum integrated with field-based practice, reflection, and application including professional practice. SIT offers master's degrees in Teaching (ESOL, French, Spanish), Intercultural Relations, International Education. Sustainable Development, Organizational Management, Conflict Transformation, and a self-design option. SIT also offers 5 undergraduate study abroad programs in over 45 countries. **Dates:** Call for details. **Costs:** Call for details. **Contact:** Admissions, School for International Learning, P.O. Box 676, Kipling Rd., Brattleboro, VT 05302; 800-336-1616, fax 802-258-3500; admissions@sit.edu, [www.sit.edu].

TEFL Programs in Boston. The Boston Language Institute offers full-time and part-time teaching training programs: no previous teaching experience required; practical classroom experience before you leave; career guidance; certificate recognized internationally. **Dates:** Every month. **Costs:** $2,495. **Contact:** Yeny Kim, Program Coordinator, TEFL, The Boston Language Institute, 648 Beacon St., Boston, MA 02215; 617-262-3500 ext 228, fax 617-262-3595; tefl@boslang, [www.teflcertificate.com].

Venezuela

SUNY Cortland at the VEN-USA Institute. Students enroll at the VEN-USA Institute of International Studies and Modern Languages in Mérida, located in the heart of the Venezuelan Andes. Sessions include 10-week semester, 15-week semester, 2 6-week summer sessions or academic year. All levels of Spanish proficiency can be accommodated. Homestays. Latin American Studies; Venezuelan history, culture, and folklore. Most classes taught in Spanish with a limited number in English. Human services internships available to qualified students who are fluent in Spanish. **Dates:** Fall: 10-week semester late Sep-mid-Dec, 15-week semester late Aug-mid-Dec; spring: 10 week semester mid-Feb-end of Apr, 15-week semester early Jan-end of Apr; summer: session 1 late May-early Jul, session 2 early Jul-mid-Aug. **Costs:** Fall and spring 10-week semester $3,500, 15-week semester $4,400; summer $2,500 per 6-week session. Teacher's Institute $1,984 (includes tuition), SUNY tuition, insurance, airfare or spending money not included. **Contact:** Office of International Programs, Box 2000, SUNY Cortland, Cortland, NY 13045; 607-753-2209, fax 607-753-5989; koppl@cortland.edu, [www.studyabroad.com/suny/cortland].

West Africa

African Art and Culture in Mali. A positive yet realistic immersion in the culture and art of Mali. Students will have the unique opportunity to become familiar with traditional and modern Malian life and to apprentice with an artist, artisan, or musician in accordance with their own particular goals and interests. **Dates:** Jun-Aug. **Costs:** Contact office for details. **Contact:** Antioch Education Abroad, Antioch College, 795 Livermore St., Yellow Springs, OH 45387; 800-874-7986, fax 937-769-1019; aea@antioch-college.edu, [www.antioch-college.edu/aea].

Worldwide

Always Your Best Link, Language Link. Quality complete immersion Spanish language programs in Ecuado, Peru, Guatemala, Costa Rica, Mexico, and Spain. Academic credit available through U.S. accredited university. Excursions with included trips to Machu Picchu, Amazon jungle programs, beach programs, homestays, all ages, all levels, easy enrollment through our U.S. office, now in its 14th year of excellent service. **Dates:** Start any Monday, year around. **Costs:** Starting at $175 per week, tuition and homestay. **Contact:** Kay Rafool, Director, Language Link, P.O. Box 3006, Peoria, IL 61612; 800-552-2051 or 309-692-2961, fax 309-692-2926; info@langlink.com, [www.langlink.com].

American Int'l. Youth Student Exchange Program (AIYSEP). Nonprofit AIYSEP offers high school exchange programs for students in Europe, Australia, New Zealand, America, and many other countries. Area counselors are located in Europe, U.S., Australia, New Zealand, South America, Peru, Canada, and Japan. **Dates:** Year, semester, and summer programs. **Costs:** Year $3,995-$6,000, semester $3,495-$4,200, summer $1,900-$3,500. **Contact:** American International Youth Student Exchange, 200 Round Hill Rd., Tiburon, CA 94920; 800-347-7575 or 415-435-4049, 415-499-7669, fax 415-499-5651; AIYSEP@aol.com, [www.aiysep.org].

Boston Univ. International Programs. Offering internship and language/liberal arts, fine arts, archaeology, engineering, and tropical ecology programs in 40 locations on 6 continents and in 9 different languages. Course offerings range from intermediate-level language and liberal arts study through advanced-level, direct enrollment in local universities. Internship programs combine coursework with participation in local work life. Application materials: 2 references, transcript, essays, and academic approval. **Dates:** Fall, spring, and summer (length varies). **Costs:** $4,800-$17,311; application fee: $45. **Contact:** Boston Univ., International Programs, 232 Bay State Rd., 5th Fl., Boston, MA 02215; 617-353-9888, fax 617-353-5402; abroad@bu.edu, [www.bu.edu/abroad].

Travel Safety Information for Students

Council Travel has created a free pamphlet of safety travel tips for students abroad and their advisers. Request copies from: 617-218-2119; groups@counciltravel.com. Council also recommends that students consult the following web sites:

www.counciltravel.com. America's leading student travel organization web site has updated travel safety tips and airline information.

http://travel.state.gov. U.S. Dept. of State consular reports on all countries, travel warnings, info on getting or replacing U.S. passport.

www.passporthelp.com. Info on how to get a passport ASAP (also call 800-367-1818).

www.cdc.gov/travel. Center for Disease Control info on travel vaccinations required to visit a particular country and country information on outbreaks and epidemics.

www.faa.gov. FAA (Federal Aviation Administration).

www.xe.net. Currency exchange.

www.hiayh.org. Hostelling International.

lonelyplanet.com. Destination and health info, question and answer bulletin board.

www.travel.roughguides.com. Travel guidebook info.

www.timeout.com. Comprehensive city guides and entertainment listings.

www.smarterliving.com. Travel web site.

www.usitworld.com. Council Travel's worldwide partner.

www.istc.org. International Student/Teacher/Youth card web site (ISIC, ITIC, GO25).

CCIS. The College Consortium for International Studies (CCIS) is a nonprofit membership organization of over 120 2-year and 4-year U.S. colleges and universities. Member institutions offer semester, summer, and short-term study abroad opportunities for U.S. undergraduate students in 30 countries around the world. **Dates:** Call for details. **Costs:** Call for details. **Contact:** College Consortium for International Studies, 2000 P St., NW, Suite 503, Washington, DC 20036; 800-453-6956, fax 202-223-0999; info@ccisabroad.org, [www.ccisabroad.org].

Cooperative Center for Study Abroad. Study abroad programs in English-speaking countries such as Australia, Caribbean, England, Ireland, Kenya, New Zealand, and Scotland taught by faculty from consortium-member schools. Credit available. Eight-week internships available in London and Ireland. **Dates:** May-Mar. **Costs:** From $2,295-$6,595 includes air transportation, accommodations, and some meals. **Contact:** Dr. Michael A. Klembara, Executive Director, CCSA, Northern Kentucky Univ., Highland Heights, KY 41099; 859-572-6512, fax 859-572-6650; ccsa@nku.edu, [www.nku.edu/ccsa].

Council on Int'l. Education Exchange. With over 300 offices and 800 professionals world-wide, Council's main mission is to promote better cultural and global understanding. Through its work abroad and study abroad program for high school and university students, families, and educators. **Dates:** Vary. **Costs:** Vary. **Contact:** Council on Int'l. Education Exchange, 52 Poland St., London W1V 4JQ, England; 011-44-207-478-2000; infouk@councilexchanges.org, [www.councilexchanges.org].

ERDT/SHARE! Exchange Program. ERDT/ SHARE! provides American students, ages 16 to 18, opportunities for summer, semester, or academic year homestays/study abroad. Language proficiency, academic standing, maturity are criteria for selection. Students live with host families and, depending upon program selected, attend local school or language school. ERDT/ SHARE! Also provides opportunities for American families to host international high school exchange students. **Dates:** Vary with type of program selected and academic year dates. Student and host family applications are accepted year round. **Costs:** $1,500-$7,000 (depending on program), excluding transportation and personal expenses. **Contact:** Roger Riske, President, 475 Washington Blvd., Suite 220, Marina del Rey, CA 90292; 800-321-3738, 310-821-9977, fax 310-821-

9282; info@erdtshare.org, [www.erdtshare.org].

Friends World Program-Comparative Religion. A 9-month program in comparative religion and culture. Students study for three 10-week terms in Taiwan, India, and Israel. The field course is based on experiential approaches, emphasizing participation, observation, and involvement in local religious life. Culture's relation to religion and social change is emphasized. **Dates:** Early Sep-mid-May. **Costs:** $28,260 for year 2000-2001. Includes tuition, travel, room and board, fees and books. **Contact:** Admissions, Friends World Program, 239 Montauk Hwy., Southampton, NY 11968; 631-287-8474; fw@southampton.liunet.edu, [www.southampton.liu.edu/fw].

Global Campus. Select from a growing list of programs in Spain, Ecuador, England, France, India, Kenya, Mexico, Senegal, and Venezuela. Curriculum may include language, culture, area studies, international development, and much more with integrated classroom options. Internships are available for credit at many sites. Open to all students and professionals. **Dates:** Academic year, semester, quarter, and summer options. **Costs:** From $2,100-$17,325. Includes tuition, study abroad, registration fees, room and board, and excursions. **Contact:** Global Campus, Study Abroad, Univ. of Minnesota, 230 Heller Hall, 271 19th Ave. S, Minneapolis, MN 55455; 612-626-9000, fax 612-626-8009; UMabroad@umn.edu, [www.UMabroad.umn.edu].

Global Service Corps (GSC), a project of Earth Island Institute, creates opportunities for adult participants to live in Tanzania and Thailand homes while volunteering on health, education and environment community service and development projects. These service-learning programs emphasize grass-roots collaboration on the local level, mutual transfer of skills, and cross-cultural understanding. Our goals are to provide developing communities with the means to function more sustainably, and to widen the perspectives of participants as responsible global citizens. Project areas: HIV/AIDS prevention, health care, Buddhism immersion, environmental education, English language instruction and sustainable agriculture. Undergraduate and Graduate level credits qualifying for financial aid available. **Dates:** Year round. Contact GSC office or check the web site for specific starting dates **Costs:** Approx. $1,800-$2,000 for 2-4 week project trips: $595 per month for 2-6 month long-term extensions; $2,815-$3,145 for summer and semester college internships.

Includes extensive pre-departure preparation and in-country expenses (hotel and homestay room and board, orientation, training, project expenses, transportation, excursions). Airfare not included, discounted international airfare available. **Contact:** Global Service Corps., 300 Broadway, Suite 28, San Francisco, CA 94133; 415-788-3666 ext 128, fax 415-788-7324,; gsc@earthisland.org, [www.globalservicecorps.org].

High School Abroad. Programs provide an opportunity for long-term, in-depth immersion in another culture. Participants live with a host family and attend a local high school. Programs are available in Australia, France, Germany, Ireland, Japan, Netherlands, South Africa, Spain, and Sweden.

Dates: Semester and year programs start in Aug/Sep and Jan/Feb. **Costs:** Approx. $5,000-$7,000 for full year. **Contact:** Outbound Dept., Center for Cultural Interchange, 17 N. 2nd Ave., St. Charles, IL 60174; 888-ABROAD1, fax 630-377-2307; info@cci-exchange.com, [www.cci-exchange.com].

International Honors Program. Three different academic programs are offered by the International Honors Program in 2001-2002. Global Ecology is a 2-semester program of around-the-world study and travel to England, Tanzania, India, the Philippines, and Mexico with academic coursework in ecology, anthropology, economics, and environmental issues. Challenges of a Global Culture is a 1-semester program of study and travel with a regional concentration in Nepal and Tibet, with academic coursework in anthropology, history, and language. Cities in the 21st Century is a 1-semester program of study and travel to India, South Africa, and Brazil with academic coursework in urban studies, anthropology, sociology, economics, and political science.

Dates: Global Ecology: Sep 2001-May 2002 (deadline Mar 15); Challenges of a Global Culture: Aug-Dec 2001 (deadline Mar 15); Cities in the 21st Century: Jan-May 2002 (deadline Oct 2001). **Costs:** Global Ecology: $24,650 plus airfare; includes tuition, room and board. Challenges of a Global Culture or Cities in the 21st Century: $13,850 plus airfare, includes tuition, room and board. Estimated airfare for each program is $3,900. Financial aid is available. **Contact:** Joan Tiffany, Executive Director, International Honors Program, 19 Braddock Pk., Boston, MA 02116; 617-267-0026, fax 617-262-9299; info@ihp.edu, [www.ihp.edu].

International Student Exchange. Nacel Open Door is a nonprofit organization dedicated to promoting international understanding and language education. We believe it is essential for young people to develop a deeper awareness of their role as citizens of the world through direct experience in other cultures and languages, and we are committed to providing accessible and affordable programs.

Dates: Jun, Jul, and Aug. Fall semester and academic year. **Costs:** From $1,855 including roundtrip international airfare and comprehensive medical insurance. **Contact:** Programs Abroad Director, Nacel Open Door, Inc., 3410 Federal Drive, Suite 101, St. Paul, MN 55122; 800-622-3553, 651-686-0080, fax 651-686-9601; mhindes@nacelopendoor.org, [www.nacelopendoor.org].

InterStudy Programs. InterStudy offers integrated study abroad opportunities for undergraduate students in Ireland, England, Scotland, Wales, Belgium, South Africa, and the tropical island of Mauritius. Students are enrolles for a semester or a year, taking credit-rated courses at selected universities. All InterStudy students have guaranteed housing.

Dates: Fall and spring or full year. **Costs:** Programs start at $7,500. Contact organization for individual program fees. **Contact:** InterStudy, 63 Edward St., Medford, MA 02155; 800-663-1999 or 781-391-0991, fax 781-391-7463.

Marist International Internships. Internship and study abroad programs in Australia, England, Ireland, Italy, and Spain. Programs combine internships and course work at host institutions. Homestays are available at select sites.

Dates: Fall and spring semesters and full academic year. **Costs:** Average program fee is $11,500. **Contact:** Carol Toufali, Marist College, 3399 North Rd., Poughkeepsie, NY 12601; 845-575-3330, fax 845-575-3294; international@marist.edu, [www.marist.edu/international].

NYU Study Abroad. Fall, spring, summer study abroad programs in Buenos Aires, Florence, London, Madrid, Paris, and Prague (many additional locations in summer). Courses in English or in native language of host country. Scholarships available to NYU and visiting students based on financial need and merit.

Dates: Vary by site. **Costs:** Fall or spring semester $12,168 for tuition, fees, and numerous excursions and local events (2000-2001 rates). Room and board charges vary by site and type of housing selected. Summer fees vary by site and program. **Contact:** Study Abroad Admissions, New York Univ., 7 E. 12th St., 6th Fl., New York, NY 10003-4475; 212-998-4433, fax 212-995-4103; studyabroad@nyu.edu, [www.nyu.edu/abroad/go].

Overseas Studies at Univ. of Haifa. The Dept. of Overseas Studies at the Univ. of Haifa, Israel offers a wide variety of fully accredited courses for a year, semester, or summer in the humanities, arts and social sciences. The program features a kibbutz-university program, a psychology honors program, internships, the Summer Hebrew Ulpan and other summer courses. **Dates:** Contact for details. **Costs:** $5,760 per semester, $9,140 per year. Includes tuition fee, housing, and activities. **Contact:** Dept. of Overseas Studies, Univ. of Haifa, Haifa 31905, Israel; 011-972-4-8240766, fax 011-972-4-8240391; overseas@research.haifa.ac.il, [www.haifa.ac.il].

PAX Abroad. Offers opportunities for high school students; homestay programs in Ecuador, France, Germany, and Spain for 1 semester or full year. Some custom academic programs available. Summer adventures to Australia, Ecuador, Spain, and Brazil for soccer. **Dates:** Semester or full year. Summer. **Costs:** Varies. **Contact:** PAX Abroad, PAX-Program of Academic Exchange, 71 Arch St., Greenwich, CT 06830; 800-555-6211, fax 203-629-0486; academicexchange@pax.org, [www.pax.org].

Penn Summer Abroad. Academic programs granting Univ. of Pennsylvania credits. Courses focusing on language, culture, economics, theater, anthropology, cinema, art history, traditional folk medicine, performing arts, and religion. Several programs offer homestays, some offer internships. **Dates:** Mid-May-late Aug (2-8 weeks). **Costs:** Tuition: $1,695 per course. Living costs vary. **Contact:** Elizabeth Sachs, Penn Summer Abroad, College of General Studies, Univ. of Pennsylvania, 3440 Market St., Suite 100, Philadelphia, PA 19104-3335; 215-898-5738, fax 215-573-2053; summerabroad@sas.upenn.edu, [www.sas.upenn.edu/CGS].

School for International Training. The NEASSC accredited college of World Learning, School for International Training (SIT) is a global leader in international and intercultural education, offering the following graduate degrees: MA in Teaching (academic year and summer formats), MA in Intercultural Service, Leadership, and Management, MA in Intercultural Service, MA in Interational Education, MA in Intercultural Relations, MA in Sustainable Development, MA in Conflict Transformation, and a MS in Organizational Management. Based on the powerful integration of theory and practice, all SIT programs combine classroom and field-based learning. SIT's masters degrees are designed to produce learned practitioners who have a commanding knowledge of the theoretical bases of their professions, possess essential skill, honed and tested through practice, and have a solid awareness of themselves—their capabilities, values, and ethics. **Dates:** Academic year: Sep-May. Summer MAT program, 2 summers from mid-Jun-Aug, with an academic year internship in between. **Costs:** Tuition from $19,500-$27,000. **Contact:** Admissions, School for International Training, P.O. Box 676, Kipling Rd., Brattleboro, VT 05302; 800-336-1616 or 802-257-7751, fax 802-258-3500; admissions@sit.edu, [www.sit.edu].

Service Learning Programs. The International Partnership for Service-Learning, founded in 1982, is an incorporated not-for-profit organization serving colleges, universities, service agencies, and related organizations around the world by fostering programs that link community service and academic study. Countries include: Czech Republic, Ecuador, England, France, Jamaica, U.S., Russia, Israel, India, Mexico, Philippines, and Scotland. Students gain hands-on experience in an international community service agency. We also offer a Master's degree in International Service. **Dates:** Summer, semester, year, or intersession. **Costs:** Vary. **Contact:** The International Partnership for Service-Learning, 815 2nd Ave., Suite 315, New York, NY 10017; 212-986-0989, fax 212-986-5039; pslny@aol.com, [www.ipsl.org].

SIT Study Abroad. This program challenges college and university students to put knowledge into practice as they learn graduate credits in one of 57 interdisciplinary programs in over 50 countries around the world. Through a rigorous integration of classroom and field-based learning, students develop a profound understanding of issues of critical global importance, such as conflict transformation, the environment, and the arts and social change. To date over 21,000 students have chosen to study abroad with SIT. **Dates:** Fall and spring semesters (vary). **Costs:** From $10,600-$13,700. Includes room and board, tuition, international transport, health and accident insurance, all field trips and related fares, and other direct program expenses.

Contact: Admissions SIT Study Abroad, SIT, P.O. Box 676, Kipling Rd., Brattleboro, VT 05302; 888-272-7881, 802-257-7751, fax 802-258-3296; admissions@sit.edu, [www.sit.edu].

Summer Seminars, Internships, Volunteering. Visit 1 to 4 cities. Topics include International Business and Economics, Comparative Education, Historical Literature, Social Service Systems, and other crosscultural studies. Emphasis on personal interaction between students and European professionals and providing a holistic cultural experience. Two- to 5-week programs. Three to 6 credit hours—undergraduate, graduate, or audit basis—through the Univ. of Missouri-Kansas City.

Dates: Early summer. **Costs:** Approx. $2,000 (does not include airfare). **Contact:** People to People International, Collegiate and Professional Studies Abroad, 501 E. Armour Blvd., Kansas City, MO 64109-2200; 816-531-4701, fax 816-561-7502; internships@ptpi.org, [www.ptpi.org/studyabroad].

SUNY Brockport Study Abroad. Semester, year, and summer study programs in Costa Rica, Mexico, France, and Vietnam. SUNY Brockport's language programs offer the opportunity to study abroad while fully immersing oneself into the language and culture of the country. Programs provide enrollment and immersion opportunities at foreign universities, with transcripts provided by a U.S. accredited 4-year academic institution.

Dates: Vary by program: call or visit web site. **Costs:** Vary by program: call or visit web site. **Contact:** Office of International Education, SUNY College at Brockport, 350 New Campus Dr., Brockport, NY 14420; 800-298-7869, fax 716-637-3218; overseas@brockport.edu, [www.brockport.edu/studyabroad].

SUNY Oswego Study Abroad. Programs in Australia, China, Costa Rica, Czech Republic, France, Germany, Hungary, Ireland, Italy, Japan, Mexico, Native America, New Zealand, Puerto Rico, Slovakia, Spain, and U.K. Courses available in all academic disciplines. Internships and student-teaching at select sites.

Dates: Approx. fall, spring, summer, and winter session. **Costs:** Vary by program. **Contact:** SUNY Oswego, Office of Int'l. Education, 102 Rich Hall, Oswego, NY 13126; 888-467-9346, 315-341-2477; intled@oswego.edu, [www.studyabroad.com/suny/oswego/oswegohome.htm].

Thunderbird. Thunderbird, The American Graduate School of International Management, offers students an opportunity to gain knowledge and experience in the global business environment through various programs located around the globe that emphasize exposure to other cultures, political and economic systems and language.

Dates: Spring, summer, fall, and winter, in addition to 2-week mini-terms (interims) throughout the year. **Costs:** Depends upon the number of courses taken. **Contact:** Thunderbird Overseas Programs, 15249 North 59th Ave., Glendale, AZ 85306; 602-978-7252, fax 602-978-7419; overseas@t-bird.edu, [www.t-bird.edu/overseas].

Trent International. Trent Univ.'s international study and exchange programs provides students with an opportunity to spend an academic study year abroad. Students take regular courses and examinations and credits are counted toward their undergraduate degree. Available in most disciplines. Orientation and special services for visiting students.

Dates: Full academic year, some semester programs available. Sep-Dec and Jan-Apr. **Costs:** Differs according to program but generally includes Trent's tuition and often residence. **Contact:** Cynthia Bennett Awe, Int'l. Programs and Services Manager, Trent Univ., Peterborough, ON, K9J 7B8, Canada; fax 705-748-1626; cawe@trentu.ca.

Visions. Visions community service summer programs for teenagers combine community service, outdoor adventure and exploration, intercultural activities at sites in Peru, Alaska, Montana, South Carolina Sea Islands, Australia, and 5 Caribbean islands. Co-ed groups of 24 students and 6 staff live in cross-cultural host communities for up to 4 weeks.

Dates: Late Jun-late Jul, first weeks of Aug; 4-week or 3-week sessions. **Costs:** $2,400-$3,500 depending on program site and length. **Contact:** Joanne Pinaire, Visions, P.O. Box 220, Newport, PA 17074; 717-567-7313, 800-813-9283, fax 717-567-7853; visions@pa.net, [www.visions-adventure.org].

TEN

VOLUNTEERING & INTERNSHIPS
BEST RESOURCES AND PROGRAMS

Regardless of your background or area of interest, there are volunteer options to suit your needs. Becoming part of this global movement will forever change your perspective on travel and on life. A listing of best volunteer programs starts on page 159. A listing of best internship programs starts on 177. Programs based in more than one country are listed under "Worldwide."

Volunteer Organizations and Publications

Alternatives to the Peace Corps: A Directory of Third World and U.S. Volunteer Opportunities by Joan Powell. 2001. 128 pp. $9.95 plus s/h from Food First Books; foodfirst@foodfirst.org, [www.foodfirst.org]. Order online or from LPC Group, 1436 Randolph St., Chicago, IL 60607; 800-243-0138. Thoroughly researched guide to voluntary service, study, and alternative travel overseas and in the U.S. with organizations which "address the political and economic causes of poverty."

Archaeological Fieldwork Opportunities Handbook compiled by Margo Muhl Davis. 2000. 154 pp. $15 ($12 members of AIA) plus $4 s/h from Kendall/Hunt Publishing Co., Order Dept., 4050 Westmark Dr., Dubuque, IA 52002; 800-228-0810. A comprehensive list compiled by the Archaeological Institute of America of almost 300 archaeological fieldschools, volunteer positions, and programs throughout the world with openings for volunteers, students, and staff. AIA also publishes Archaeology magazine, which lists volunteer opportunities in the Old World (Mar/Apr) and the New World (May/Jun). For membership in AIA or subscriptions, call 617-353-9361 or fax 617-353-6550.

Archaeology Abroad, 31-34 Gordon Square, London WC1H 0PY, U.K.; archabroad@ucl.ac.uk, [www.britarch.ac.uk/archabroad/index.html]. Two bulletins each year in April and November. Lists worldwide projects for volunteers and professionals.

CCIVS Publications Lists. Available from: Coordinating Committee for International Voluntary Service (CCIVS), c/o UNESCO, 1 rue Miollis, 75732 Paris, Cedex 15, France; 011-33-1-45-68-49-36, fax 011-33-42-73-05-21; ccivs@unesco.org, [www.unesco.org/ccivs]. (Publications include The Volunteer's Handbook.) Information on civilian and youth service worldwide. Price of one publication is 7 International Reply Coupons.

Global Work: InterAction's Guide to Volunteer, Internship and Fellowship Opportunities. 95 pp. (oversize). $10 plus $4 s/h from Interaction, Publications Dept., 1717 Massachusetts Ave., NW, Suite 801, Washington, DC 20036; 202-667-8227, fax 202-667-8236; publicationsia@ **interaction.org, [www.interaction.org].** Describes opportunities in U.S. and abroad with over 70 major organizations working in international relief and development. Most require professional skills though some are open to students. Indexes for location and type of work.

Green Volunteers: The World Guide to Voluntary Work in Nature Conservation edited by Fabio Ausenda. 1999. Vacation Work (U.K.). Available for $19.95 from Seven Hills. Information on conservation organizations that accept volunteers and how to apply.

How to Live Your Dream of Volunteering Overseas by Joseph Collins, Stefano DeZerega, and Zahara Heckscher. 2002. 550. $19.95. Penguin-Putnam; [www.volunteeroverseas.org]. New book provides a comprehensive, authoritative overview of volunteering abroad, and includes in-depth profiles of 65 volunteer placement organizations and evaluations to help volunteers assess whether the organization is right for them.

How to Serve and Learn Effectively: Students Tell Students by Howard Berry and Linda A. Chisholm. 1992. 77 pp. $7 from Partnership for Service Learning, 815 2nd Ave., Suite 315, New York, NY 10017; 212-986-0989, fax 212-986-5039; pslny@aol.com, [www.ipsl.org]. Reality-testing and exploration of motivations for students considering volunteering overseas. Not a directory of opportunities.

International Directory of Voluntary Work by Louise Whetter and Victoria Pybus. 2000. 319 pp. Vacation Work (U.K.). $15.95 from Peterson's. Directory of over 700 agencies offering volunteer jobs and how to apply. Most comprehensive listing of volunteer opportunities in Britain and Europe of any directory.

International Volunteer Programs Association (IVPA). A professional association for international volunteer programs, IVPA sets standards for programs and lists those adhering to them on its web site in a searchable database at [www.volunteerinternational.org].

International Volunteer Projects (Council). Free brochure from Council Exchanges, 633 3rd Ave., 20th Fl., New York, NY 10017; 888-COUNCIL, fax 212-822-2649; info@councilexchanges.org, [www.councilexchanges.org/vol]. Describes over 600 short-term summer voluntary service options available through Council in over 25 countries of Europe, Africa, and North America.

International Workcamp Directory: A Listing of Hundreds of Volunteer Projects Located in 50 Countries (SCI-IVS). Updated each Apr. $5 postpaid (or free on their web site) from SCI-International Voluntary Service, 814 NE 40th St., Seattle, WA 98105; 206-545-6585; sciinfo@sci-ivs.org, [www.sci-ivs.org]. Describes

short-term volunteer options in Europe, Africa, Asia, and North America available through SCI-IVS. Web site has links to many other volunteer organizations.

International Workcamper. Free brochure available from Volunteers for Peace (VFP), International Workcamps, 1034 Tiffany Rd., Belmont, VT 05730-0202; 802-259-2759, fax 802-259-2922; vfp@vfp.org, [www.vfp.org]. The VFP International Workcamp Directory (280 pp.), available each Apr for $20 from VFP (or free on their web site), describes over 2,000 short-term voluntary service placements in over 70 countries available through VFP for the summer and fall of the year of publication.

Just Act - Working For Global Justice: A Directory of Progressive Organizations. Just Act: Youth Action for Global Justice, 333 Valencia St., #101, San Francisco, CA 94110; 415-431-4204, fax 415-431-5953; info@justact.org, [www.justact.org]. Includes information on global justice organizations working in the U.S. and internationally ($8). Also available: Pros and Cons of the Peace Corps: articles and interviews with former Peace Corps volunteers ($7).

Kibbutz Volunteer by Victoria Pybus. 2000. 223 pp. Vacation Work. $17.95 from Seven Hills. The most up-to-date and comprehensive resource on volunteering in Israel.

Making a Difference: College Volunteers Abroad, and Making a Difference: American Volunteers Abroad by Bob Gilner. 2000. $39.95 (individuals) or $79.95 (institutions) for each video from: Bob Gilner Productions, P.O. Box 596, Boulder Creek CA 95006; fax 831-338-7381; bgliner@hotmail.com, [www.docmakeronline.com/VolunteersAbroad.html]. Outstanding hour-long videos, made onsite by an award-winning filmmaker, provide first-hand insight into the rewards and realities of volunteering abroad through programs offered by established U.S.-based organizations. College Volunteers Abroad looks at programs intended for college students, American Volunteers Abroad for adult volunteers.

Nepal Volunteer Handbook. 2001. $10 hard copy from Scott Dimetrosky (free for members), Himalayan Explorers Club, P.O. Box 3665, Boulder, CO 80307-3665; 303-998-0101, fax 303-998-1007; info@hec.org, [www.hec.org]. Publication by nonprofit organization offers potential volunteers everything they will need to know about volunteering in Nepal, including a personal skills assessment, background on the

CHOOSING A PLACEMENT ORGANIZATION

PAST VOLUNTEERS OFFER ADVICE

By Joseph Collins, Stefano DeZerega, and
Zahara J. Heckscher

The number of international volunteer programs is growing, and it can be difficult to make your way through all the brochures and web sites describing the myriad of options. But it is worth taking the time to carefully consider the various programs available. Many past volunteers offer the following advice: "Don't just select the first program that comes along, as I did. Investigate the different options." The following tips will help you heed their advice and make an informed decision about which international volunteer program is right for you.

1. **Assess your interests.** Before you start exploring different volunteer options, take the time to explore your own interests. Consider the major issues in choosing a program such as where you want to go and for how long, the type of work you want to do, your living situation, and whether you want a rural or urban placement.

2. **Think about your special needs and aspirations.** Consider the various components of your identity—including age, ability, race, and sexual orientation—and identify the factors that are most important to you. Also think about your vision of volunteering. How much staff support do you need? What are you looking for in your daily work environment? Do you want to volunteer alone or in a group?

3. **Create a vision.** List the characteristics you are looking for in an organization. Include logistics such as costs and length of volunteer stay as well as more philosophical issues such as the organization's approach to development. Since you probably won't find an organization that matches your vision perfectly, circle the qualities that are most important to you.

4. **Refer to the listing of organizations.** For example, if your goal is to work in Africa for a year or more in the educational field, create your own list of groups that have all at your specified characteristics. See www.volunteerinternational.org web site for a searchable database of programs.

5. **Begin your research.** Conduct preliminary research by visiting the organizations' web sites. Also try a general web search to find "unofficial" information.

6. **Narrow your list.** Figure out the top two to four organizations. If you don't find any groups that meet your specifications, you may want to broaden your search by focusing on one or two primary factors to judge organizations.

7. **Create a list of questions.** Based on any concerns you have from the web sites, your personal values, and any special needs, create a list of questions for staff and or alumni.

8. **Contact the organization to ask your questions.** These days, email may be the best way to communicate. Ask your questions and request contact information for program alumni as well as information regarding the application process. Verify that the organizations still operate in the country where you want to go, and note any changes in fees or programs.

9. Contact alumni. Ask them hard questions about their experiences and try to get contact information for people who they volunteered with who might be more critical of the program than they are.

10. Choose. Select the organization that matches your interests and aspirations most closely and begin the application process.

11. Get it in writing. No matter how nice the people you talk to are, get a written document explaining fees, benefits, insurance issues, and refund policies.

history of foreign assistance in Nepal, tips for ensuring a worthwhile experience, and information on over 50 volunteer leads.

The Peace Corps and More: 175 Ways to Work, Study, and Travel at Home and Abroad by Medea Benjamin and Miya Rodolfo-Sioson. 1997 (next edition 2002). 126 pp. $8.95 from Global Exchange.

Peace Corps Information Packet. The Peace Corps, 1111 20th St., NW, Rm. 8436, Washington, DC 20526; 800-424-8580; [www.peacecorps.gov]. Peace Corps seeks individuals to serve as volunteers in overseas communities in the areas of education, small business development, the environment, health, youth development, and agriculture. Tour is 27 months with $6,075 readjustment allowance upon completion of service. Must be U.S. citizen, over 18, in good health, and have education and/or experience relative to programs.

Response: Volunteer Opportunities Directory of Catholic Network of Volunteer Service. 2001 (revised annually). 100 pp. Free (donations accepted) from CNVS, 4121 Harewood Rd., NE, Washington, DC 20017; 800-543-5046 or 202-529-1100, fax 202-526-1094; volunteer@cnvs.org. Also online at [www.cnvs.org]. Directory of lay mission opportunities in the U.S. and abroad.

South American Explorers Volunteer Opportunities Information Packet. Latest update: May 2001. 50 pp (oversize packet, not a book). Updated 3-4 times a year. $6 for non-members, $ 4.50 for members, postpaid from South American Explorers, 126 Indian Creek Rd., Ithaca, NY 14850; [www.samexplo.org]. Volunteer possibilities located mainly in Ecuador, Peru, and Bolivia, some in Brazil, Chile, and Costa Rica, with local and U.S.-based organizations. Divided into categories of environment, education, arts and culture, agriculture, human rights, general, working with children, and working with women.

So, You Want to Join the Peace Corps . . . What to Know Before You Go by Dillon Banerjee. 2000. 178 pp. $12.95 from Ten Speed Press, P.O. Box 7123, Berkley CA 94707; 800-841-BOOK or 510-559-1600; [www.tenspeed.com]. Comprehensive information in a question and answer format on topics ranging from applying and training to returning home. A must-read for anyone considering Peace Corps and valuable for others considering volunteering abroad.

Volunteer Vacations: Short-Term Adventures That Will Benefit You and Others by Bill McMillon. 1999. 390 pp. $16.95 from Chicago Review Press, 814 N. Franklin St., Chicago, IL 60610; 312-337-0747. Describes more than 250 organizations sponsoring weekend to- 6-week projects in the U.S. and abroad.

Volunteer Programs

Australia

Conservation Volunteers Australia. CVA is a national, nonprofit, nonpolitical organization undertaking practical conservation projects including tree planting, seed collection, flora/fauna surveys, endangered species projects, coastal restoration, habitat protection, track construction, and weed eradication. Volunteers work in teams of 6-10; all training is provided.

Dates: Year round in all states and territories; choose any Friday throughout the year as starting date. **Costs:** Six-week Conservation Experience Package: AUS$966 includes all food, accommodations, and project-related transport within Australia. **Contact:** CVA, P.O. Box 423, Ballarat, Victoria 3353, Australia (please include IRC); 011-61-3-5333-1483, fax 011-61-3-5333-2166; info@conservationvolunteers.com.au, [www.conservationvolunteers.com.au].

Willing Workers on Organic Farms (WWOOFING). Learn organic growing while living with a host family. Fourteen hundred hosts in Australia or travel the world with over 600 hosts worldwide, on every continent, where you work in exchange for food and board.

Dates: Year round. **Costs:** AUS$45 single, AUS$50 double (add $5 for postage outside of Australia). **Contact:** WWOOF Australia, Buchan, Victoria 3885, Australia; 011-61-3-5155-0218, fax 011-61-3-5155-0342; wwoof@wwoof.com.au, [www.wwoof.com.au].

Canada

WWOOF-Canada (Willing Workers on Organic Farms). In exchange for your help (4-6 hours per day, 5-5 1/2 days per week) you receive accommodations, meals, and an interesting and valuable experience. Host farms/homesteads in every region of Canada, East to West . . . over 400 hosts.

Dates: Year round. Most opportunities early spring to late fall. **Costs:** $30 per person includes membership plus 2 International Postal Coupons. **Contact:** WWOOF-Canada, RR 2, S. 18, C. 9 Nelson, BC, V1L 5P5, Canada; 250-354-4417; wwoofcan@uniserve.com, [www.members.tripod.com/~wwoof].

Caribbean

Historic Preservation. CVE recruits volunteers to work on historic preservation projects throughout the Caribbean. We work with local agencies: national trusts, museums, and historical societies.

Dates: One-week trips throughout year: Dominica Feb 3-10, Nevis Slave Research Mar 17-27, Virgin Gorda Mar 31-Apr 7, Nepal Sep. **Costs:** $500-$1,000 per week. **Contact:** CVE, Box 388, Corning, NY 14830; 607-962-7846; ahershcve@aol.com, [www.cvexp.org].

Central America

Cultural Program in Belize. Belize has a variety of cultures living side by side and intermingling, yet keeping their individual identities (Kriol, Spanish, Garifuna, Mayan, Chinese, Lebanese, British, and more). Cultures change with each new generation. Program participants observe the current lifestyles and trends as well as generation perspectives of change within the cultures.

Dates: Year round, 3-week sessions. **Costs:** $499. **Contact:** Ms. Mary Kay Sweet, Cornerstone Foundation, 9 Blancaneaux St., San Ignacio, Cayo District, Belize, Central America; 011-501-92-2373; sweetmaryk@btl.net, [www.peacecorner.org].

Sea Turtle Nesting Protection. Volunteers work with biologists to collect important information on nesting population. Volunteers count and tag turtles, learn about sea turtle conservation and biology, and visit nearby forests and local communities.

Dates: Summer and fall. **Costs:** Approx. $1,000 per week. **Contact:** Randall Arauz, Sea Turtle Restoration Project, P.O. Box 400, Forest Knolls, CA 94933; 506-236-6017, fax 506-235-0836; rarauz@sol.racsa.co.cr.

Central and Eastern Europe

Bridges for Education, Inc. Bridges for Education sends volunteer teachers to teach conversational English in summer. Three weeks teaching, 1 week travel. Educated adults (including families) and college students pay roundtrip airfare and BFE administrative expenses. Since 1984 about 750 teachers to 8 countries, serving 7,000 students from 27 countries with Ministry of Ed, UNESCO.

Dates: Summer, Jul, and Aug. **Costs:** Approx. $2,000, depending on departure and destination points. **Contact:** Margaret Dodge, Applications Coordinator 8912 Garlinghouse Rd., Naples, NY 14512; 716-534-9344; mdodge@frontiernet.com, [www.bridges4edu.org].

Central European Teaching Program. English conversation teachers urgently needed! Provide an essential service to public schools in Central Europe by teaching English (or German, French, Literature, or History) in Hungary, Poland, Romania, and other countries. No foreign language skills required. Extensive support plus free housing, health insurance, and local salary provided.

Dates: Sep-Jun or Jan-Jun. **Costs:** Placement fee: $2,000. **Contact:** Amy Berigtold, CETP, Beloit College, Box 242, 700 College St., Beloit, WI 53511; 608-363-2619; cetp@beloit.edu, [www.beloit.edu/~cetp].

Costa Rica

COSI (Costa Rica Spanish Institute). COSI offers high quality instruction with a very professional and organized staff. We provide the unique possibility of taking Spanish classes in San José and at Manuel Antonio National Park (beach and rainforest).

Dates: Year round. **Costs:** Prices start at $315 per week including 20 hours of instruction in mini groups of a maximum of 5 students, books, homestay, cultural activities, access to email, airport pickup. **Contact:** COSI, P.O. Box 1366-2050, San Pedro, San José, Costa Rica; 011-506-234-1001, fax 011-506-253-2117; office@cosi.co.cr, [www.cosi.co.cr].

Learn Spanish While Volunteering. Assist with the training of Costa Rican public school teachers in ESL and computers. Assist local health clinic, social service agencies, and environmental projects. Enjoy learning Spanish in the morning, volunteer work in the afternoon/evening. Spanish classes of 2-4 students plus group learning activities; conversations with middle class homestay families (1 student or couple per family). Homestays and most volunteer projects are in a small town near the capital, San José.

Dates: Year round, all levels. Classes begin every Monday (except Mar 25-29 and Dec 14-Jan 5), volunteer program is continuous. **Costs:** $345 per week for 26 hours of classes and group activities including Costa Rican dance and cooking classes. Includes tuition, meals, homestay, laundry, all materials, weekly 3-hour cultural tour, and airport transportation. $25 one-time registration fee. **Contact:** Susan Shores, Registrar, Latin American Language Center, PMB 123, 7485 Rush River Dr., Suite 710, Sacramento, CA 95831-5260; 916-447-0938, fax 916-428-9542; lalc@madre.com, [www.madre.com/~lalc].

WORK FOR PEACE
WORKCAMPS OFFER VOLUNTEERS AN INEXPENSIVE ALTERNATIVE

By April Thompson

For good-hearted paupers, workcamps offer an attractive alternative to volunteer projects requiring large amounts of time and money. "The typical 'Third World program' covers everything from inoculations to airfare, but it can cost as much as $4,000 for a month-long program," says Peter Coldwell, founder of Volunteers for Peace (VFP), in Belmont, VT. The largest of three U.S. organizations linking volunteers to workcamps, WFP has placed over 10,000 Americans abroad since 1982.

VFP's small program fee of $175 to $300 per camp covers organizational expenses. "I still can't believe that for $175 I lived, ate, played, and worked in a remote village in central France in the heart of a valley summer," said Angela Kolter, a former VFP volunteer.

Worldwide, roughly 150 organizations coordinate more than 2,200 projects. Each group places volunteers abroad in exchange for receiving foreign volunteers into its domestic programs. By virtue of a body-for-body swap, money never needs to change hands between groups. Any local organization—be it a church, arts group, or state park branch—can coordinate a camp to help with a community project. The local host group provides everything from tools to leaders, often with financial support from the community and government.

The work varies widely from site to site. A group may excavate a medieval Jewish necropolis in Spain, plant mango trees in Thailand, or set up a summer music festival in Norway. Projects often involve the environment, arts, social services, archeology, construction, and historic preservation. Volunteers may sleep in a school, church, private home, community center, or even a tent. Some groups cook and clean for themselves; others eat meals donated by a local family or restaurant. Most camps arrange evening and weekend excursions to local attractions, whether a city cultural tour or a trip to a national park.

Workcamps are for a mature audience only, Coldwell cautions. Volunteers must make their own travel arrangements and inform themselves about their host countries. Because camp conditions vary so widely, volunteers must come with an open mind as well as an open heart.

"None of us realized we would be giving 100 percent for 14 hours a day, yet we loved it," said Sandy Stefanowicz, who volunteered with a children's program in Ireland.

Work Not War

Workcamps originated with Pierre Ceresole, a Swiss pacifist and Quaker. In 1920 Ceresole led a small international team in reconstructing a French village destroyed during World War I. He hoped that such projects would provide an alternative to military service.

Ceresole's efforts evolved into Service Civil International (SCI), a volunteer service organization that now has 33 branches worldwide (sidebar). SCI's volunteer-run U.S. branch sends about 50 Americans abroad each year, according to Traudi Krausser, volunteer coordinator.

Workcamps are well established in Western Europe, where service projects have continued since Ceresole's postwar effort. The region now is saturated with workcamps—several hundred in Germany alone. European camps often recruit unemployed youth to help organize projects, Krausser said.

In the 1980s VFP concentrated on exchanges across the Iron Curtain. Today, not only Eastern and Central Europe but developing nations in Asia, Africa, and Latin America abound with new projects, according to Coldwell. Several countries hosting camps, such as Azerbaijan, Israel, and Northern Ireland, face political turmoil that can lead to violence. Volunteers in these areas sign up at their own risk.

"We rely on information from our partners. If a country's residents feel an area is safe, that's what we tell our volunteers," explained Coldwell.

"Here was this place so devastated and destroyed and yet the people were the most beautiful I ever met," said Hau Truong, a volunteer in Bosnia. "They seemed more real to me, unspoiled by the things we take for granted in the West."

A Transforming Experience

Ultimately, volunteers get back much more than the time and tiny amount of money they give. By working, living, and playing with people from a variety of countries and cultures, volunteers transcend a country's tourist facade and transform their own sense of the world.

"People cared enough to travel around the world to help a small town called Allemont," said Patrick Nolen of his camp in France. "Through our experiences, we created a magic that penetrated the boundaries not only of our minds but also our countries."

Molli Grant, who volunteered in the Czech Republic, summed it up: "When representatives from 10 different countries get together and hold hands and pitchforks for two weeks, I call that peace. Mission accomplished."

Ecuador

Academia Latinoamericana. Proud to be the friendliest Spanish school you have ever known. Family owned and operated. The program offers language study at 9 levels, for complete beginners through advanced. Experienced staff, native Ecuadorians. Carefully selected host families within walking distance of school. Exclusive "Cloud Forest and Galápagos" extension program, volunteer program. U.S. college credit available.

Dates: Year round. **Costs:** $255 per week. Includes 20 hours of lessons, 7 days with host family, 2 meals per day, transfer, services at the school, and teaching material. **Contact:** Suzanne S. Bell, Admissions Director, USA/International, 640 East 3990 South, Suite E, Salt Lake City, UT, 84107; 801-268-4608, fax 801-265-9156;; ecuador@access.net.ec, [www.latinoschools.com].

El Salvador

CRISPAZ. Offers 3 programs: 1) Volunteer program is designed for individuals who wish to spend a minimum of 1 year living and working in a marginalized urban or rural community. Volunteers donate their time, skills, and interests as they work alongside Salvadorans in areas such as literacy, health care, community organization, education, agriculture, appropriate technology, youth work, etc. 2) El Salvador Encounters are 7 to 10 days long and offer the opportunity to explore a different reality and build relationships with people. 3) The Summer Internship Program is designed to provide an intensive learning and service experience in a poor community in El Salvador. Homestays with Salvadoran families.

Dates: Ongoing programs. Encounters are generally facilited 10-12 times per year. **Costs:** $70 per day per person includes in-country travel, accommodations, and meals. Airfare not included. Long term volunteers responsible for living expenses, generally through sponsorship by community or organization, and airfare. A small stipend is provided to volunteer upon re-entry. Health insurance included. CRISPAZ can faciliate fundraising for volunteer placement. **Contact:** CRISPAZ, Stan de Voogd or Jennifer Collins, 319 Camden, San Antonio, TX 78215; 210-222-2018, fax 210-226-9119; crispaz@igc.apc.org, [www.crispaz.org].

Europe

World PULSE Young Ambassadors. World PULSE is a scholarship-based international volunteer program for young adults in the San Francisco Bay Area. Participants do volunteer work and attend workshops in the Bay Area from November-June. In the summer, they travel abroad to join peers from around the world for 2-3 weeks on a volunteer 'workcamp.'

Dates: November to August. **Costs:** $350-$500 World PULSE sponsors the rest. **Contact:** Bettina Mok, Director World PULSE, 663 13th St., Oakland, CA 94612; 510-451-2995, fax 510-451-2996; info@worldpulse.org, [www.worldpulse.org].

France

Archaeological Excavations. Excavations, drawing, mapping in a medieval town.

Dates: Jul-Sep. **Costs:** Contact organization for details. **Contact:** Service Archaeologique de Douai, 191 rue Saint Albin, F59500 Douai, France; 011-33-3-2771-3890, fax 011-33-3-2771-383; arkeos@wanadoo.fr.

Restoration of Medieval Buildings. Volunteers restore and maintain medieval buildings and sites, including 2 fortified castles at Ottrott, Alsace, destined as cultural and recreational centers. We provide participants with both cultural enrichment and physical exercise.

Dates: Jul, Aug, Aug (1999). **Costs:** Approx. FF550 (1999). **Contact:** Chantiers d'Études Médiévales, 4 rue du Tonnelet Rouge, 67000 Strasbourg, France; 011-33-88-37-17-20; libertysurf.fr, [http://perso.libertysurf.fr/castrum].

Israel

Kibbutz Programs: Volunteer, Ulpan (Work and Study Program). Kibbutz Volunteers live and work on a kibbutz in Israel. Work can vary: agriculture, services, education, or industry. The volunteer program is for 2-6 months. Ulpan students live on kibbutz for 5 months where they work 3 days and study Hebrew 3 days a week. The program offers trips and tours in Israel as well as social and educational activities. It is a great way to explore your Jewish heritage and get connected with your Jewish roots. Kibbutzes are located throughout Israel.

Dates: Ulpan: 5 months, starting every month. Volunteers live and work-full week on Kibbutz in return for room and board. Volunteer: minimum 2 months, all year. **Costs:** Ulpan: $250 registration fee, $600 program fee and $80-$145 insurance. Volunteer: $150 registration and insurance. **Contact:** Dov Abramson, Director of Admissions, Kibbutz Program Center, 633 3rd Ave., 21st Fl., New York, NY 10017; 800-247-7852, fax 212-318-

6134; ulpankad@aol.com,
[www.kibbutzprogramcenter.org].

Volunteering at Archaeological Digs. A listings
of digs recruiting volunteers can be found on the
web site of the Israel Ministry of Foreign Affairs:
[www.mfa.gov.il/mfa/go.asp?MFAH00wk0].

Dates: Spring and summer. **Costs:** Vary.
Contact: Addresses on the web site.
[www.mfa.gov.il/mfa/go.asp?MFAH00wk0].

Latin America

Volunteer Positions. In Costa Rica, Mexico,
Guatemala, Ecuador, Argentina, Peru, Bolivia.
Various positions in the fields of health care,
education, tourism, ESL, business, law,
marketing, administrative, environmental, and
social work. Additional customized options
available. Four weeks to 6 months. Inexpensive
lodging in homestays or dorms. Some positions
provide free room and board.

Dates: Year round. Flexible start dates. **Costs:**
$350 placement and application fee. Travel
insurance and pre-departure preparation
included. Lodging costs depend on location.
Contact: AmeriSpan Unlimited, P.O. Box
40007, Philadelphia, PA 19106; 800-879-6640,
fax 215-751-1100; info@amerispan.com,
[www.amerispan.com].

Nepal

Insight Nepal Volunteering and Tours.
Volunteer placements for 3 months in Nepali
communities. Program includes week-long
language course and homestay, 1 week trekking,
and 3-day jungle safari. Cultural experience
tours of 2 to 6 weeks are also available. Nepali
Director, Naresh, is a competent and reliable
host committed to expanding cross-cultural
understanding.

Dates: Feb, Apr, Aug, Oct. Tours start year
round. **Costs:** $800 program fee, $40 application fee. Tour fees vary. **Contact:** Naresh M.
Shrestha, Director, Insight Nepal. U.S. contact
and former volunteer: Holly Noonan, P.O. Box
957, Camden, ME 04843; holly@ringing
mountain.com.; insight@mos.com.np,
[www.insightnepal.org].

Volunteer Nepal Himalaya. The Himalayan
Explorers Club places volunteer English teachers
in Nepal to teach conversational English for 3
months in the spring and fall. Volunteer
teachers receive intensive teacher and language
training. Qualifications: 18 years and older;
some travel/camping experience, willingness to
learn and give.

Dates: Fall (Sep-Dec), and spring (Feb-May).
Costs: $1,000 donation to the Himalayan
Explorers Club 501(c)(3) plus travel and
homestay expenses. **Contact:** Jane Sabin-Davis
or Scott Dimetrosky, Himalayan Explorers Club;
888-420-8822; scott@hec.org, jsd@vcinet.com,
[www.hec.org].

Volunteer Nepal! This program is designed to
meet the needs of participants who desire more
than typical tourist experience. It provides
volunteer service opportunities for people who
are genuinely interested in learning about a new
and different community and culture while
contributing their time and skills to benefit
worthwhile community service throughout
Nepal.

Dates: Feb, Apr, Aug, and Oct. Other dates
can be arranged. **Costs:** $650 (for whole
program) includes pre-service training, language
instruction, homestay, hiking, lectures on
different topics, meditation, cultural orientation
tour, transportation from airport and within the
country, trekking, whitewater rafting, jungle
safari, volunteering, food and accommodations,
etc. **Contact:** Rajesh Shrestha, Director, Cultural
Destination Nepal, GPO Box #11535,
Kathmandu, Nepal; 011-977-1-426996, fax
011-977-1-426996; cdnnepal@wlink.com.np,
[www.volunteernepal.org.np].

Romania

Child Development Program. Romanian
Children's Relief sponsors experienced, degreed
professionals in child development (OT, Ed,
MSW, etc.) fields to go to Romania and train
caregivers in pediatric hospitals and orphanages.
Programs are in Bucharest and Bistrita,
Romania.

Dates: Vary. Minimum 2-year commitment.
Costs: RCR pays for housing, living stipend,
transportation, and health insurance. **Contact:**
Eileen McHenry, Romanian Children's Relief,
P.O. Box 107, Southboro, MA 01772; 508-303-
6299; emmc2@aol.com.

United Kingdom and Ireland

**The National Trust for Scotland Thistle
Camps.** Thistle Camps are practical outdoor
conservation working holidays which take place
on trust properties at beautiful and remote
locations all over Scotland. Anyone who is
reasonably fit and over 16 years can join.

Dates: Mar-Oct. **Costs:** £35-£100 for 1 to 3
weeks. All food, training, travel from/to pick up/
/dropoff points, accommodations is provided.
Contact: Julia Downes, NTS, 28 Charlotte Sq.,

COMMON HOPE
WORKING WITH FAMILIES IN GUATEMALA

By Julie Kremen

We planned to study Spanish in Guatemala for three months and spend nine months volunteering," said Zach Thomas, a volunteer at Antigua's Common Hope for more than two years. "We saw a lot of projects; however, we knew immediately when we came to Common Hope that it was different. "They deliver what they promise."

Common Hope, a nonprofit organization, provides impoverished Guatemalan children, families, and communities with healthcare, education, and housing. Its goal is to empower the families to permanently lift themselves out of poverty while maintaining their dignity and independence. Through its Family Development Center in Antigua and other satellite projects in Guatemala, it works with up to 2,200 children and their families. Common Hope believes that a child's health depends on the health of the family; when a mother attends one of their nutrition classes, her children benefit.

Common Hope accepts many types of volunteers, from people just passing through to long-term volunteers who commit for a year or more. Long-term volunteers must be fluent (or very close to it) in Spanish and commit to the program for at least a year. Those who want to become a long-term volunteers but lack Spanish skills can live off site and take Spanish classes. (Expect to pay about $125 per week for homestay, meals, and private instruction at one of Antigua's 75 Spanish schools.) Once proficient in Spanish the volunteer becomes full time and lives on the premises. Short-term volunteers live off site and fund their own stay.

In addition to those who volunteer on site, from 20-30 volunteer workteams of 10-16 people travel to Guatemala each year and stay 7-10 days. They pay their own expenses but live on the premises. Projects include constructing new houses, organizing the library, working at the project's medical clinic, etc. Through training lectures and interaction with the Guatemalan staff, the sponsored children, and the children's families, they learn about the culture and life in Guatemala.

Long-term volunteers and workteams must apply in advance to the St. Paul office. Short-term volunteers should inquire in advance but can also contact the project leader in Antigua and arrange for a tour and interview. Contact: Common Hope, P.O. Box 14298, St. Paul, MN 55114; 651-917-0917, fax 651-917-7458; info@mn.commonhope.org, [www.commonhope.org]. In Guatemala: Tel./fax 832-4111; Info@guate.commonhope.org. (In Guatemala, the project is called Familias de Esperanza.)

Edinburgh EH2 4ET, Scotland; 011-44-131-243-9470, fax 011-44-131-243-9444; mhume@nts.org.uk.

Time for God. TFG provides volunteer opportunities for 9-12 months for young adults aged 18-25 to do youth work in churches, recreational work with homeless and the mentally ill, and to assist people with learning difficulties. TFG provides training and a spiritual development program.

Dates: Begins Sep or Jan for 9-12 months. **Costs:** £2,000 includes board, lodging, and stipend. **Contact:** Tracy Phillips, TFG, Chester House, Pages Ln., London N10 1PR, U.K.; 011-44-181-883-1504; tracytfg@cs.com.

Worcestershire Lifestyle. Full-time volunteer workers are required to act as the arms and legs of people with physical disabilities who wish to live independently in their own home. Duties include personal care, household tasks, and sharing leisure interests. Free accommodations are provided in Worcestershire or Herefordshire and £58.88 per week.

Dates: Vacancies are on-going. **Costs:** Contact organization for details. **Contact:** Worcestershire Lifestyles, Woodside Lodge, Lark Hill Rd., Worcester WR5 2EF, U.K.; 011-44-1905-350686, fax 011-44-1905-350684.

Work on Organic Farm in Scotland. Daily help with dairy goats, friendly sheep, and in organic kitchen garden in stress-free, beautiful countryside near Sea (Dornoch Firth). Home-produced food (vegetarian), comfortable caravan, pocket money. Can take paying guests.

Dates: Any time throughout summer. **Costs:** Getting here (North of Inverness). **Contact:** Pam Shaw, The Rhanich, Edderton, Tain Rossshire, Scotland, 1V19 1LG; 011-44-1862-821-265.

United States

Rethinking Tourism Project. The Rethinking Tourism Project, an Indigenous organization based in Minnesota, offers volunteer opportunities for students and others to work with us in our home office. Volunteers learn about responsible tourism and international development issues from the Indigenous perspective. Non-paid positions and require a 3-month commitment. Offers individualized tours to Mexico.

Dates: Contact organization for details. **Costs:** Contact organization for details. **Contact:** Rethinking Tourism Project, 366 North Prior Ave., Suite 203, St. Paul, MN 55104; 651-644-9984, fax 651-644-2720; RTProject@aol.com, [www.rethinkingtourism.org].

TEFL Programs in Boston. Explore the World through Teaching! Full-time and part-time teaching training programs; no previous teaching experience required; practical classroom experience before you leave; career guidance; certificate recognized internationally.

Dates: Sep 10, Oct 15, Nov 26. **Costs:** $2,495. **Contact:** The Boston Language Institute, TEFL, 648 Beacon St., Boston, MA 02215; 617-262-3500 ext 288, fax 617-262-3595; tefl@boslang.com, [www.teflcertificate.com].

Worldwide

A Cultural Immersion Experience. Immerse yourself in exotic cultural and geographical landscapes! Serve communities by volunteering your time and energy. Actively engage with local people through home stays, language study, cultural seminars, a village trek, a volunteer service project and more. Make friends and make a contribution through these extraordinary immersion programs in Nepal, Peru, and India.

Dates: Summer: 6 weeks (Jul-Aug), semester: 2-4 months (Sep-Dec and Jan-Apr). **Costs:** Summer $1,800, semester programs: from $2,500. **Contact:** David, Program Director, International Cultural Adventures, 507 Stackpole Rd., Durham, ME 04222; 888-339-0460, 207-926-5311, fax 208-728-7338; icadventures@usa.net.

Amity Volunteer Teachers Abroad (AVTA). The AVTA program is a teaching exchange program offering participants a unique opportunity for cultural immersion while serving as a volunteer teacher or teaching assistant. Candidates must be a native English-speaking university graduate with background in tutoring or teaching, and have previously traveled or lived abroad.

Dates: Northern hemisphere: Sep-Jun; Jan-Jun. Southern hemisphere: Mar-Dec; Jul-Dec. Shorter assignments (1-3 months) can be arranged for experienced teachers. **Costs:** $500 for an assignment in Latin America; $1,200 for assignments in Africa. **Contact:** Amity Institute, 10671 Roselle St., Suite 101, San Diego, CA 92121; 858-455-6364, fax 858-455-6597; www.amity.org, [www.amity.org].

Amizade Volunteer Programs. Amizade is a nonprofit organization dedicated to promoting volunteerism, providing community service, encouraging collaboration, and improving cultural awareness in locations around the world. Amizade offers programs for individuals and customizes programs for groups in Brazil, Bolivia, Australia, Nepal, Thailand, as well as the Navajo Nation and the Greater Yellowstone Region, USA.

Work in the Middle Kingdom
Internship Opportunities for Students in China

By Christopher Moore

Adding work on top of study experience abroad demonstrates to employers that one can function professionally in a foreign environment and an overseas job can be the stepping stone to a life of foreign work and adventure. At the least, it will be an exciting time of learning and challenge. (For the most comprehensive compilation of information and advice on paid jobs abroad for students and recent graduates, see the 2001 edition of *Work Abroad: The Complete Guide to Finding a Job Overseas* published by Transitions Abroad Publishing.)

My job destination was China. As it moves toward full membership in the World Trade Organization, China offers the student or recent graduate a wealth of possibilities to gain international work experience.

Many positions in multinational organizations in China do not require a knowledge of the language. In addition, many opportunities for English teachers, writers, and editors are advertised in publications targeted at the foreign community in China. I recently saw the following statement on a Chinese web site: "There are more English speakers in China than in America." True or not, there are many Chinese who speak English and many more who want to learn.

The best place to start a job search in China is at the American Chamber of Commerce. Here you can network and find out about job availability throughout the country (the Chamber also offers its own internships). You can order the Chamber's directory of companies in China that employ foreigners and possibly nail down an internship before you leave the U.S. (see below).

How I Did It

I went to my adviser and announced my plan to intern in Beijing. What kind of academic credit, if any, could I get?

Surprisingly, my adviser accepted this vague proposal without questioning how I would implement it. Now the pressure was on me: I had to go to Beijing and find an internship.

When I arrived in Beijing I looked for jobs advertised in the local expat publications to get a feel for the job market and contacted whomever I could think of for possible leads. I looked at Internet sites for promising openings; I went to the Chamber of Commerce and looked through their directory of U.S. companies operating in China; I made a list of potential employers in which I was interested and contacted the most attractive ones—whether they had advertised openings or not. Then I sent cover letters and resumes to the eight organizations I especially liked. From these first contacts I obtained five interviews and in the end I had four offers to choose from.

At first I worked in the market research division of Unisono, a Dutch company whose focus is the Chinese marketplace. I am now interning with UNESCO in Beijing.

Living and working in China and taking part in its daily life is exhilarating. I enjoy the Chinese and love the expatriate environment, which permits one to get to know and make friends with people from around the world.

How You Can Do It

All you need is a resume, a positive attitude, and an appropriate work uniform. Be prepared with these necessities and you'll lose no time. I have talked with many student interns in Beijing and can safely say that an internship can begin—if one searches diligently—within two to four weeks after arrival in China.

Finding a position in China is similar to a job search anywhere. My experience has been concentrated in Beijing. But one could easily find similar possibilities in all business-oriented areas of China.

Internship Contacts

- **The Department of State** has several student employment programs, some in Washington, DC and others in embassies overseas. For info write: Attn: Student Programs, U.S. Department of State, Recruitment Division, SA-1, 2401 E St., NW, 5th Fl., Washington, DC 20522; [www.state.gov/www.careers].
- **MOGPA**, a nonprofit organization that arranges 6- to 12-month professional work assignments and internships for corporations in Asia with U.S. students and recent graduates, operates in China and Japan. Proficiency in the language is required. Contact: 2345 Rice St., Suite 200, Saint Paul, MN 55113; info@mogpa.org, [www.Mogpa.org].
- **The American Chamber of Commerce**, a great launching point for networking and researching companies, publishes a directory of all U.S. companies operating in China and hosts a monthly social. It offers a resume service in which you can advertise to companies in China that you are looking for an internship. Contact: Room 1903, China Resource Bldg., 8 Jianguomenbei Dajie, Beijing 100005, China; 011-86-10-8519-1920; AmCham@AmCham-China.org.cn, [www.AmCham-China.org.cn].
- **Canada-China Business Council** offers services similar to the American Chamber of Commerce and also hosts a social every month that is good for networking and finding out about job availability. Contact: Suite 1802 CITIC Bldg., 19 Jianguomen-wai Dajie, Beijing 100004, China; 011-86-10-6512-6120; [www.ccbc.com].
- **The U.S.-China Business Council**, a useful source for company information, has a human resource link to many Asian job sites. This is the principal organization of U.S. companies engaged in trade and investment in the Peoples Republic of China. It offers its own internships. Contact: 1818 N. St., NW, Suite 200, Washington, D.C. 20036; 202-429-0340; [www.uschina.org].
- **The United Nations** has various internship and fellowship programs. Each department has a separate internship administration, so you must contact the department you are interested in. For information on the UN Development Fund in China contact: UNDP China, 2 Liangmahe Nan Lu, Beijing 100600, China; 011-86-10-6532-3731; registry.cn@undp.org, [www.un.org].

Web Sites

- **Teach in China** [www.cbw.com/teaching] describes conditions for teachers and contains articles from people who have taught in China. It will match you with a position for up to six months at no cost.
- **www.JobOK.com** is a Hong Kong, Macau, Mainland China job site.
- **www.ChinaNow.com** has a classified section where one can search for housing and jobs wanted and offered, including teaching.
- [**www.unpof.net**] is a UN site. Under the internship hyperlink is a listing of various internships around the world with organizations other than the UN.
- **City Weekend,** Full Link Plaza Tower B, Suite 1212, Chao-yangmenwai Dajie 18, Beijing 100020, China; 011-86-10-6588-1341, [www.cityweekend.com.cn].

Dates: Contact Amizade for specific dates. **Costs:** Ranges from $450 to $2000, airfare not included. Fee is tax deductible. **Contact:** Michael Sandy, Executive Director, 367 South Graham St., Pittsburgh, PA, 15232; 888-973-4443, fax 412-648-1492; volunteer@amizade.org, [www.amizade.org].

BTCV-Conservation Holidays. Program of practical conservation holidays at locations around the U.K. and worldwide. No experience necessary, just energy and enthusiasm. You could be drystone walling in the English Lake District or turtle monitoring in Thailand.

Dates: Year round. **Costs:** From £45-£1,000 includes food and accommodations. **Contact:** BTCV, 36 St. Mary's St., Wallingford, Oxfordshire OX10 0EU, U.K.; 011-44-1491-821600, fax 011-44-1491-839646; information@btcv.org, [www.btcv.org].

Conservation Expeditions. Frontier is an international conservation and research NGO which works in threatened tropical environments to protect endangered habitats and wildlife through research and practical projects. Offers self-funding volunteers the opportunity to work on overseas projects for 10 or 20 weeks. Full training is provided, leading to a qualification.

Dates: Jan-Mar, Apr-Jun, Jul-Sep, and Oct-Dec of each year. **Costs:** Volunteers must raise approx. GBP 2,500 plus airfare for 10 weeks. **Contact:** Research Assistant Coordinator, Frontier, 77 Leonard St., London EC2A 4QS, U.K.; 011-44-20-7613-2422, fax 011-44-20-7613-2992; enquiries@frontierprojects.ac.uk, [www.frontier.ac.uk].

Cross-Cultural Solutions. Experience the vibrant, colorful culture of China, India, Ghana, Russia, China, or Peru and make a difference at the same time. This unique short- or long-term volunteer programs enable volunteers to work with local social service organizations in fields as diverse as healthcare, education, skills training, and arts/recreation. Volunteers receive continual professional support from our U.S. and local staff. No skills or experience required—only a desire to help and learn.

Dates: Year round. **Costs:** Approx. $1,950 for 3 weeks covers in-country transportation, accommodations, board, and support. International airfare, insurance, and visa not included. Program fee is tax deductible. **Contact:** Cross-Cultural Solutions, 47 Potter Ave., New Rochelle, NY 10801; 800-380-4777 or 914-632-0022, fax 914-632-8494; info@crossculturalsolutions.org, [www. crossculturalsolutions.org/transabroad.html].

Franciscan Mission Service. FMS prepares and sends Catholic women and men for extended assignments among oppressed and poor peoples of Africa, Asia, and Latin America. Volunteers are needed to work in the areas of health care, social service, education, agriculture and community organizing. Allow a different culture to expand your worldview.

Dates: Jan-Apr 2002; Sep-Nov 2002-2003. **Contact:** Megeen White, Co-director, Franciscan Mission Service, P.O. Box 29034, Washington, DC 20017; 877-886-1762, fax 202-832-1778; fms5@juno.com.

Global Service Corps (GSC), a project of Earth Island Institute, creates opportunities for adult participants to live in Tanzania and Thailand homes while volunteering on health, education and environment community service and development projects. These service-learning programs emphasize grass-roots collaboration on the local level, mutual transfer of skills, and cross-cultural understanding. Our goals are to provide developing communities with the means to function more sustainably, and to widen the perspectives of participants as responsible global citizens. Project areas: HIV/AIDS prevention, health care, Buddhism immersion, environmental education, English language instruction and sustainable agriculture. Undergraduate and Graduate level credits qualifying for financial aid available.

Dates: Year round. Contact GSC office or check the web site for specific starting dates **Costs:** Approx. $1,800-$2,000 for 2-4 week project trips: $595 per month for 2-6 month long-term extensions; $2,815-$3,145 for summer and semester college internships. Includes extensive pre-departure preparation and in-country expenses (hotel and homestay room and board, orientation, training, project expenses, transportation, excursions). Airfare not included, discounted international airfare available. **Contact:** Global Service Corps., 300 Broadway, Suite 28, San Francisco, CA 94133; 415-788-3666 ext 128, fax 415-788-7324,; gsc@earthisland.org, [www.globalservicecorps.org].

International Opportunities Clearinghouse. The Clearinghouse offers: directories of organizations that work in the international development field and offer internships in the U.S. and overseas; information packs (regional or topical) with materials from 15-30 volunteer programs in one's area of interest; and a research and referral service in which ODN researches various options and provides contacts with organizations that best fit an individual's interests.

HIMALAYAN HOMESTAYS
NEPAL PROGRAM IS IDEAL FOR FIRST-TIME VOLUNTEERS

By Simon Lynch

Insight Nepal is a cross-cultural exchange program promoting appreciation and understanding of traditional Nepali life. The organization recruits volunteers of any age to work in local schools or education centers for three to four months. Participants are mainly based in the town of Pokhara, a beautiful community strung out along the Phewa Tal lake with the Himalayan mountains providing a sensational backdrop.

The orientation phase of the program in Kathmandu lasted for one week. It started with a whirlwind tour of the city's main sights conducted by the program's director.

Pokhara is a total contrast to Kathmandu. The atmosphere is relaxed, with cows in the middle of the street. The program really began for us here as we split up and moved in with our host families. The program's rule is that at least one family member speaks some English, but the similarities among the families stop there. The house of my family had an inside bathroom, hot water, phone, and TV. Other participants' homes had none of that.

The first priority was to communicate with our host families. Fortunately, spoken Nepali is not difficult to learn. After five days of language classes and practice with our families in the evenings, everyone could manage a few practical phrases.

After classes we were taken to local monasteries and temples. In the end, we asked for a few of the local trips to be dropped so we could get some sleep.

The second phase of the program consisted of two separate cultural excursions. We spent three days roaming the jungle on foot or on the back of an elephant looking for the elusive one-horned rhino, followed by a 1-week trek into the Himalayan foothills staying in local villages. We wandered through the mountains and across footbridges, photographing frisky gray monkeys and meeting traders and porters.

The trails are the freeways that connect the various communities, and they are filled with countless people eager to chat. A highlight was watching the morning sun rise over an isolated hill illuminating 15 peaks all around us.

The final but most important phase of the program was the work placement itself. I worked at Pardi government school. The children aged 4-17 were mostly from the poorest groups in Nepal, including the untouchable caste. Classes took place in tiny dark rooms with 50 to 70 students per class. There was no electricity or running water, and the school had almost no money to pay for books or paper. I worked 10 a.m. to 4 p.m., six days a week and was always thoroughly exhausted at the end of the day.

Most Western teachers would beg for such appreciative students, however, teaching was a 2-way lesson: I tried to explain the difference between "to hear" and "to listen" and the students taught me five new Nepali words as reward. Their appreciation made me work doubly hard.

Class sizes were the main difficulty. Teaching sports to 100 children on dried mud courts with just one volleyball was a new challenge that took a few attempts to get right.

Some might question why children from the poorest groups of society in Nepal need to learn English. Nepal's major source of income is now tourism and Pokhara has become the gateway to the Himalayas. Thousands of visitors descend on the town each year for trekking, whitewater rafting, and jungle safaris. People in Pokhara see the economic potential in welcoming visitors and want to learn English.

Insight Nepal is an ideal program for those who are looking to volunteer in a developing country for the first time. Experience is not necessary and the three distinct phases allow you to interact with other participants, thus giving you a good support network. Once at your school, contact with the program organizers becomes minimal, but this didn't prove to be a problem. We eventually made Nepali friends, and participants usually met up on days off.

Insight Nepal is a for-profit organization. The $800 fee for the 3-month program covers accommodations, meals, excursions, hotel stays, and the language course. Also included is a 1-week trekking excursion and a 3-day jungle safari in Chitwan National Park. It does not include the air ticket to Nepal, entry visa and subsequent visa extensions. None of the fees go toward the work placement.

Nepal has beautiful mountains and scenery, but its people left the real impression on me. A highlight was participating in the Hindu festival of light (tihar) with the students and my host family. During the five-day celebration dogs, cows and family brothers, including me, received tika, a blessing in the form of a red mark placed on the forehead. The streets are lit with candles to welcome Ramma, the personification of the god Vishnu, back from exile. Students danced in the streets to traditional songs while the teachers and I collected money to pay for schoolbooks.

Dates: Vary by program. **Costs:** Vary by program. **Contact:** Wendy Phillips, Overseas Development Network, 333 Valencia St., Suite 325, San Francisco, CA 94103; (415) 431-4204, fax (415) 431-5953; odn@igc.org, [www.igc.orgodn].

International Volunteer and Cultural Exchange Programs.
Cross-Cultural Solutions offers life-changing volunteer programs and "insight" cultural tours in Asia, Africa, Latin America, the Caribbean, and Eastern Europe. Volunteers typically work in the areas of education, healthcare, and community development for 2 weeks to 6 months. Cultural tours range from 7 to 18 days.

Dates: Year round. **Costs:** Programs begin at $1,700 and vary depending on duration and country. **Contact:** Volunteer Coordinator, Cross-Cultural Solutions, 47 Potter Ave., New Rochelle, NY 10801; 914-632-0022 or 800-380-4777, fax 914-632-8494; info@crossculturalsolutions.org, [www.crossculturalsolutions.org].

International Volunteer Program.
IVP provides 6-week summer volunteer placements in nonprofits in France and the U.K. Volunteer placements include work with at-risk youth, elderly, handicapped, and homeless individuals. The administrative fee covers roundtrip airfare and room and board during the whole 6-week program.

Dates: Jun 20-end of July **Costs:** $1,500. **Contact:** Rebecca Jewell, International Volunteer Program, 210 Post St., Suite 502, San Francisco, CA 94108; 415-477-3667, fax 415-477-3669; rjewell@ivpsf.com, [www.ivpsf.com].

Int'l. Volunteer Placements.
Volunteer placements in Puerto Rico, Costa Rica, Mexico, Ecuador, New Zealand, and Australi include working with forest conservation, wildlife rescue, rural schools, farming, and environmental education. Individually arranged. Volunteers live with host families or bunkhouse lodging at a project site.

Dates: Year round. From 1 or 2 weeks. **Costs:** Placement fees $600-$1,000. **Contact:** John Lee or Debbie Jacobs, Explorations in Travel, Inc., 1922 River Rd.,275 Jacksonville Stage Rd., Brattleboro, VT 05301; 802-257-0152 or 802-257-2784; explore@sover.net, www.exploretravel.com.

Jewish Volunteer Corps.
The Jewish Volunteer Corps sends skilled Jewish men and women to provide technical assistance and training in the fields of health, agriculture, business, and education to communities in the developing world. JVC volunteers work with local grassroots nongovernmental organizations throughout Latin America, Asia, and Africa from 1 to 12 months.

Dates: Year round, minimum 1 month. **Costs:** JVC covers airfare, emergency evacuation insurance, volunteers cover all other costs. **Contact:** American Jewish World Service, 45 W. 36th St., 10th Fl., New York, NY 10018; 212-736-2597, fax 212-736-3463; jvcvol@jws.org, [www.ajws.org].

Research/Conservation Expeditions to Canada and Nepal.
In Canada help monitor population trends and changes on record and document flora and fauna species. Live the life of a field biologist and learn. In Nepal visit rural areas in the Central-Hill region to document and record the use of rare and endangered medicinal plants. Results will be used to help establish protected areas.

Dates: Canada: Jun-Aug (2 weeks). Nepal: Mar-Aug (2 weeks). **Costs:** Canada $425-$499 per person (14 days). Nepal $999 per person (14 days). **Contact:** Dave Jolly, Executive Director, EARTHQUEST (Canada) for the Environment, P.O. Box 24142, London, Ontario, Canada N6H SC4; 519-642-9988; earthquest@hotmail.com, [www.geocities.com/earthquestcanada].

Service Learning Programs.
The International Partnership for Service-Learning, founded in 1982, is an incorporated not-for-profit organization serving colleges, universities, service agencies, and related organizations around the world by fostering programs that link community service and academic study. Countries include: Czech Republic, Ecuador, England, France, Jamaica, U.S., Russia, Israel, India, Mexico, Philippines, and Scotland. Students gain hands-on experience in an international community service agency. We also offer a Master's degree in International Service.

Dates: Summer, semester, year, or intersession. **Costs:** Vary. **Contact:** The International Partnership for Service-Learning, 815 2nd Ave., Suite 315, New York, NY 10017; 212-986-0989, fax 212-986-5039; pslny@aol.com, [www.ipsl.org].

Teach in Africa, Asia, Latin America.
WorldTeach. Based at Harvard Univ. for 15 years, WorldTeach provides opportunities for individuals to make a meaningful contribution to international education by living and working as volunteer teachers in developing countries in Africa, Asia, and Latin America. Offers 8-week summer teaching programs to qualified adults 18 years of age and older, involving either English or basic computer/internet instruction. WorldTeach also offers 1 year and semester teaching placements for college graduates.

Dates: Jun 20-Aug 20 (summer); long-term programs depart through the year. **Costs:** Summer $3,990; year/semester $4,990-$5,990. Includes international roundtrip airfare, health insurance, orientation and training, room and board, and full-time in-country staff support. **Contact:** WorldTeach, Center for International Development, Harvard Univ., 79 John F. Kennedy St., Cambridge, MA 02138; 800-483-2240 or 617-495-5527, fax 617-495-1599; info@worldteach.org, [www.worldteach.org].

Volunteers for Peace. Over 2,000 short-term voluntary service projects in over 70 countries. An opportunity to complete meaningful community service while abroad. Programs last 2-3 weeks; work includes construction, renovation, environmental, social work, refugee programs, education, arts, etc.

Dates: May-Sep; some programs run all year. **Costs:** $200 (some camps have extra fee). Volunteer pays transportation costs. **Contact:** Volunteers for Peace, 1034 Tiffany Rd., Belmont, VT 05730; 802-259-2759, fax 802-259-2922; vfp@vfp.org, [www.vfp.org].

World Wide Volunteer Services. Volunteering? WWVS is a personalized service locating challenging volunteer positions and negotiating placements to meet your special interests and skills. Opportunities are global, of long or short duration (including summers). Placements usually provide free room and board.

Dates: Year round. **Costs:** Vary. **Contact:** Director, WWVS, P.O. Box 3242, West End, NJ 07740; 732-571-3215; worldvol@aol.com, [http://welcome.to/volunteer_services].

Youth International. An experiential education program focusing on international travel and intercultural exchange, adventure, community service, and homestays. Teams of 14, aged 18-25, travel together for 1 semester to Asia (including the Philippines, Thailand, India, and Nepal) or Africa (including Kenya, Tanzania, Botswana, and Namibia). Assist refugees, hike the Himalayas, live with and help an African tribe, scuba dive, and much more.

Dates: Every year, early Sep-mid-Dec, and early Feb-late May. **Costs:** $7,500 including airfare. **Contact:** Brad Gillings, Youth International, 1121 Downing St., #2, Denver, CO 80218; 303-839-5877, fax 303-839-5887; director@youthinternational.org, [www.youthinternational.org].

Internship Organizations and Publications

Academic Year Abroad and Short-Term Study Abroad. The most comprehensive and authoritative directories of study abroad. Indexes for internships, practical training, volunteering, and student teaching list over 1,300 programs, most of which charge tuition and give academic credit. Available free online at [www.iiepassport.org].

American-Scandinavian Foundation: "Study in Scandinavia." 2001 (annual). 54 pp. Free from ASF, 58 Park Ave., New York, NY 10016; 212-879-9779, fax 212-249-3444; [www.amscan.org]. Web site lists both study and work programs. Paid internships in Scandinavia in engineering, teaching English as a foreign language, business, and agricultural fields. Apply for internships by late Dec. Fee $50. ASF also assists with obtaining work permits for Scandinavia. "Study in Scandinavia" is available only on the ASF web site.

Association for International Practical Training (AIPT)/International Association for the Exchange of Students for Technical Experience (IAESTE). Information and applications available from AIPT/IAESTE, 10400 Little Patuxent Pkwy., Suite 250, Columbia, MD 21044-3510; 410-997-2200, fax 410-992-3924; aipt@aipt.org, [www.aipt.org]. Nonprofit organization provides paid internships in over 60 countries in engineering and science (apply by late Dec.), and in tourism and hotel and restaurant management. They can also assist in obtaining work permits for career-related practical training in most fields.

CDS International, Inc. Free booklet and applications available from CDS, 871 United Nations Plaza, 15th Fl., New York, NY 10017-1814; 212-497-3500, fax 212-497-3535; info@cdsintl.org, [www.cdsintl.org]. Web site lists both study and work programs. Offers paid internships in Scandinavia in engineering, teaching English as a foreign language, business. Apply for internships by late Dec. Fee $50. (If accepted a $200 refundable deposit is required to hold position).

Directory of International Internships: A World of Opportunities edited by Charles A. Gliozzo and Vernicka K. Tyson. 1998 (new edition expected 2002). 4th edition. 162 pp. Michigan State Univ. Career Services and Placement. $25 postpaid from Michigan State Univ., Career Services and Placement, Attn: Directory of International Internships, 113 Student Services Bldg., East Lansing, MI 48824; 517-355-9510 ext. 146, fax 517-353-2957,

By Susan Griffith

Volunteer and experience Australia. The main conservation organization in Australia, the Australian Trust for Conservation Volunteers, accepts large numbers of volunteers to help on its 1,500 projects around the country including tree planting, erosion control, seed collection, track maintenance, surveying endangered flora and fauna, and habitat and heritage restoration. A fee of AUS$20 a day covers transportation, food, and accommodations in caravans, hostels, shearers' huts, bunkhouses, or tents. Further details are available from the ATCV National Office, Box 423, Ballarat, Victoria 3353; 011-03-5333-1483; [www.atcv.com.au].

Western Australia: One way to spend time in a remote part (or any part) of the state of Western Australia is to join the volunteer program organized by the Conservation & Land Management Department (CALM) of Western Australia [www.calm.wa.gov.au], open to anyone aged 16-70. Most projects are land based, but a few are in marine environments such as the breathtaking Ningaloo Marine Park. This 260-kilometer stretch of coral is the undiscovered rival to the Great Barrier Reef.

CALM arranges accident insurance and training, but accommodations are not normally provided in remote places. Details are available from the Volunteer Coordinator at CALM (Locked Bag 104, Bentley Delivery Centre, WA 6893; 011-61 8-9334-0251). For people with a conservation background or relevant skills, CALM also runs an Educational Work Experience Program. Placements of one or two weeks are arranged by individual park or forest rangers either in the national parks near Perth or in more remote locations.

Queensland: If you have a background in marine biology or you are a scuba diver you may want to volunteer with one of the marine research stations along the coast of Queensland. The Australian Institute of Marine Science (AIMS) is located in a national park at Cape Ferguson, 50 kilometers from Townsville in Queensland (PMB No. 3, Townsville Mail Centre, Qld 4810; 011-61-7-4753-4240; visitor_coord@aims.gov.au, [www. aims.gov.au]). AIMS runs a visitor scheme and a program for volunteers with appropriate skills. For example, qualified scuba divers accompany research trips, often to assess damage to the Great Barrier Reef. Overseas applicants must have a working visa and medical certificate.

The Heron Island Research Station (Great Barrier Reef, via Gladstone, Qld 4680) has been known to offer free accommodations in exchange for about four hours of work a day. For other possibilities contact the relevant departments of James Cook Univ. or the Univ. of Queensland at St Lucia (Brisbane).

For land-based opportunities, a research station in northern Queensland operated by the Australian Tropical Research Foundation (PMB 5, Cape Tribulation, Qld 4873; 011-61-7-40-98-00 63; austrop@austrop.org.au, [www. austrop.org.au]) welcomes over 50 volunteers a year to carry out tasks like caring for a resident population of flying foxes (large bats). Volunteers are expected to work long hours around the research station and must pay $70 a week (U.S.) to cover basic expenses.

New South Wales: The National Parks & Wildlife Service of New South Wales does not run a structured volunteer program, so in this state of tremendous environmental contrasts and 68 National Parks it is better to concentrate your efforts on exploring rather than on volunteering.

The NSW National Parks and Wildlife Service (43 Bridge St., Hurstville, NSW 2220, Australia [www.npws.nsw.gov.au]) can provide further information if you have a specific interest in certain habitats, wildlife, or zoology. Once in Sydney you can pick up the detailed *Guide to NSW National Parks* from the NPWS office in Cadman's Cottage, 110 George St. in The Rocks (011-61 2-9247-5033). Park rangers run a Discovery program of guided activities such as rockpool rambles and snorkeling expeditions. Details are available at their web site, or by phoning 1300 36 1967 (within Australia).

[www.isp.msu.edu/InternationalInternships].
This is the most comprehensive directory of both academic and non-academic internships located abroad. Describes experiential educational opportunities offered through educational institutions, governmental and private organizations-for academic credit, for pay, or simply for experience. In-depth profiles of more than 200 internship programs offered by over 160 organizations. Very useful cross-indexes by subject and country. Highly recommended.

A Handbook for Creating Your Own Internship in International Development by Natalie Foster and Nicole Howell (Just Act: Youth Action for Global Justice, 333 Valencia St., #101, San Francisco, CA 94110; 415-431-4204, fax 415-431-5953; info@justact.org, [www.justact.org]). The handbook includes a workbook to help evaluate your skills, motivations, and learning objectives, as well as practical advice. See Just Act's directory of opportunities in the volunteer section below.

International Cooperative Education Program. Free information from ICE, 15 Spiros Way, Menlo Park, CA 94025; 650-323-4944, fax 650-323-1104; ICEmenlo@aol.com, [www.icemenlo.com]. Offers 450 paid summer internships for students with knowledge of foreign languages (German, Finnish, French, Italian, Chinese, Japanese) in Europe and Asia. U.S. or Canadian citizens preferred. Apply by Feb. Fee of $800.

International Health Electives for Medical Students. American Medical Student Association. $15 from AMSA Resource Center, 1902 Association Dr., Reston, VA 20191; 703-620-6600 ext. 217, 800-767-2266, fax 703-620-5873; amsarc@www.amsa.org, [www.amsa.org]. Overseas internships for third- or fourth-year medical students. Related titles, A Student's Guide to International Health ($8), and Cross-Cultural Medicine: What to Know Before You Go ($8), Creative Funding for International Health Electives ($5) also available from AMSA. Most publications available free on AMSA web site.

The Internship Bible by Mark Oldman and Samer Hamadeh. 2001 (annual). 621 pp. $25. Princeton Review. Distributed by Random House, available through Velarde Publicity; 212-572-2870, fax 212-572-6026; [www.review.com]. Directory describes in detail paid and unpaid internships offered by nearly 900 mostly nonacademic organizations, around 120 of which have overseas branches. Indexes for location, field, benefits, level of study, minority programs, and deadlines.

Internships International. Free information from Judy Tilson, Director, P.O. Box 480, Woolwich, ME 04579-0408; 207-443-3019, fax 207-442-7942; intintl@aol.com, [rtpnet.org/~intintl]. Organization offers unpaid, not-for-credit internship placements in all fields for college graduates (or seniors who need an internship for graduation) in London, Paris, Dresden, Florence, Dublin, Santiago, Budapest, Glasgow, Melbourne, and Capetown. Fee of $800 ($1,000 for Dublin).

LEAPNow: Lifelong Education Alternatives & Programs. Brochure available from web site or LEAPNow, P.O. Box 1817, Sebastopol, CA 95473; 707-829-1142, fax 707-829-1132; info@leapnow.org, [www.leapnow.org]. Over 20,000 options in 129 countries and 20 years' experience tailoring custom programs for people of all ages and backgrounds. Academic credit available for all programs.

Peterson's Study Abroad and Summer Study Abroad. Study abroad directories list over 3,500 programs, over 800 of which offer internships, listed in a special index. Most are for academic credit.

U.S. Department of State Student Intern Program. Free brochure and application from U.S. Department of State, Intern Coordinator, HR/REE SA-1, 2401 E St., NW, 5th Fl., Washington, DC 20522; email for hard-copy application: internbook@socent.org. Apply online: [www.state.gov/employment]. Nearly 1,000 mostly unpaid internships in international relations annually, in Washington and abroad. Only for enrolled students who will continue studies after the internship. Competitive. Deadlines: Nov 1 (summer), Mar 1 (fall), Jul 1 (spring).

Women in International Security: Online International Internships Directory by Women in International Security. 1999 (continuously updated). Web site includes detailed descriptions of internships offered by more than 250 international organizations, primarily in the Washington, D.C. area as well as a few overseas locations; info@wiis.org, [www.wiis.org].

Internship Programs

Australia

Australian Internships. Interns are placed with research teams, Australian employers, political administrations, etc., for periods ranging from 6 weeks to a year. The positions are unpaid. Homestay (or other) accommodations are included. Placement is arranged to suit the individual provided 4 months notice is given.

Most placements are in Queensland or New South Wales. Fields: marine and wildlife biology, business, etc. No academic credit offered. Unlimited internships. Prerequisites: a) High School Graduates, b) Professional Development for Graduates and Junior/Senior college students.

Dates: Year round. Application deadline: Four months before start date. **Costs:** $2,990 (includes room and board) for 6-week professional development program. Application fee: $500. **Contact:** Dr. Maurice A. Howe, Education Australia, P.O. Box 2233, Amherst, MA 01004; 800-344-6741, fax 413-549-0741; edaust@javanet.com.

Custom Designed Internsips. AustraLearn will facilitate enriching and educational internships in Australia. Focus: diversity of fields such as International Business, Sports and Fitness, Marine Biology, Education, Public Policy, Public Relations, and more. Available to all interested students undergraduate and graduates and working professionals. Academic credit can be arranged through home university.

Dates: Year round, from 6-week minimum to 52 weeks maximum. Lead-time must be at least 4 months prior to intended date of departure. **Costs:** Starts at $3,560 for 6-week program. Prices are adjusted based on desired length of internship. Includes internship placement, homestay with 2 meals or shared accommodations without meals, liaison services in Australia, and airport transfers. Call for more information. **Contact:** AustraLearn: North American Center for Australian Universities. CSU Denver Center, 110 16th St., Denver, CO 80202; 800-980-0033, fax 303-446-2214; studyabroad@australearn.org, [www.australearn.org].

Univ. of the Sunshine Coast. Australia's newest university offers students a truly Australian experience. Located 1 hour from Brisbane, on the Sunshine Coast, USC offers courses in a wide range of disciplines, outstanding faculty, small classes, individualized attention, strong program of support services and cultural activities. Internships available with the required prior academic preparation. Student apartments adjacent to campus.

Dates: Session I: early Feb-end of Jun; Session II: mid-Jul-early Dec. **Costs:** Approx. $4,700 per semester includes orienation in the U.S. and Australia, 20 weeks of housing with food allowance, Australian health insurance, USC tuition, administrative fees. Airfare and SUNY tuition not included. **Contact:** Office of International Programs, P.O. Box 2000, SUNY Cortland, Cortland, NY 13045; 607-753-2209, fax 607-753-5989; koppl@cortland.edu, [www.studyabroad.com/suny/cortland].

Belize

Internships in Belize. Experience living and working in an English-speaking developing country. Internships are available in most disciplines. Interns live with host families. Following a 1-week orientation, participants work full time with various agencies and organizations. Must be self-starters. Journals and written projects are submitted for assessment at the end of program. Academic credit offered: 15-16 credits per semester. Required: 2.5 cumulative GPA, strong performance in major, maturity, and adaptability. Junior or senior status.

Dates: Fall and spring, 16-17 weeks each. **Costs:** Estimate: $4,400 includes internship supervision, room and board, health insurance, local transportation, international airfare, full-day orientation prior to departure in Cortland, and 1-week orientation upon arrival in Belize. SUNY tuition not included. **Contact:** Office of International Programs, Box 2000, SUNY Cortland, Cortland, NY 13045; 607-753-2209, fax 607-753-5989; studyabroad@cortland.edu, [www.studyabroad.com/suny/cortland].

Costa Rica

Learn Spanish While Volunteering. Assist with the training of Costa Rican public school teachers in ESL and computers. Assist local health clinic, social service agencies, and environmental projects. Enjoy learning Spanish in the morning, volunteer work in the afternoon/evening. Spanish classes of 2-4 students plus group learning activities; conversations with middle class homestay families (1 student or couple per family). Homestays and most volunteer projects are in a small town near the capital, San José.

Dates: Year round, all levels. Classes begin every Monday (except Mar 25-29 and Dec 14-Jan 5), volunteer program is continuous. **Costs:** $345 per week for 26 hours of classes and group activities including Costa Rican dance and cooking classes. Includes tuition, meals, homestay, laundry, all materials, weekly 3-hour cultural tour, and airport transportation. $25 one-time registration fee. **Contact:** Susan Shores, Registrar, Latin American Language Center, PMB 123, 7485 Rush River Dr., Suite 710, Sacramento, CA 95831-5260; 916-447-0938, fax 916-428-9542; lalc@madre.com, [www.madre.com/~lalc].

Europe

Internship Program. CCI's Discovery Abroad Internship Program gives students (18-25) the opportunity to participate in a volunteer internship in France, Germany, Ireland, Italy, or the U.K. Internships provide exciting opportunities for language and cross-cultural immersion and valuable work experience. Participants live with a host family for the duration of the program and will be placed in an internship related to their course of study.

Dates: Year round. **Costs:** One month approx. $2,000, 2 months approx. $2,900, 3 months approx. $3,400. **Contact:** Outbound Department, Center for Cultural Interchange, 17 N. 2nd Ave., St. Charles, IL 60174; 888-ABROAD1, fax 630-377-2307; karen@cci-exchange.com, [www.cci-exchange.com].

Internships in Europe/E.P.A. The Univ. of Rochester and Educational Programs Abroad sponsor programs in London, Bonn, Brussels, Madrid, and Paris that combine coursework with unpaid internships for academic credit. Fields include politics, law, business, health science, and the arts. Available to juniors, seniors, and recent graduates. Requirements: 3.0 GPA or better, and at least 2 years of college-level language study where appropriate.

Dates: Sep-Dec, Jan-Apr; 2 summer terms of 8 weeks each. **Costs:** Semester programs range from $6,700-$9,850; summer $5,400. **Contact:** Jacqueline Levine, Director, Center for Study Abroad, Univ. of Rochester, Rochester, NY 14627; 716-275-7532, fax 716-461-5131; abroad@mail.rochester.edu, [www.rochester.edu/College/study-abroad/europe/index.html].

Prehistoric and Tribal Art. Apprenticeship in prehistoric and tribal art: research, editing, international relations, museums, and exhibitions planning, evaluation and definition of rock art and of art objects. Minimum stay: 3 months; stage 6 months or 12 months. Specialization courses and field school. Details upon request.

Dates: Year round. **Costs:** Contact sponsor. **Contact:** Prof. Emmanuel Anati, Centro Camuno di Studi Preistorici (CCSP), 25044 Capo di Ponte, BS, Italy [www.rockart-ccsp.com].].

Western Europe

First Choice/Ski Bound. First Choice leases and runs 30 hotels and 40 chalets in European ski resorts. Recruits over 850 staff to work in resorts each year. Positions include hotel/bar/restaurant managers, chefs (all grades), kitchen porters/night porters, bar staff, general assistants maintenance staff. A job with First Choice provides the opportunity to travel, meet many new friends, improve language skills, and learn to ski while gaining valuable job experience. Training is carried out in house either prior to departure or while in resort. Offers attractive package that includes travel to and from resort, medical insurance, personal belonging insurance, food, accommodations, and either a free or subsidized lift pass (dependent on position).

Dates: Contact organization for details. **Costs:** Contact organization for details. **Contact:** Applications should be made in writing with a resume: First Choice Ski Lakes and Mountains Division, Olivier House, 18 Marine Parade, Brighton BN2 1TL, U.K.; 011-44-1273-677777, fax 011-44-1273-600486.

Germany

Internship Programs. This program is designed for American college seniors or recent graduates in business, hotel management, engineering, or technical fields who want 6-12 months of practical on-the-job training in an international environment. Individuals are placed in paid internships with companies that match their professional interests.

Dates: Programs begin the first day of each month. **Costs:** Application fee: Participants responsible for airfare, housing, and living expenses. **Contact:** Isabell Kowalk, CDS International, Inc., 871 United Nations Plaza, 15th Fl., New York, NY 10017; 212-497-3500; info@cdsintl.org; [www.cdsintl.org].

Learn German and Discover Berlin. GLS, one of the leading institutions teaching German as a foreign language in Germany, offers various levels of German all year round (age 16 and up), preparation for all language certificates, business German, German for bankers and lawyers. Special feature: internships in German companies. GLS has accreditation with some U.S. universities.

Dates: Year round. **Costs:** Price example: $1,080 standard 4-week course and apartment share. **Contact:** GLS Sprachenzentrum, Barbara Jaeschke, Managing Director, Kolonnenstrasse 26, 10829 Berlin, Germany; 011-49-30-780-08-90; fax 011-49-30-787-41-92; germancourses@gls-berlin.com, [www.german-courses.com].

Latin America

Internship Positions. In Costa Rica, Mexico, Guatemala, Ecuador, Argentina, Peru, Bolivia. Various positions in the fields of health care, education, tourism, ESL, business, law, marketing, administrative, environmental, and social work. Additional customized options available. Four weeks to 6 months. Inexpensive lodging in homestays or dorms. Some positions provide free room and board.

Dates: Year round. Flexible start dates. **Costs:** $350 placement and application fee. Travel insurance and pre-departure preparation included. Lodging costs depend on location. **Contact:** AmeriSpan Unlimited, P.O. Box 40007, Philadelphia, PA 19106; 800-879-6640, fax 215-751-1100; info@amerispan.com, [www.amerispan.com].

Russia and the NIS

ACTR Business Russian Language and Internship Program. This program combines a curriculum focusing on the language of Russian business communication with a 20-hour per week internship in a U.S. or Russian business, NGO, or government agency. The program emphasizes speaking and reading skills for business communications, commercial document preparation, and reading the Russian business press.

Dates: Summer term, academic year, fall and spring. **Costs:** Summer $6,000, fall/spring terms $9,000, academic year $15,000. **Contact:** Graham Hettlinger, Gabriel Coleman, or Terrence Graham, Program Officer, ACTR, 1776 Massachusetts Ave., NW, Suite 700, Washington, DC 20036; 202-833-7522, fax 202-833-7523; hettlinger@actr.org, [www.actr.org].

Scandinavia

Training Program. Two- to 6-month positions in engineering, chemistry, computer science, agriculture, business, TEFOL. Most positions are in Finland and Sweden.

Dates: Contact organization for details. **Costs:** $50 application fee. **Contact:** Training, The American-Scandinavian Foundation, 58 Park Ave., New York, NY 10016; 212-879-9779, fax 212-686-2115; trainscan@amscan.org, [www.amscan.org].

United Kingdom and Ireland

AIFS International Internship Program in London. A 1-semester program awarding 12 to 18 credits for an unpaid internship in London. Placements are in international business, finance, marketing, international relations, education, media, museums and galleries, art and design firms, theater and entertainment, and politics. Individual attention given to clarify and set goals as well as support during placement.

Dates: Sep-Dec; Jan-May. **Costs:** $11,000 includes tuition, housing, and one way flight to London from any of 32 U.S. cities. **Contact:** AIFS, River Plaza, 9 West Broad St., Stamford, CT 06902-3788; collegeinfo@aifs.com, [www.aifs.com/java/us/aifsay_s/ukintem/int.htm].

AIU London Study and Internship Program. AIU's central London campus offers a U.S.-accredited curriculum and a multicultural population. Study abroad students take courses in International Business, Communication, Liberal Arts, Fashion Design/Marketing, Interior Design, Visual Communication, and Media Production. Program features include comprehensive student services, activities/travel, furnished apartment accommodations, and scholarships and financial aid.

Dates: Five regular academic quarters: fall (Oct-Dec); winter (Jan-Mar); spring (Mar-May); summer I (Jun-Jul); summer II (Aug-Sep). Special 4-week summer sessions as well. **Costs:** Three classes $4,900; 4 classes $5,700; 2 classes and internship $4,900. **Contact:** American InterContinental Univ., 6600 Peachtree-Dunwoody Rd., 500 Embassy Row, Atlanta, GA 30328; 800-255-6839, fax 404-965-8006; studyabroad@aiuniv.edu, [http://studyabroad.aiuniv.edu].

Hansard Scholars Programme. An opportunity for students to become involved in the workings of the British government and British politics, accompanied by a comprehensive study of British politics and British public policy. Students are mainly assigned internships with Members of Parliament, but also to political parties, think tanks, and pressure groups. Prerequisites: 2 or more years of college. Application materials: transcript, 2 letters of recommendation, an essay, and a personal statement.

Dates: Spring: mid-Jan-early Apr; summer: mid-May-late Jul; fall: late-Sep-mid-Dec. **Costs:** £5,350 per semester (includes housing and London travel costs, and a series of study visits and social events). **Contact:** Melanie Rimmer, Programme Coordinator, The Hansard Society, St. Philips, Building North, Sheffield St., London WC2A 2EX, U.K.; 011-44-171-955-7713, fax 011-44-171-955-7492; hansard@lse.ac.uk, [www.hansard-society.org.uk].

Internship Program in Wales. International work experience by the sea in Wales. Business, media, leisure, local government, law, administration, social work, and more. Accommodations in university housing; orientation; assessment, and transcript. Four credits. See web site for details.

Dates: Summer 2002, late May-mid Jun. **Costs:** Approx. $2,000 includes accommodations. **Contact:** Emma Frearson, American Studies Exchange Office, Univ. of Wales Swansea, Singleton Park, Swansea SA2 8PP, Wales, U.K.; 011-44-1-792-295135, fax 011-44-1-792-295719; e.frearson@swansea.ac.uk, [www.swan.ac.uk/sao].

Internship Program. We personally design internship packages, both in New York and London to suit individual needs and career interests. Internships are available year round in just about any field imaginable.

Dates: Year round. **Costs:** From $995 year round internship to $4,995 London summer internship packages (4 weeks). Includes program, theater, trips, room and partial board. **Contact:** Janet Kollek Evans, Director, American Assn. of Overseas Studies, 51 Drayton Gardens, Suite 4, London SW10 9RX, U.K.; 800-EDU-BRIT, aaos2000@hotmail.com, [www.worldwide.edu/uk/aaos].

London Internship Program. A pioneer of supervised work experience, Middlesex Univ. offers one of the widest range of internships in the U.K. Year-long opportunities are available to gain experience in business, politics, community, and health, amongst others. All internships are project-based, academically supervised, and carry academic credit. Internships can be taken alongside other university courses.

Dates: Fall, spring, or summer semester. **Costs:** Approx. $1,950 (tuition and internship). **Contact:** Valdev Chaggar, Registry Admissions, Middlesex Univ., White Hart Ln., London N17 8HR, U.K.; 011-44-203-362-5782, fax 011-44-208-362-5649; admissions@mdx.ac.uk.

Univ. of North London. SUNY Cortland celebrates its 29th consecutive year at UNL. Over 400 courses are offered. Fields of study include education, natural sciences, humanities, communications, social sciences, business, health, theater arts, fine arts, and others. Direct enrollment with British students. Credits per semester: 12-16. Pre-arranged housing in flats in the Bayswater district. Full- and part-time internships available.

Dates: Fall: late-Sep-mid Dec; spring: end of Jan-mid-May. **Costs:** Estimates: $7,800 per semester; academic year: $13,000. Estimates include full-day orientation in the U.S., application fee, pre-arranged apartment rental, meals, commuter ticket on underground,

London tour and Thames cruise, insurance, roundtrip airfare from N.Y., transportation from airport to downtown London upon arrival, passport, books and supplies, various cultural activities, administrative fees. SUNY tuition and spending money not included. **Contact:** Office of International Programs, Box 2000, SUNY Cortland, Cortland, NY 13045; 607-753-2209, fax 607-753-5989; studyabroad@cortland.edu, [www.studyabroad.com/suny/cortland].

Worldwide

Association for Int'l. Practical Training (AIPT). AIPT is the foremost provider of worldwide on-the-job training programs for students and professionals seeking international career development and life-changing experiences. AIPT arranges workplace exchanges in hundreds of professional fields, bringing employers and trainees together from around the world. AIPT's online placement service PINPOINT matches individuals seeking training opportunities with appropriate training positions in their field.

Dates: Year round. **Costs:** Vary. **Contact:** Customer Service Representative, AIPT, 10400 Little Patuxent Pkwy., Suite 250, Columbia, MD 21044-3519; 410-997-2200, fax 410-992-3924; aipt@aipt.org, [www.aipt.org].

Boston Univ. International Programs. Offering internship and language/liberal arts, fine arts, archaeology, engineering, and tropical ecology programs in 40 locations on 6 continents and in 9 different languages. Course offerings range from intermediate-level language and liberal arts study through advanced-level, direct enrollment in local universities. Internship programs combine coursework with participation in local work life. Application materials: 2 references, transcript, essays, and academic approval.

Dates: Fall, spring, and summer (length varies). **Costs:** $4,800-$17,311; application fee: $45. **Contact:** Boston Univ., International Programs, 232 Bay State Rd., 5th Fl., Boston, MA 02215; 617-353-9888, fax 617-353-5402; abroad@bu.edu, [www.bu.edu/abroad].

Directory of International Internships. The Directory is a comprehensive guide to international internships sponsored by educational institutions, government agencies, and private organizations. The Directory consists of 170 pages which includes subject and location indexes, international internship opportunities, and a bibliography.

Dates: Up-to-date, 4th ed., revised in late 1998. **Costs:** $25 includes s/h. **Contact:** Charles Gliozzo, Michigan State Univ., Rm. 209,

International Center, E. Lansing, MI 48824; 517-353-5589, fax 517-353-7254; gliozzo@pilot.msu.edu, [www.isp.msu.edu].

Global Service Corps (GSC), a project of Earth Island Institute, creates opportunities for adult participants to live in Tanzania and Thailand homes while volunteering on health, education and environment community service and development projects. These service-learning programs emphasize grass-roots collaboration on the local level, mutual transfer of skills, and cross-cultural understanding. Our goals are to provide developing communities with the means to function more sustainably, and to widen the perspectives of participants as responsible global citizens. Project areas: HIV/AIDS prevention, health care, Buddhism immersion, environmental education, English language instruction and sustainable agriculture. Undergraduate and Graduate level credits qualifying for financial aid available.

Dates: Year round. Contact GSC office or check the web site for specific starting dates **Costs:** Approx. $1,800-$2,000 for 2-4 week project trips: $595 per month for 2-6 month long-term extensions; $2,815-$3,145 for summer and semester college internships. Includes extensive pre-departure preparation and in-country expenses (hotel and homestay room and board, orientation, training, project expenses, transportation, excursions). Airfare not included, discounted international airfare available. **Contact:** Global Service Corps., 300 Broadway, Suite 28, San Francisco, CA 94133; 415-788-3666 ext 128, fax 415-788-7324,; gsc@earthisland.org, [www.globalservicecorps.org].

IAESTE (United States). Founded in 1948, the International Association for the Exchange of Students for Technical Experience (IAESTE) is an international network that coordinates paid international internships for students in technical fields such as engineering, computer science, mathematics, natural/physical sciences, architecture, and agricultural science. IAESTE United States has represented IAESTE in America since 1950.

Dates: Application deadline for 2002 internships is January 1, 2002. **Costs:** $25 application fee, $175 participation fee. **Contact:** Customer Service Representative, 10400 Little Patuxent Pkwy., Suite 250, Columbia, MD 21044-3519; 410-997-3069, fax 410-997-5168; aipt@aipt.org, [www.aipt.org/iaeste.html].

Internships International. Quality, nonpaying internships in London, Paris, Dublin, Dresden, Santiago, Budapest, Melbourne, Bangkok, and Glasgow, and Capetown. Internships in all fields, from 8 weeks to 6 months. Open to college graduates and seniors requiring an internship to graduate.

Dates: Based on individual's needs. **Costs:** $800 program fee for all cities except Dublin ($1,000). **Contact:** Judy Tilson, Director, Internships International, P.O. Box 480, Woolwich, ME 04579-0480; 207-443-3019, fax 207-442-7942; intintl@aol.com, [http://rtpnet.org/~intintl].

Marist International Internships. Internship and study abroad programs in Australia, England, Ireland, Italy, and Spain. Programs combine internships and course work at host institutions. Homestays are available at select sites.

Dates: Fall and spring semesters and full academic year. **Costs:** Average program fee is $11,500. **Contact:** Carol Toufali, Marist College, 3399 North Rd., Poughkeepsie, NY 12601; 845-575-3330, fax 845-575-3294; international@marist.edu, [www.marist.edu/international].

MAST Experience Abroad. A chance to learn first-hand under the guidance of innovative and successful farmers, agribusiness operators, and horticulturists around the world. Spend 2 to 12 months training on a farm or agricultural, horticultural, or forestry business in one of 15 countries. Develop lifelong friendships with your host family and colleagues. Gain a personal and professional learning experience that will shape your life. Single men and women between the ages of 18 and 30.

Dates: Jan, Mar, Jun, Sep. Other dates available. **Costs:** $400 program fee. **Contact:** Susan VonBank, MAST International, Univ. of Minnesota, 1954 Buford Ave., #395, St. Paul, MN 55108; 800-346-6278, 612-624-3740; mast@tc.umn.edu, [www.mast.agri.umn.edu].

ELEVEN

EDUCATIONAL TRAVEL
BEST PROGRAMS

Ann Waigand, our first educational travel editor, writes: "I discovered Transitions Abroad 25 years ago, just as I headed out to graduate study in Germany. Within two years I completed a graduate degree, settled down with my first job, and assumed the door to study abroad was closed. On the contrary. Over the past 25 years the number of adults participating in study abroad or attending short-term classes overseas has exploded." Programs based in more than one country are listed under "Worldwide." (Credit-bearing courses can be audited, often at reduced cost.)

Argentina

Argentina I.L.E.E. Located in downtown Buenos Aires. Dedicated exclusively to teaching Spanish as a foreign language. Small groups and private classes year round. All teachers hold master's degrees in education or literature and have been full-time Spanish professors for years. Method is intensive. Excellent social-cultural activities program. Student body is international, 40 percent from Central Europe. Highly recommended worldwide. Ask for individual references in U.S. Please visit web site for full information and photos.
Dates: Year round. **Costs:** Four-week intensive program (20 hours per week) including homestay $1,460; 2 weeks $730. Private classes $19 per hour. Registration fee (includes books) $100. **Contact:** Daniel Korman, I.L.E.E., International Director, Av. Callao 339, 3 Fl. (1022), Buenos Aires, Argentina; Tel./fax 011-54-11-47827173; info@ilee.com.ar, [www.ilee.com.ar].

Argentum, Univ. Blas Pascal. Argentum, The Institute for International Education at Universidad Blas Pascal in Córdoba, Argentina, is a Spanish language and culture program for undergraduate, graduate, and high school students providing language and culture courses as well as a wide variety of standard university courses. Participants are paired up with a tutor who acts as a bridge to the Argentine culture.
Dates: Session 1: Mar-Jun; session 2: Aug-Nov; intensive: Jun-Jul, Jul-Aug. **Costs:** Semester $6,100; intensive $2,200; intensive 3-week program $1,900. Includes tuition, room and board, organized group excursions. **Contact:** Marta Rosso-O'Laughlin, Argentum, P.O. Box 99, Medford, MA 02153; Tel./fax 978-318-0421; mrosso@aol.com, [www.worldwide.edu/argentina/argentum].

Canada

English Dramatic Literature Field Study. A visit to the Stratford Festival, seeing 6-8 plays, followed by a week of classes at Ball State Univ.
Dates: Jun. **Costs:** $900 (2001). **Contact:** William T. Liston, Prof. of English, Ball State Univ., Muncie, IN 47306-0460; 765-285-8473, fax 765-285-3765; 00wtliston@bsu.edu.

Research Expeditions. Join our research team and participate in fieldwork on blue, fin, humpback, and minke whales in the Gulf of St. Lawrence and Sea of Cortez. Small groups; experienced field biologists.
Dates: Jun-Oct. **Costs:** CAN$1,895 for 7 days includes hotel and all meals. **Contact:** Mingan

Island Cetacean Study, 285 Green St., St. Lambert, QC, J4P 1T3 Canada; Tel./fax 418-949-2845; mics@globetrotter.net, [www.rorqual.com].

Study English or French at POiNT3 in Montréal! We offer Intensive English and Intensive French, as well as North American Business Communication, TOEFL Preparation, and Learning Vacation programs. Our teachers are excellent, our classes are small, and we organize extra-curricular activities to help students to practice the language that they are learning. In addition, students have access to the Internet and language learning CD-ROMs, as well as to books and videos. We also offer students free weekly language workshops. Accommodation is available with one of our friendly host families, in a student residence, or in a furnished apartment.

Dates: Year round. Start dates every two weeks. Start dates for complete beginners every 4 weeks. **Costs:** Intensive French $260 USD for 2 weeks (44 hours), Intensive English $286 USD for 4 weeks (50 hours) **Contact:** POiNT3 Language Center, 404 Saint-Pierre Street, Suite 201, Montréal, PQ, Canada H2Y 2M2; 514-840-7228, fax 514-840-7111; info@point-3.com, [www.point-3.com].

China

Excavation Practicum in Xi'an. In collaboration with Xi'an Jiastong Univ. and the Archaeological Institute in Xi'an, Chian the Sino-American Field School of Archaeology offers credit. Archaeological Practicum (field work) and Chinese Art and Culture. In English.

Dates: Jul 2-Aug 2. **Costs:** Deposit $200; participation fee $3,795. **Contact:** Dr. Alfonz Lengyel, Fudan Museum Foundation, 4206 73rd Terr. E., Sarasota, FL 34243; Tel./fax 941-351-8208; fmfsafsa@juno.com.

Costa Rica

COSI (Costa Rica Spanish Institute). COSI offers high quality instruction with a very professional and organized staff. We provide the unique possibility of taking Spanish classes in San José and at Manuel Antonio National Park (beach and rainforest).

Dates: Year round. **Costs:** Prices start at $315 per week including 20 hours of instruction in mini groups of a maximum of 5 students, books, homestay, cultural activities, access to email, airport pickup. **Contact:** COSI, P.O. Box 1366-2050, San Pedro, San José, Costa Rica; 011-506-234-1001, fax 011-506-253-2117; office@cosi.co.cr, [www.cosi.co.cr].

Costa Rican Language Academy (C.R.L.A.). Costa Rican owned and operated language school offers first-rate Spanish instruction in a warm and friendly environment. Teachers with university degrees. Small groups or private classes. Volunteer opportunities. Included free in the programs are airport transportation, coffee and natural refreshments, Internet, excursions, Latin dance, Costa Rican cooking, and conversation classes to provide students with complete cultural immersion.

Dates: Year round (start anytime). **Costs:** $155 per week or $235 per week for program with homestay. All other activities and services included at no additional cost. **Contact:** Costa Rican Language Academy, P.O. Box 1966-2050, San José, Costa Rica; fax 011-506-233-5065. In the U.S.: 800-854-6057; crlang@sol.racsa.co.cr, [www.learn-spanish.com].

Learn Spanish While Volunteering. Assist with the training of Costa Rican public school teachers in ESL and computers. Assist local health clinic, social service agencies, and environmental projects. Enjoy learning Spanish in the morning, volunteer work in the afternoon/evening. Spanish classes of 2-4 students plus group learning activities; conversations with middle class homestay families (1 student or couple per family). Homestays and most volunteer projects are in a small town near the capital, San José.

Dates: Year round, all levels. Classes begin every Monday (except Mar 25-29 and Dec 14-Jan 5), volunteer program is continuous. **Costs:** $345 per week for 26 hours of classes and group activities including Costa Rican dance and cooking classes. Includes tuition, meals, homestay, laundry, all materials, weekly 3-hour cultural tour, and airport transportation. $25 one-time registration fee. **Contact:** Susan Shores, Registrar, Latin American Language Center, PMB 123, 7485 Rush River Dr., Suite 710, Sacramento, CA 95831-5260; 916-447-0938, fax 916-428-9542; lalc@madre.com, [www.madre.com/~lalc].

Living Among the Giant Grasses. Work with and learn about tropical bamboos, one of the world's fastest growing renewable resources while you experience rural Costa Rican life in a wild river setting. This program offers a general orientation on the subject of bamboo, including opportunities to work in a tropical garden, participate in the development of a small bamboo plantation, and assist in the work of a bamboo furniture maker and sculptor.

Tango and Spanish in Buenos Aires
Even the Tourists Are from Latin America

By Catherine M. Thomas

Buenos Aires is a vibrant, cosmopolitan city of 12 million where you can immerse yourself in a lively, fascinating culture while studying Spanish. I spent one month there at the Instituto de Lengua Española para Extranjeros (ILEE), a few steps from Calle Corrientes, the Buenos Aires equivalent of Broadway.

ILEE attracts students from all over the world. The instructors—who use the "direct method," meaning that only Spanish is spoken—are seasoned professionals with graduate degrees in education or literature. The school hosts walking tours of various Buenos Aires neighborhoods daily at 5 p.m. and more extensive outings on Saturdays.

Although Buenos Aires has a reputation for being an expensive city, I did not find it to be so. The peso is equal to the dollar, so you always know exactly how much you are spending. A subway ride costs 60 cents. Most of the museums are free. Delicious coffee, served with a "medialuna" (an Argentine croissant) and a small glass of fresh-squeezed orange juice, costs $1.50. A tender filet mignon large enough for two diners is $9.

Then there's the Argentine tango: a passionate, sensual, and dramatic dance invented in Buenos Aires in the late 19th century. You can see it danced for free in the city's pedestrian-only streets and plazas; you can pay to see it performed in countless theaters and nightclubs, or, on any given day, you can choose from at least five different "milongas" (a milonga is a large room with live or recorded music and a good dance floor surrounded by tables where people gather to dance tango socially). Many milongas are preceded by a free group class. In professional dance schools tango classes generally cost $8-$9 for a 2-hour group session. Private lessons are also widely available.

No matter how you decide to spend your free time, you will have plenty of opportunities to practice your Spanish. Few people speak English in Buenos Aires, and nearly all the signs and menus are in Spanish only. Even the tourists are mostly from other South American countries.

Group classes at ILEE cost $240 per week for 20 hours of instruction. You can begin any day, year round. A $100 registration fee covers training materials and a placement test. The school can help arrange convenient homestays with private rooms, with meals or without, or nearby accommodations in 3-star hotels. The price range is $500 to $1,000 per month for singles. My furnished, well-located, privately-owned apartment cost $800 a month. If you would prefer studying in a smaller Argentine city, you might want to try ILEE's new branch school in Córdoba.

Contact: Daniel Korman, International Director, Instituto de Lengua Española para Extranjeros (ILEE), Avenida Callao 339, 3rd Fl., Buenos Aires, Argentina; Tel./fax 011-54-11-4782-7173; ilee@overnet.com.ar, [www.ilee.com.ar].

Dates: Year-round, 1 month sessions, beginning the 1st of each month. **Costs:** $750 for 1st month, $600 each additional month. Includes private sleeping space, shared bath, meals. Airfare not included. **Contact:** Brian Erickson, Apdo. 295-7210 Guapiles, Costa Rica; fax 011-506-710-2264; brieri99@yahoo.com.

Spanish in Costa Rica and Special Offers "2 x 1". The Instituto de Español "Costa Rica" is a specialized institution in the teaching of the Spanish language and Latin American culture and traditions. Our course includes tours and housing with selected Costa Rican families. We are unique in offering super special packages "2 x 1" for couples of friends enrolling together.

Dates: New courses start every Monday year round. **Costs:** From $190. **Contact:** Mrs. Sabina de Serrano, Director, Instituto de Español "Costa Rica," P. O. Box 1405, 2100 Guadalupe, San José, Costa Rica; 011-506-2806622, fax 011-506-2834733; iespcr@sol.racsa.co.cr, [www.professionalspanish.com].

Ecuador

Academia Latinoamericana. Proud to be the friendliest Spanish school you have ever known. Family owned and operated. The program offers language study at 9 levels, for complete beginners through advanced. Experienced staff, native Ecuadorians. Carefully selected host families within walking distance of school. Exclusive "Cloud Forest and Galápagos" extension program, volunteer program. U.S. college credit available.

Dates: Year round. **Costs:** $255 per week. Includes 20 hours of lessons, 7 days with host family, 2 meals per day, transfer, services at the school, and teaching material. **Contact:** Suzanne S. Bell, Admissions Director, USA/International, 640 East 3990 South, Suite E, Salt Lake City, UT, 84107; 801-268-4608, fax 801-265-9156; ecuador@access.net.ec, [www.latinoschools.com].

Europe

Budapest Semesters in Mathematics. A rigorous mathematics program for students attending colleges and universities in North America majoring in mathematics or computer science. Classes taught in English by eminent Hungarian professors. Unlike any other program you will ever encounter. Mix it all with a world as warm and friendly as Budapest, and it's paradise.

Dates: Spring: Feb-May; fall: Sep-Dec. **Costs:** Tuition: $3,890 plus $300 refundable housing deposit. **Contact:** Dr. Paul D. Humke, Director, Budapest Semesters in Mathematics, St. Olaf College, Northfield, MN 55057; 800-277-0434, 507-646-3114; budapest@stolaf.edu, [www.stolaf.edu/depts/math/budapest].

En Famille Overseas. Homestays in friendly families in France, Spain, and Germany. All ages. Language courses or one-to-one tuition available.

Dates: One week or more year round. **Costs:** £65 fees. One week full board approx. £200-£350 plus tuition and fees (2002). **Contact:** En Famille Overseas, 60B Maltravers St., Arundel, BN18 9BG, U.K.; 011-44-1903-883266, fax 011-44-1903-883582; enfamilleoverseas@aol.com.

ICCE Educational Travel Programs. Learn the language, study the culture. French Riviera, Paris, Aix-en-Provence, Italian Riviera della Versilia, Spanish Costa del Sol. Also summers in Tokyo and Beijing. For credit or just for pleasure. More program—less cost. For students of all ages.

Dates: Call for details. **Costs:** From $2,479 and up (2 weeks). Includes airfare, tuition, room and board. **Contact:** Dr. Stanley I. Gochman, ICCE, 5 Bellport Ln., Bellport, NY 11713; 631-286-5228.

The European Centre. This travel-study program for adults offers continuing education in the heart of the Alps: Innsbruck, Austria. Attend challenging seminars in history, opera, literature and the arts, as well as German language and culture. On the weekends, travel with us to Venice and Vernoa and to Prague and Bohemia.

Dates: Jul. **Costs:** $3,295 double occupancy, single supplement of $350 (2000). **Contact:** Irene B. Ziegler, PhD, Univ. of New Orleans, Metropolitan College, ED114, New Orleans, LA 70148; 504-280-7318, fax 504-280-7317;; iziegler@uno.edu, [www.uno.edu/~inst/Welcome.html].

France

Aromatherapy Summer School. Run by the prestigious state licensed Australasian College USA and held in the heart of Provence at the height of the lavender harvest. Includes French cuisine, instruction, and instructional tours, accommodations and transfers. Credit toward the state licensed Diploma in Aromatherapy. Curriculum changes annually.

Dates: Summer 2002 dates to be confirmed. **Costs:** 2001: $1,950; 2002 to be confirmed. **Contact:** Erika Petersen, Australasian College USA, 530 1st St., P.O. Box 57, Lake Oswego, OR 97034; 800-487-8839, fax 503-636-0706; achs@herbed.com, [www.herbed.com].

French Language Learning Vacations. Learn French while discovering the chateaux of the Loire Valley, the secrets of Provence, or the sandy beaches of the Mediterranean. Our programs are designed for independent travelers sharing a passion for the French culture and lifestyle. We offer a choice of locations in Tours, Aix-en-Provence, Montpellier, Paris, or Nice.

Dates: Two or more weeks year round. **Costs:** Two-week packages range from $825-$1,265. Includes classes, housing and fees. **Contact:** Jim Pondolfino, French-American Exchange, 3213 Duke Street, #620, Alexandria, VA 22314; 800-995-5087, fax 703-823-4447; faetours@erols.com, [www.faetours.com].

Immersion Course in French. Intensive 2-4 week course for professional adults in Villefranche (next to Nice) overlooking the French Riviera's most beautiful bay; 8 hours a day with 2 meals. Audiovisual classes, language lab, practice sessions, discussion-lunch. Evening film showings, evening outings with teachers, excursions to cultural landmarks. Accommodations in comfortable private apartments.

Dates: Courses start Jan, Feb, Mar, May, Jun, Aug, Sep, Oct, Nov, Dec. **Costs:** Tuition fees: Dec-Apr Euro 200/4 weeks; May-Nov EURO 2,650/4 weeks. Accommodations: Dec-Apr EURO 300-EURO 800/4 week; May-Nov EURO 350-EURO 900/4 weeks. **Contact:** Frédéric Latty, Institut de Francais, 23, avenue General Leclerc, 06230 Villefranche Sur Mer, France; 011-33-493-01-88-44, fax 011-33-493-76-92-17; instfran@aol.com, [www.institutdefrancais.com].

Language and Cooking Classes. Dr. Janice Ovadiah offers a menu of French study programs for many needs, budgets, and durations. Accommodations include homestays, hotels, college campuses, or chateau lodgings. Participants may choose to study in accredited schools in Paris, on the French Riviera, or in other attractive French cities. French-language programs and 1-week courses in French cuisine are available during the summer and throughout the year. Programs cater to both general students and business professionals for leisure or intensive study.

Dates: Year round. **Costs:** Rates vary according to length of program. **Contact:** Dr. Janice E. Ovadiah, 303 W. 66 St., New York, NY 10023; 212-724-5823, fax 212-294-5145; jovadiah@aol.com.

Learn French in Paris with OISE. Brand new school in Latin Quarter! Traditional building, contemporary interior, excellent study facilities. Highly targeted, results-based intensive courses for general, professional, and exam preparation purposes. Small groups (maximum 8) and/or individual tuition, 10-30 lessons per week. Accommodations provided; excellent social program; friendly dynamic team. Courses for all levels start every Monday.

Dates: Year round. **Costs:** $360 per week (based on 20 lessons), homestay accommodations $230 per week. **Contact:** Claire Jannot (Principal), OISE Paris, 71 bis rue de Vaugirard F-75006 Paris, France; 011-33-142-22-01-98, fax 011-33-142-22-03-31; info@oise.net, [www.oise.net/paris].

Germany

Learn German in Heidelberg. The OISE School of German is on the top floor of smart, modern building with panoramic city views from school roof terrace. Intensive courses for general, professional, and exam preparation purposes. Small groups (maximum 8) and/or individual tuition, 10-30 lessons per week. Accommodations provided, excellent social program, friendly dynamic team. Courses for all levels start every Monday.

Dates: Year round. **Costs:** $360 per week (based on 20 lessons), homestay accommodations $165 per week. **Contact:** Matthias Brotel (Principal), Poststrasse 48, D-69115 Heidelberg, Germany; 011-49-62-21-90-58-20, fax 011-49-62-21-90-58-2-11; info@oise.net, [www.oise.net/heidelberg].

Greece

Greek Folk Dances and Culture. Workshops on Greek dance (traditional and ancient) including general courses on Greek culture (music, costume, language, etc.).

Dates: Summer 1998. **Costs:** $200 a week. **Contact:** Alkis Raftis, Greek Dances Theatre, 8 Schoiou St., GR-10558, Plaka, Athens, Greece; 011-30-1-3244395.

Guatemala

Art Workshops in Guatemala. We provide 10-day workshops in a wide variety of arts, including backstrap weaving; photography; creative writing; papermaking, beading, book, fiber, and visual arts. All classes are held in Antigua, Guatemala.

Dates: Classes held during Jan, Feb, Mar, Apr, Jul, Oct, and Nov. **Costs:** Approx. $1,850. Includes airfare from U.S., lodging, tuition, field trips, and all ground transportation. **Contact:** Liza Fourre, Director, Art Workshops in Guatemala, 4758 Lyndale Ave. S, Minneapolis, MN 55409-2304; 612-825-0747, fax 612-825-6637; info@artguat.org, [www.artguat.org].

Honduras

Honduras Conservation Corps. Participants live with Honduran and international volunteers while working on environmental conservation projects to benefit small communities in rural Honduras. Two-week work camp setting. Registration for more than 1 camp accepted. Spanish language and knowledge of environmental issues are welcomed but not required.

Dates: Jul 7-22; Jul 21-Aug 5; Aug 13-30; Aug 4-19; Sep 1-15. **Costs:** $200 per camp includes room and board plus $50 initial registration fee. Airfare not included. **Contact:** Partners of the Americas, 1424 K St., NW, Suite 700, Washington, DC 20005; 800-322-7844 ext. 227 or 114.; dm@partners.net, [www.partners.net].

India

Art and Architecture of India. Led by Dr. Don Stadtner, PhD, Indian Art History, UC Berkeley, this tour highlights ancient art and architecture of north India including paintings, sculpture, textiles, marble, bronzes, and temples. Special presentations by directors and curators of museums in Delhi, Bombay, and others.

Dates: Feb 11-Mar 3, 2002. **Costs:** From $5,350 double occupancy. **Contact:** Spirit of India, P.O. Box 446, Mill Valley, CA 94942; 888-367-6147, 415-381-5861, fax 415-381-6919; inquire@spirit-of-india.com, [www.spirit-of-india.com].

Israel

Pardes Institute of Jewish Studies. For over 25 years, Pardes has set the standard for rigorous study of Jewish texts in an open environment. At Pardes, students acquire technical and conceptual understandings of the sources. Pardes welcomes Jewish men and women from all backgrounds.

Dates: Year, semester, winter, and summer learning opportunities available. **Costs:** Depends upon length of time in Israel. **Contact:** Paula Steisel, American Pardes Foundation, 136 E. 39th St., New York, NY 10016; 212-447-4333, fax 212-447-4315; pardesusa@aol.com, [www.pardes.org.il].

Italy

Centro di Lingua Italiana I Malatesta. In the morning we offer group and individual courses, up to 7 lessons a day. In the afternoon, cultural courses such as History of Art, Italy Today, Italian Cookery, Italian for Business, Italian for Tourism, Language of Libretti, History of Opera, Diction.

Dates: One-, 2-, and 3-week classes year round. **Costs:** Costs vary by duration and type of course, starting at LIT530,000 for 1 week. **Contact:** Centro di Lingua and Cultura Italiana, I Malatesta, G. d'Augusto 144, 47900 Rimini, Italy; 011-390-541-56487, fax 011-390-541-21088; imalatesta@tn.nettuno.it, [www.akeor.it/imalatesta].

Italiaidea in Rome. All levels and formats of Italian language study from intensive short-term "survival Italian" to advanced, semester-long courses, business Italian, conversation, and flexible scheduling. For nearly 20 years we have been offering college credit courses at U.S. college and university programs in Italy; we now offer academic assistance and travel and study assistance to client institutions. Housing including homestays or shared apartments possible.

Dates: Year round. **Costs:** Sixty-hour group course EURO 423.49, 25-hour one-on one program EURO 692.05, 24-hour business Italian EURO 258.22; registration fee EURO 20.65. **Contact:** Carolina Ciampaglia or Dana Prescott, Piazza della Cancelleria 85, 00186 Roma, Italy; 011-390-0668307620, fax 011-390-066892997; italiaidea@italiaidea.com, [www.italiaidea.com].

Language Courses by the Sea. The courses: conversation course (2 hours a day); main minigroups (4 hours a day); intensive (main course plus 6 private lessons); indvidual tuition. Special courses: tourist industry, commercial Italian for import/export; small group (max. 6 students). Sports (sailing, catamaran, surfing); excursions (Calabria, Sicily). Accommodations in apartments.

Dates: Mar 6-Nov 24. **Costs:** Two-week course includes single room LIT1,010,000. **Contact:** Caffè Italiano Club, Largo A. Pandullo 5, 89861 Tropea (VV), Italy; 011-390-0963-60-32-84, 011-390-0963-61786; caffeitaliano@tin.it, [www.paginegialle.it/caffeital].

Study Italian in Florence or Tuscan Town. Study Italian in a 16th century Renaissance palace in the center of Florence or in a classic Tuscan town just 30 minutes from the sea. Koiné Center's professional language teachers and small class sizes encourage active participation by each student. Cultural program, guided excursions, choice of accommodations including host families.

Dates: Year round; starting dates each month. **Costs:** Two-week intensive program $325; 3 weeks $395; homestay accommodations from $220 for 2 weeks. **Contact:** In North America: Talking Traveler, 800-274-6007, fax 503-274-

ANTARTIC MARINE EXPEDITIONS
THE ULTIMATE IN EXOTIC LEARNING HOLIDAYS

By Robin and Arlene Karpan

We recently returned from a trip offered by Marine Expeditions, which claims to have the lowest prices anywhere. The experienced Canadian-based company, whose slogan is "to the ends of the earth," uses Russian ships and an international crew. The small ships leave from Ushuaia on the southern tip of Argentina and sail the 600 miles or so to the Antarctic peninsula. Most passengers opt for package deals that include airfare from major North American gateways. But you can also begin the trip in Ushuaia, an attractive option if you want to combine Antarctica with travels to other parts of South America.

The least expensive option (a shared cabin for four) from Ushuaia is just under $2,000 for an 8-day trip, including meals, all shore excursions, the lecture series, taxes, and port charges. We took the 10-day trip, which was about $200 more. Longer trips take in the Falkland Islands and South Georgia Island in addition to Antarctica.

The trip was a wonderful learning experience. The food and accommodations were excellent, with none of the pretense or conspicuous consumption of major cruise ship lines. The bridge was almost always open to visitors, and the Russian captain and crew were happy to explain routings and map readings. We were especially impressed with the knowledge of the expedition leaders. An extensive onboard lecture and film series covered everything to do with Antarctica: geography, wildlife, politics, the Antarctic Treaty, and famous explorers such as Scott, Amundsen, Shackleton, and Admiral Byrd. Each day after we arrived at the northernmost Antarctic islands we made landings by Zodiac and visited such places as Gentoo, Chinstrap, and Adelie penguin rookeries where we could walk amongst the nests without disturbing the birds.

Contact Marine Expeditions: 800-263-9147; info@marineex.com, [www.marineex.com].

9004. In Italy: Dr. Andrea Moradei, Koiné Center, Via Pandolfini 27, 50122 Firenze, Italy; 011-390-55-213881, [www.koinecenter.com]; homestay@teleport.com, [www.talkingtraveler.org].

Mexico

Cemanahuac Educational Community. Trips are highly educational, with college credit (graduate and undergraduate) available. Countries include Mexico, Belize, Costa Rica, and Guatemala. Focus areas include history, anthropology, archaeology, social issues, cooking and cuisine, and popular and folk art. Previous groups include teachers, social workers, artists, senior citizens, chefs, museum members, alumni groups, and other adult participants. Each trip individually planned.

Dates: Travel seminars can be held at any time of the year. **Costs:** Dependent on requirements and length of the field study trips. **Contact:** Vivian B. Harvey, Educational Programs Coordinator, Cemanahuac Educational Community, Apartado 5-21, Cuernavaca, Morelos, Mexico; 011-52-7-3186407, fax 011-52-7-312-5418. U.S.: 1321A Lake Shore Dr., Columbus, OH 43204; 614-487-0965; cemanahuac@compuserve.com, [www.cemanahuac.com].

Center for Bilingual Multicultural Studies. Intensive semester or intensive Spanish language programs for executives, bilingual teachers, healthcare professionals, seniors, nurses, high school students. Group-5 system, 40 class hours per week include Spanish class, Latin American courses and lectures, housing with Mexican host family or guest residence; excursions to historical and archaeological sites. Students enrolled may attend the university courses at no additional cost.

Dates: Year round starting every Monday. **Costs:** Registration fee $100; tuition $200 per week; lodging $168 per week, Plan A. **Contact:** Javier Espinosa, President, San Jeronimo #304, Col. Tlaltenango, Cuernavaca, Mor. 62179, Mexico; 011-527-317-10-87, fax 011-527-3-17-05-33; U.S. 800-932-20-68; admission@bilingual-center.com.mx, [www.bilingual-center.com].

Intensive Spanish in Yucatan. Centro de Idiomas del Sureste, A.C. (CIS), founded in 1974, offers 3-5 hours per day of intensive conversational Spanish classes with native-speaking, university-trained professors. Maximum 6 students per group, average 3. Program includes beginner courses to very advanced with related field trips and recom-mended optional homestay. Also special classes in business, legal, medical vocabulary, or Mayan studies.

Dates: Year round. Starts any Monday, except last 2 weeks in Dec. **Costs:** Tuition (3 hours per day program: $370 first 2 weeks, $135 each additional week); tuition 5 hours per day programs $570 first 2 weeks, $235 each additional week. **Contact:** Chloe C. Pacheco, Director, Centro de Idiomas del Sureste, A.C., Calle 14 #106 X25, col. Mexico, CP 97128, Mérida, Yucatán, Mexico; 011-52-99-26-11-55 or 011-52-99-26-94-94, fax 011-52-99-26-90-20; cisnorte@prodigy.net.mx, [www.cisyucatan.com.mx].

Mar de Jade Ocean-front Center, Chacala, Nayarit. Celebrating our 20th year as a center for responsible tourism, we are located in the fishing village of Chacala on its beautiful beach north of Puerto Vallarta. For 15-years, our volunteer/study program has been offering opportunities to guests to learn Spanish and put it to use in rural community volunteer projects, including a medical clinic, an after school program for children, a community kitchen and garden project, ESL classes, and house construc-tion. Guests gain insight into local culture through volunteering. Surrounded by lush jungle with the warm, clear Pacific at our door, they enjoy swimming, surfing, hiking, horseback riding, snorkeling, kayaking, whale-watching, and other excursions. Our calendar of retreats include yoga, meditation among others as well as our teen summer camp.

Dates: Year round. **Costs:** All rates are per person per night and include accommodations and 3 meals daily. Rates start at $60 per person per night for shared accommodations (up to 4 in a room), or $1,200 for 21 day/20 night optional volunteer program. Doubles, singles, suites, master suites, and apartments available. Add 15 percent tax to all rates. Reduced 3-week rates available in May, June, September, October. Children welcome. Optional Spanish classes: $80 per week with minimum of 6-night stay. Group rates available. **Contact:** In Mexico, Tel./fax 011-52-322-21171; Tel. 011-52-322-23524. U.S. mailing address: PMB 078-344, 705 Martens Ct., Laredo, TX 78041-6010; info@mardejade.com, [www.mardejade.com].

Nepal

Sojourn Nepal. Sojourn Nepal is a 12-week program comprised of homestay, language study, lectures, village stay, trekking, and opportunities for apprenticeships in a vast variety of areas. Cultural immersion at its finest.

Dates: Fall and spring semesters. **Costs:** $6,500 all inclusive. Offers fall/spring 11 weeks to Nepal and Tibet $7,000; 6 weeks summer to Nepal and Tibet $4,450; Ladahk $3,750. Airfare not included. **Contact:** Jennifer Warren, Sojourn Nepal, 2440 N. 56th St., Phoenix, AZ 85008; Tel./fax 602-840-9197; snepal@aol.com, [www.sojournnepal.org].

Spain

=**elemadrid**=. Learn Spanish at home and in Madrid! Spanish courses in small groups or private tuition for adults, professionals, Spanish teachers, unique program of Spanish culture classes, Spanish conversation, art seminars, Spanish dances, leisure activity courses, fascinating weekend excursions. Free Spanish word of the month. Conjugate Spanish verbs online.

Dates: Courses start every other Monday year round. **Costs:** Courses $235-$1,075 per week, culture classes included; accommodations $90-$980 per week; art seminars, dancing classes, leisure activity courses, and weekend excursions vary. **Contact:** =elemadrid=, Calle Serrano 4, 28001 Madrid, Spain; Tel./fax 011-34-91-432-4540/41; hola@elemadrid.com, [www.elemadrid.com].

Intensive Spanish Courses, Seville. CLIC IH, one of Spain's leading language schools, is located in the heart of Seville, the vibrant capital of Andalusia, and boasts a beautifully renovated Sevillian mansion as its center. Year-round intensive Spanish language courses, business Spanish, and official exam preparation are taught by highly qualified and motivated native teachers. CLIC IH combines professionalism with a friendly atmosphere. Academic credits available. Accommodations are carefully selected and we offer a varied cultural program as well as exchanges with local students.

Dates: Year round. **Costs:** Approx. $859 for a 4-week Spanish course and homestay, individual room, 2 meals per day. **Contact:** Bernhard Roters, CLIC IH Seville, C/ Albareda 19, 41001 Sevilla, Spain; 011-34-95-450-2131, fax 011-34-95-456-1696; clic@clic.es, [www.clic.org].

Learn Spanish in Madrid with OISE. Centrally located permanent school in the heart of Madrid's business district boasting state-of-the-art facilities. Intensive courses for general, professional, and exam preparation purposes. Small groups (maximum 8) and/or individual tuition, 10-30 lessons per week. Accommodations provided, excellent social program, friendly dynamic team. Courses for all levels start every Monday.

Dates: Year round. **Costs:** $360 per week (based on 20 lessons), homestay accommodation $215 per week. **Contact:** Robin Gravina (Principal), Orense 81, E-28020 Madrid, Spain; 011-34-91-571-2994, fax 011-34-91-570-0596; info@oise.net, [www.oise.net/madrid].

United Kingdom and Ireland

British Studies at Oxford. This program of study in one of the world's most prestigious universities offers undergraduate and graduate credit in art history, business, communication, drama, education, English literature, history, and political science taught by Oxford Univ. professors. The participants live in private rooms tidied daily by the college staff, who also serve 3 bountiful and tasty meals a day in the Great Hall. Field trips are an integral part of each course as well as group trips to the theater in Stratford-upon-Avon and London.

Dates: Summer: Jun 30-Jul 20; Jul 21-Aug 10; or Jun 30-Aug 10. **Costs:** $3,350 for 3 weeks; $6,050 for 6 weeks. Includes 4 or 8 credits, travel in Britain for course related events, theater, entrance to museums, dinners in country inns, and many field trips. Overseas travel not included. **Contact:** Dr. M.B. Pigott, Director, British Studies at Oxford, 322 Wilson Hall, Oakland Univ., Rochester, MI 48309-4401; 248-652-3405 or 248-370-4131, fax 248-650-9107; pigott@oakland.edu, [www.oakland.edu/oxford].

Summer Academy. Summer Academy offers study holidays at 11 British universities. The course fee includes full accommodations for 6 to 7 nights, tuition fees, and course-related excursions. Study topics include: heritage, the arts, countryside, and creative writing. Accommodations are in single rooms in university residence halls. Locations include: Aberystwyth, Bangor, Bristol, Canterbury, Durham, Exeter, Glasgow, Norwich, Sheffield, Southampton, Stirling, and York.

Dates: Jun-Aug. **Costs:** £480-£585 (2002). **Contact:** Andrea McDonnell, Marketing and Reservations Coordinator, Summer Academy, Keynes College, The Univ., Canterbury, Kent CT2 7NP, U.K.; 011-44-1227-470402/823473, fax 011-44-1227-784338; summeracademy@ukc.ac.uk, [www.ukc.ac.uk/sa/index.html].

UNH Cambridge Summer Program. Join us this summer in Cambridge, England, for the study of English, history, and the humanities at Cambridge Univ. We offer small classes and challenging courses, fine theater and excursions in England and Scotland, intellectual community among staff and students, and banquets and socializing in traditional English style—all in beautiful surroundings.

Dates: Six weeks Jul-Aug. **Costs:** $4,725. **Contact:** Margaret Love-Denman, Director, UNH Cambridge Summer Program, Hamilton Smith Hall, 95 Main St., Durham, NH 03824-3575; Tel./fax 603-862-3962; cambridge.program@unh.edu, [www.unh.edu/cambridge].

Univ. of Cambridge Summer Schools. Intensive study in Cambridge as part of an international community. Plenary lectures and special subject courses are offered, together with evening activities and excursions. Both multi-disciplinary and specialist-subject programs are available.

Dates: Jul and Aug. **Costs:** Tuition from £510-£740, accommodations from £285-£1,040 (2001 prices, 2002 TBA). **Contact:** International Division, Univ. of Cambridge, Madingley Hall, Cambridge CB3 8AQ, U.K.; 011-44-1954-280398, fax 011-44-1954-280200; intenq@cam.ac.uk, [www.cont-ed.cam.ac.uk/IntSummer].

Yeats International Summer School. Themes: The Poetry and Plays of Yeats—cultural and critical contexts, predecessors, contemporaries, successors, gender, politics, nationalism, postcolonialism, contemporary Irish poetry and drama, representing history.

Dates: Jul-Aug. **Costs:** $525 or £335 (2000). **Contact:** Yeats Society, Hyde Bridge, Sligo, Ireland [www.yeats-sligo.com].

Worldwide

Bicycle Africa/Cuba/Ecuador/Asia. Educational, people-to-people bicycle tours to all parts of Africa, Cuba, and Nepal. Cycling difficulty is moderate. Each tour is unique; all focus on the diversity of the culture, social institutions, and environment and the complexity of the history, economy, and society. Programs are led by area studies specialists.

Dates: Jan and Aug (Uganda), Feb and Aug (Tanzania/Kenya), Apr (Tunisia), Jun (Ecuador), Jul-Aug (South Africa, Zimbabwe, Malawi, Tanzania, Uganda), Sep-Oct (Eritrea/Ethiopia), Oct-Nov (Senegal/Guinea/Mali), Nov-Dec (Burkina Faso/Togo/Benin/Ghana), Nov-Apr (Cuba), Jan (Nepal). **Costs:** $990-$1,490 plus airfare for 2 weeks. Includes food, lodging, guides, and fees. **Contact:** International Bicycle Fund/Bicycle Africa, 4887 Columbia Dr. S. #T, Seattle, WA 98108-1919; Tel./fax 206-767-0848; ibike@bike.org, [www.ibike.org/ibike].

Conservation Expeditions. Frontier is an international conservation and research NGO which works in threatened tropical environments to protect endangered habitats and wildlife through research and practical projects. Offers self-funding volunteers the opportunity to work on overseas projects for 10 or 20 weeks. Full training is provided, leading to a qualification.

Dates: Jan-Mar, Apr-Jun, Jul-Sep, and Oct-Dec of each year. **Costs:** Volunteers must raise approx. GBP 2,500 plus airfare for 10 weeks. **Contact:** Research Assistant Coordinator, Frontier, 77 Leonard St., London EC2A 4QS, U.K.; 011-44-20-7613-2422, fax 011-44-20-7613-2992; enquiries@frontierprojects.ac.uk, [www.frontier.ac.uk].

Discovery Tours. Worldwide educational travel programs of the American Museum of Natural History (65 in 2001) are accompanied by curatorial and its scientific staff.

Dates: Year round. **Costs:** $3,198-$32,950. **Contact:** Richard Houghton, Discovery Tours, American Museum of Natural History, CPW at 79th St., New York, NY 10024-5192; discovery@amnh.org, [www.amnh.org].

Earthwatch Institute. Unique opportunities to work with leading scientists on 1- to 3-week field research projects worldwide. Earthwatch sponsors 160 expeditions in over 30 U.S. states and in 60 countries. Disciplines include archaeology, wildlife management, ecology, ornithology and marine mammalogy. No special skills needed—all training is done in the field.

Dates: Year round. **Costs:** Tax deductible contributions ranging from $695-$3,995 support the research and cover food and lodging expenses. Airfare not included. **Contact:** Earthwatch Institute, 3 Clocktower Pl., Suite 100, Box 75, Maynard, MA 01754-0075; 800-776-0188; info@earthwatch.org, [www.earthwatch.org].

ERDT/SHARE! Exchange Program. ERDT/SHARE! provides American students, ages 16 to 18, opportunities for summer, semester, or academic year homestays/study abroad. Language proficiency, academic standing, maturity are criteria for selection. Students live with host families and, depending upon program selected, attend local school or language school. ERDT/SHARE! Also provides opportunities for American families to host international high school exchange students.

Dates: Vary with type of program selected and academic year dates. Student and host family applications are accepted year round. **Costs:** $1,500-$7,000 (depending on program), excluding transportation and personal expenses. **Contact:** Roger Riske, President, 475 Washing-

THE ARTS IN NORTHERN IRELAND
ABUNDANT OPPORTUNITIES FOR VISITORS TO PARTICIPATE

By Rhonda Strickland

For the visitor to Northern Ireland there is an abundance of opportunities for studying or participating in the arts—or just having a good time attending events and seeing the real Northern Ireland. The organizers of the many organizations and festivals are very friendly and open to outsiders. They want North Americans to see that Northern Ireland has a rich cultural and artistic life and is not just a hotbed of troubles.

The Verbal Arts Center is a busy drop-in resource center in Londonderry where you can obtain information on literary events, join a writing workshop, attend a reading or "poetry slam," purchase publications by Irish authors, and use the Center's computer database to find the latest on Irish writers and events. In addition to being a hub for local literary arts, the center also aims to be a "window into international literature." It regularly sponsors an international storytelling festival.

In Belfast, the Arts Council of Northern Ireland runs the "Artslink" office, where you can find arts events throughout the province. You can check their database, or get a monthly broadsheet listing festivals and events.

Belfast is also home to the Creative Writers' Network, an umbrella organization bringing together writers' groups from all over Northern Ireland. They organize writing courses in all genres.

And if you're an aspiring screenplay writer, the Northern Ireland Film Commission is worth checking out. They connect script writers with production companies and offer helpful publications on how to get started making films. As for live theatre, the Shankhill Theatre Company in Belfast, is open to anyone who wants to act or write drama for production.

In Belfast, the Linen Hall Library features a regular monthly schedule of lectures on literary and historical issues. In their pleasant café you are actually encouraged to linger over coffee or lunch while reading their library materials.

Most events are free. Dates and opening times vary, so call or write for information:

Verbal Arts Center: Located in the Cathedral Old School on London St., within the walled city section of Londonderry. Open 9-5:30 Mon.-Fri. Call Sam Burnside, 011-44-1504-266946; [www.verbart.demon.co.uk].

Artslink: The Arts Council of Northern Ireland, MacNeice House, 77 Malone Rd., Belfast, Northern Ireland T9 6AQ. Call Mathew Hendry, 011-44-1232-385200.

West Belfast Festival, Culturalann Mnacadaim O'Faich, 216 Falls Rd., Belfast, Northern Ireland. Call Georde Murtagh, 011-44-1232-313440.

Belfast Folk Festival, 249 Cavehill Rd., Belfast, Northern Ireland. Call Nigel Martin, 011-44- 1232-711547.

Bangor Aspects Festival of Literature/Bangor Visual Arts Festival, North Down Burrough Council, Town Hall, Bangor, Northern Ireland BT20 4BT; 011-44-1247-270371.

Appalachian and Bluegrass Festival, Ulster-American Folk Park, Mellon Rd., Castledown, Omagh, County Tyrone, Northern Ireland BT78 5QY; 011-44-1662-243292, fax 011-44-1662-24241; uafp@iol.ie.

The Creative Writers' Network, 81/87 Academy St., Belfast, Northern Ireland BT1 2J5; 011- 44-1232-242910, fax 011-44-1232-312264.

Northern Ireland Film Commission, 21 Ormeau Ave., Belfast, Northern Ireland BT2 8HD.

Writing Across Borders Project and **Shankhill Theatre Company,** 1 Ballysillan Dr., Belfast, Northern Ireland BT14 8HQ; Tel./fax 011- 44-1232-391240.

Linen Hall Library, 17 Donegall Sq. N, Belfast, Northern Ireland BT1 5GD; 011-44-1232- 321707, fax 011-44-1232-43856.

ton Blvd., Suite 220, Marina del Rey, CA 90292; 800-321-3738, 310-821-9977, fax 310-821-9282; info@erdtshare.org, [www.erdtshare.org].

Global Awareness Through Experience (GATE).
GATE offers alternative tourism through immersion and feminist spiritual quest programs in Mexico, Guatemala, El Salvador and Eastern Europe. Participants connect with Third World people in face-to-face dialogue to explore social, economic, religious and cultural issues.
Dates: El Salvador: Nov 27-Dec 6, 2001; Mexico: Jan 3-13 and 21-31, Feb 5-15, Jul 2-12 and 17-27, 2002; Guatemala: Mar 20-30, 2002; Eastern Europe: May 9-20, 2002. **Costs:** $100 registration; $850-$900 (Latin America); $1,800 (Eastern Europe). Airfare not included.
Contact: Maria Friedman, GATE, 912 Market St., La Crosse, WI 54601-8800; 608-791-5283, fax 608-782-6301; GATE@ fspa.org, [www.GATE-Travel.org].

Global Service Corps (GSC), a project of Earth Island Institute, creates opportunities for adult participants to live in Tanzania and Thailand homes while volunteering on health, education and environment community service and development projects. These service-learning programs emphasize grass-roots collaboration on the local level, mutual transfer of skills, and cross-cultural understanding. Undergraduate and graduate level credits qualifying for financial aid available.
Dates: Year round. Contact GSC office or check the web site for specific starting dates
Costs: Approx. $1,800-$2,000 for 2-4 week project trips: $595 per month for 2-6 month long-term extensions; $2,815-$3,145 for summer and semester college internships. Includes extensive pre-departure preparation and in-country expenses. **Contact:** Global Service Corps, 300 Broadway, Suite 28, San Francisco, CA 94133; 415-788-3666 ext 128, fax 415-788-7324; gsc@earthisland.org, [www.globalservicecorps.org].

Independent Homestay Program. Independent Homestay Programs focus on the homestay experience. These programs are ideal for independent teen and adult travelers desiring full immersion in another culture for a short period of time.
Dates: One to 4 weeks, year round. **Costs:** Approx. $800-$1,300. **Contact:** Outbound Department, 17 N. 2nd Ave., St. Charles, IL 60174; 888-227-6231, fax 630-377-2307; info@cci-exchange.com, [www.cci-exchange.com].

Interhostel/Familyhostel. Interhostel (for adults 50 years and older) and Familyhostel (for grandparents and/or parents and school-aged children) offer study/travel programs to locations in the U.S. and all over the world. One- and 2-week programs include presentations, field trips, sightseeing, cultural and social activities, recreation. Call for a free catalog or visit our web site.
Dates: Over 75 programs throughout the year. **Costs:** U.S. programs: $600-$800; foreign programs: $2,000-$3,500. Includes meals, accommodations, activities, and foreign airfare. **Contact:** Interhostel, Univ. of New Hampshire Continuing Education, 6 Garrison Ave., Durham, NH 03824; 800-733-9753, fax 603-862-1113; learn.dce@unh.edu, [www.learn.unh.edu/interhostel].

International Volunteer and Cultural Exchange Programs. Cross-Cultural Solutions offers life-changing volunteer programs and "insight" cultural tours in Asia, Africa, Latin America, the Caribbean, and Eastern Europe. Volunteers typically work in the areas of education, healthcare, and community development for 2 weeks to 6 months. Cultural tours range from 7 to 18 days.
Dates: Year round. **Costs:** Programs begin at $1,700 and vary depending on duration and country. **Contact:** Volunteer Coordinator, Cross-Cultural Solutions, 47 Potter Ave., New Rochelle, NY 10801; 914-632-0022 or 800-380-4777, fax 914-632-8494; info@crossculturalsolutions.org, [www.crossculturalsolutions.org].

Learning Journeys. ARTIS is a nonprofit 501c(3) art agency dedicated to providing high quality international art and cultural experiences at affordable prices. Our learning journeys programs are for adults of all ages and feature free art workshops taught on location in beautiful art capitals throughout the world.
Dates: May-Aug. **Costs:** $1,000-$3,700 **Contact:** David Renfrow, ARTIS, 1616 Princeton Dr., Columbia, MO 65023; 800-232-6893, fax 573-234-2926; dfro@socket.net, [www.artis-tours.org].

Live the Language. Live the language by learning where it's spoken. Carefully selected host families complement the cultural immersion experience. Programs are available to all levels and range from weekend and week-long courses in Ensenada to 2 weeks and longer in Guadalajara, Madrid, Salamanca, Paris, and Florence. UCSD Extension credit available.
Dates: Flexible start dates each month. **Costs:** Vary. Call organization for details. **Contact:** University of California, San Diego, Extension, Travel Study Program, 9500 Gilman Dr., 0176-

Z, La Jolla, CA 92093-0176; 858-822-2747, fax 858-534-7385; travelstudy@ucsd.edu, [www.extension.ucsd.edu/travelstudy].

Skyros Holistic Vacations. We offer over 200 courses on the beautiful Greek island of Skyros and the Thai island of Ko Samet. Courses range from yoga, Tai Chi, massage, art, personal development, creative writing, and dance to drumming, voicework, drama, and bodywork. Delicious food and spectacular surroundings.

Dates: Jan-Dec. **Costs:** $1,085. **Contact:** Helen Akif, Skyros, 92 Prince of Wales Rd., London NW5 3NE, U.K.; 011-44-207-284-3065, fax 011-44-207-284-3063; connect@skyros.com, [www.skyros.com].

World Affairs Council Travel Program. All the highlights of touring plus access to political leaders and local experts who give special briefings and behind-the-scenes views. Europe, Cuba, Asia, South American, Middle East, and North America as well as a once-in-a-lifetime private jet trip cities of history.

Dates: 2002 and beyond. **Costs:** From $1,800-$32,500. **Contact:** Joan Russell, World Affairs Council, 1314 Chestnut St., Philadelphia, PA 19010; 800-942-5004 ext. 209 [www.libertynet.org/~wac].

Youth International. An experiential education program focusing on international travel and intercultural exchange, adventure, community service, and homestays. Teams of 14, aged 18-25, travel together for 1 semester to Asia (including the Philippines, Thailand, India, and Nepal) or Africa (including Kenya, Tanzania, Botswana, and Namibia). Assist refugees, hike the Himalayas, live with and help an African tribe, scuba dive, and much more.

Dates: Every year, early Sep-mid-Dec, and early Feb-late May. **Costs:** $7,500 including airfare. **Contact:** Brad Gillings, Youth International, 1121 Downing St., #2, Denver, CO 80218; 303-839-5877, fax 303-839-5887; director@youthinternational.org, [www.youthinternational.org].

TWELVE

Readers of Transitions Abroad *know that the most rewarding and least expensive overseas vacations are learning vacations. What better way to enjoy your stay in a foreign country than to start off with a period of language instruction, however brief? Not only do you have an immediate temporary home and new friends, every new word learned can be put to instant use. For a selection of the best language study web sites, see page 201.*

Argentina

Argentina I.L.E.E. Located in downtown Buenos Aires. Dedicated exclusively to teaching Spanish as a foreign language. Small groups and private classes year round. All teachers hold master's degrees in education or literature and have been full-time Spanish professors for years. Method is intensive. Excellent social-cultural activities program. Student body is international, 40 percent from Central Europe. Highly recommended worldwide. Ask for individual references in U.S. Please visit web site for full information and photos.

Dates: Year round. **Costs:** Four-week intensive program (20 hours per week) including homestay $1,460; 2 weeks $730. Private classes $19 per hour. Registration fee (includes books) $100. **Contact:** Daniel Korman, I.L.E.E.,International Director, Av. Callao 339, 3 Fl. (1022), Buenos Aires, Argentina; Tel./fax 011-54-11-47827173; info@ilee.com.ar, [www.ilee.com.ar].

Argentine Spanish Learning Center. CEDIC offers a completely integrated program of Spanish language study. Intensive classes for all levels, intermediate and advanced specialized. Flexible schedules for private or group lessons. Immersion living in a Spanish-speaking community. Living accommodations as well as social activities with Argentine families and students.

Dates: Year round. **Costs:** Two-week intensive program (40 hours) $370. Tutor classes $20. Ask about accommodations. **Contact:** CEDIC, Martin Duh or Susana Bernardi, Reconquista 715, Oficina 11, E., 1003 Buenos Aires, Argentina; Tel./fax 011-54-11-4315-1156, 011-54-11-4312-1016; cedic@tarcos.com, [www.tarcos.com/cedic].

Argentine Universities Program. COPA offers an integrated study opportunity in which undergraduate students live with Argentine host families and study with degree-seeking Argentine students. Three partner universities offer unique blends of location, academics, and student population. There is a research track available. Academic program includes optional program classes and a required Spanish course. A 6-week, non-integrated summer program is also available. All coursework is in Spanish.

Dates: Spring: Mar-Jul, fall: Jul-Dec, summer: Jun-Jul. **Costs:** Call for details. **Contact:** Cooperating Programs in the Americas, Institute for Study Abroad, 1100 W. 42nd St., Suite 305, Indianapolis, IN 46208-3345; 888-344-9299, fax 317-940-9704; COPA@butler.edu, [www.isabutler.org].

Argentum, Univ. Blas Pascal. Argentum, The Institute for International Education at Universidad Blas Pascal in Córdoba, Argentina, is a Spanish language and culture program for undergraduate, graduate, and high school students providing language and culture courses as well as a wide variety of standard university courses. Participants are paired up with a tutor who acts as a bridge to the Argentine culture. **Dates:** Session 1: Mar-Jun; session 2: Aug-Nov; intensive: Jun-Jul, Jul-Aug. **Costs:** Semester $6,100; intensive $2,200; intensive 3-week program $1,900. Includes tuition, room and board, organized group excursions. **Contact:** Marta Rosso-O'Laughlin, Argentum, P.O. Box 99, Medford, MA 02153; Tel./fax 978-318-0421; mrosso@aol.com, [www.worldwide.edu/argentina/argentum].

Learn Spanish in Argentina. Bridge-Linguatec offers intensive Spanish language programs for executives, visitors, and international students. Our highly educated and experienced instructors use Bridge-Linguatec's easy conversational approach to language instruction with groups limited to 4 students, or private classes with up to 8 hours a day. Biweekly excursions are included and homestays are available. **Dates:** Classes begin every Monday, year round. **Costs:** $325 per week for 20 hours of group classes. **Contact:** Bill Arnold, Bridge-Linguatec Int'l., 915 S. Colorado Blvd., Denver, CO 80246; 800-724-4210, 303-777-7783, fax 303-777-7246; admissions@bridgeschool.com, [www.bridge-linguatec.com].

Spanish for Foreigners. Spanish as a foreign langauge. Communication classes, friendly and relaxed atmosphere, one-on-one or small groups. Intensive and vacation courses for children, teens, or adults (all levels). Tailor-made programs for school classes and student groups. Accommodations arranged. **Dates:** Year round. **Costs:** Hourly fees range $10-$20. Matriculation fee $50. **Contact:** "Albert Schweitzer" Studio of Education and Culture, Gral. Alvear 69, 2nd Fl., Martínez 1640, Buenos Aires, Argentina; 011-54-11-4792-6322, 011-54-11-4790-6245, fax 011-54-11-4793-6888

Austria

German Courses at the University. German for beginners and advanced students, perfectionist courses, courses for students of the German language and teachers of German in foreign countries (6 levels). Lectures on German and Austrian literature, music, Austria—the country, people, and language. Special courses: commer-cial German, commercial correspondence, phonetics, conversation, communication. Excursions. **Dates:** Three sessions: Jul 7-Aug 3; Aug 4-31; Sep 1-21. **Costs:** Course fee (4 weeks): approx EURO 360. Accommodations: EURO 420. **Contact:** Magister Sigrun Inmann-Trojer, Wiener Internationale Hochschulkurse, Ebendorferstrasse 10/4, A-1010 Vienna, Austria; fax 011-43-1-405-12-5410; WIHOK@univie.ac.at, [www.univie.ac.at/WIHOK].

German Language Courses. German Language Courses for students and adults with cultural activities in Vienna (16 and over). Junior programs in Austria (age 9-16). **Dates:** Jul-Aug. **Costs:** Contact organization for details. **Contact:** Oekista, Garnisongasse 7, 1090 Vienna, Austria; 011-43-1-401-48-8820, fax 011-43-1-401-48-8800; german.course@oekista.at, [www.oek.sta.co.at].

Learn German in Vienna at Alpha Sprachinstit Austria. We offer year-round intensive German courses, cultural programs, accommodations with families. Following the system of the Goethe-Institute, courses are of highest quality and prepare for internationally recognized certificates: ZD, KDS, GDS. Modern instruction methods and materials includes computer lab, etc. **Dates:** Courses start monthly. **Costs:** EURO 422 per month intensive course. **Contact:** Alpha Sprachinstitut Austria, Canovagasse 5, Vienna A-1010, Austria; 011-43-1-503-69-69, fax 011-43-1-503-69-69-14; office@alpha.at, [www.alpha.at].

Benelux

ISOK. Homestays with language courses in Holland and, in cooperation with St. Peter's School in Canterbury, in England. **Dates:** Holland: year; England: year, not at Christmas. **Costs:** England: summer £234, other DFL184 per week; Holland: homestay DFL385 per week; lessons DFL35 per hour. **Contact:** ISOK, Mr. J.F.H. de Zeeuw, Jan-Tooropstraat 4, 2225 XT, Katwijk, Holland; 011-31-71-4013533.

Brazil

Learn Portuguese in Brazil. Bridge-Linguatec offers intensive Portuguese language programs for executives, visitors, and international students in Sao Paulo, Rio de Janeiro, Campo Grande and Victoria. Our highly educated and experienced instructors use Linguatec's easy conversational approach to language instruction with groups limited to 4 students, or private classes with up to 8 hours a day. Biweekly excursions are included and homestays are available.

Dates: Classes begin every Monday, year round. **Costs:** $325 per week for 20 hours of group classes. **Contact:** Bill Arnold, Bridge-Linguatec Int'l., 915 S. Colorado Blvd., Denver, CO 80246; 800-724-4210, 303-777-7783, fax 303-777-7246; admissions@bridgeschool.com, [www.linguatec.com.br].

Canada

College Platon English or French. Established in 1957, College Platon offers a unique learning environment. Courses taught in 28 languages in the heart of beautiful Montreal include grammar, vocabulary, conversation in a state-of-the-art facility. Complete with audiovisual, computer labs, and, most of all, experienced instructors. Enroll today.

Dates: Year round. **Costs:** Four weeks full time CAN$675; 12 weeks CAN$1,800; 24 weeks CAN$3,200. **Contact:** College Platon, Chris Kavathas, 4521 Park Ave., Montreal, PQ, H2V 4E4; 514-281-1016, fax 514-281-6275; infos@platocollege.com, [www.platocollege.com].

École de langue française de Trois-Pistoles. The oldest university-sponsored French immersion school in Canada, our school offers two 5-week sessions each year and a French Intensive session for busy adults (7-10 days). Courses are offered in the areas of French language, culture, theater, and political science. Guided by dynamic monitors, students participate in an afternoon workshop and a varied sociocultural program. Accommodations and meals, as well as an opportunity to practice French in an informal setting, provided by families in Trois-Pistoles.

Dates: May 7-Jun 8; Jul 2-Aug 3. **Costs:** CAN$1,800 plus CAN$250 program deposit ($100 refundable) (2001). **Contact:** Annie Morin, Administrative Assistant, The Univ. of Western Ontario, École de langue française de Trois-Pistoles, Univ. College 219, London, ON, N6A 3K7, Canada; 519-661-3637, fax 519-661-3799; tpistole@julian.uwo.ca, [www.uwo.ca/cstudies/tp/].

Study English or French at POiNT3 in Montréal! We offer Intensive English and Intensive French, as well as North American Business Communication, TOEFL Preparation, and Learning Vacation programs. Our teachers are excellent, our classes are small, and we organize extra-curricular activities to help students to practice the language that they are learning. In addition, students have access to the Internet and language learning CD-ROMs, as well as to books and videos. We also offer students free weekly language workshops. Accommodation is available with one of our friendly host families, in a student residence, or in a furnished apartment.

Dates: Year round. Start dates every 2 weeks. Start dates for complete beginners every 4 weeks. **Costs:** Intensive French $260 USD for 2 weeks (44 hours), Intensive English $286 USD for 4 weeks (50 hours) **Contact:** POiNT3 Language Center, 404 Saint-Pierre Street, Suite 201, Montréal, PQ, Canada H2Y 2M2; 514-840-7228, fax 514-840-7111; info@point-3.com, [www.point-3.com].

Univ. of New Brunswick ELP. Established in 1953 in eastern Canada, tradition of expertise with international clientele. Language contract base; courses designed for client needs; experienced staff; residential approach. Participants live and learn English nonstop weekdays and weekends. Classes extend into the community. Extensive diagnosis, ongoing assessment, constant quality control.

Dates: Three-week format (monthly Sep-Apr) in homestay; 5-week format (May-Jun, Jul-Aug) in university residence. **Costs:** Three weeks CAN$3,693; 5 weeks CAN$2,030. Includes tuition, materials, meals, accommodations, and weekend socio-cultural activities. **Contact:** Mrs. Mary E. Murray, Director, Univ. of New Brunswick, English Language Programme, P.O. Box 4400, Fredericton, NB, E3B 5A3, Canada; 506-453-3564, fax 506-453-3578; elp@unb.ca, [www.unb.ca/coned/elp].

Caribbean

Instituto Internacional Euskalduna. Learn Spanish in Puerto Rico! We offer communicative, learner-centered classes for all language levels. Small groups and private programs, U.S. university credit, weekly cultural activities and homestay programs with or without meals.

Dates: Classes begin every other Monday. **Costs:** Programs starting at $580. **Contact:** NESOL, Inc., Calle Navarro 56, HatoRey, PR 00918; 787-281-8013, fax 787-767-1494; studyabroad@newenglandschool.com, [www.newenglandschool.com].

Chile

Chilean Universities: Santiago. Based at the Instituto de Estudios Internacionales, the prestigious research institute associated with the Universidad de Chile, our program allows students to take two core classes in Spanish designed to acquaint U.S. undergrads with contemporary Chile. Participants take a wide variety of integrated university classes at both the Universidad de Chile and the Universidad Católica de Chile to complete their enrollment. Directed research projects available. Students live with host families. All coursework in Spanish.

Dates: Spring semester: Feb-Jul, fall semester: Jul-Dec. **Costs:** Call for details. **Contact:** Cooperating Programs in the Americas, Institute for Study Abroad, 1100 W. 42nd St., Suite 305, Indianapolis, IN 46208-3345; 888-344-9299, fax 317-940-9704; COPA@butler.edu, [www.isabutler.org].

Chilean Universities: Valparaíso. In the twin coastal cities of Valparaíso and Viña del Mar, the home to our program, students take integrated classes with Chilean students and live with a host family. Two program classes in Spanish are available to complement UCV's course offerings. All coursework in Spanish.

Dates: Spring semester: Feb-Jul, fall semester: Jul-Dec. **Costs:** Call for details. **Contact:** Cooperating Programs in the Americas, Institute for Study Abroad, 1100 W. 42nd St., Suite 305, Indianapolis, IN 46208-3345; 888-344-9299, fax 317-940-9704; COPA@butler.edu, [www.isabutler.org].

Learn Spanish in Chile. Bridge-Linguatec offers intensive Spanish language programs for executives, visitors, and international students. Our highly educated and experienced instructors use Bridge-Linguatec's easy conversational approach to language instruction with groups limited to 4 students, or private classes with up to 8 hours a day. Biweekly excursions are included and homestays are availa

Dates: Classes begin every Monday year round. **Costs:** $325 per week for 20 hours of group classes. **Contact:** Bill Arnold, Bridge-Linguatec Int'l., 915 S. Colorado Blvd., Denver, CO 80246; 800-724-4210, 303-777-7783, fax 303-777-7246; admissions@bridgeschool.com, [www.linguatec.cl].

Spanish and Latin American Studies: Santiago. Santiago offers intensive language studies fulfilling up to 2 years of university Spanish requirements in 1 semester, with additional courses in literature, business, teacher ed., history, political science. Week-long, program-oriented field trips to the south and north of Chile, homestays, and many university activities at Chilean university.

Dates: Fall semester Aug-Dec, spring semester Jan-May. **Costs:** One semester $3,980, both semesters $6,650. **Contact:** University Studies Abroad Consortium (USAC), Univ. of Nevada,

USAC323, Reno, NV 89557; 775-784-6569, fax 775-784-6010; usac@unr.edu, [http://usac.unr.edu].

China

Chinese Language and Culture. Chinese language courses are given in the morning, Mon-Fri, mainly on phonetics, oral expression, listening comprehension and Chinese characters reading/writing. Cultural courses are given in the afternoon, including Chinese painting, calligraphy, shadow boxing, and gong-fu. Optional weekend trips can also be arranged at the expense of $60.

Dates: Spring semester: Feb-Jun; fall semester: Sep-Jan; summer program: Jul-Aug. **Costs:** $1,000 for 1 semester, $1,800 for 2 semesters. **Contact:** Zhejiang University, Tang Li Int'l. College, P.O. Box 1532, Yuquan Campus, Hangzhou 310027, China; 011-86-571-7951386, fax 011-86-571-7951755; gjxzju@mail.hz.zj.cn.

Chinese Studies: Chengdu. The Chinese Studies Program offers intensive language study fulfilling up to 2 years of university language requirements in 1 semester. Additional courses in art history, economics, anthropology, political science, physics, chemistry, literature, history, and calligraphy are taught in English and offer a multidisciplinary approach to understanding the complexities of China and Asia.

Dates: Summer sessions: Jun and Jul; fall semester: Aug-Dec, spring semester: Jan-May. **Costs:** One semester $4,260; both semesters $6,860; Jun or Jul $1,480; Jun and Jul $2,760. **Contact:** University Studies Abroad Consortium (USAC), Univ. of Nevada, USAC 323, Reno, NV 89557; 775-784-6569, fax 775-784-6010; usac@unr.edu, [http://usac.unr.edu].

Princeton in Beijing. Princeton in Beijing is a high-quality intensive program in elementary, intermediate, and advanced Chinese language study for the serious language student. PiB brings together Princeton faculty, local teachers, and the textbooks of Princeton's Chinese Linguistics Project in the ultimate Chinese language environment, China's capital city of Beijing.

Dates: Jun-Aug. **Costs:** $3,900 (2000). **Contact:** 609-258-4269, fax 609-258-6984; pib@princeton.edu, [www.princeton.edu/~pib].

Costa Rica

Always Your Best Link, Language Link, Heredia and San José. Quality complete immersion Spanish language programs in 2 different locations in Costa Rica. Academic credit

Language Study Resources on the Web
Brush Up on the Country's Language and Culture Before You Go

Selected by Clay Hubbs

We never tire of reminding readers—it's our mission!—that the most rewarding and least expensive overseas vacation involves a learning component. What better way to enjoy your time in a foreign country than to start it off with a period of language instruction, however brief? Not only can this provide an immediate "ground" in a community of knowledgeable locals and like-minded travelers, every word of the new language can be put to immediate use.

On a recent trip to Ecuador my wife and I spent a week in a language school in Quito before striking out on our own. Our hosts at the school (Academia Latinoamericana) provided us with itineraries and introductions that made the rest of our trip immeasurably more satisfying than wandering around a new place independently but unprepared, or isolated with a group of strangers in a tour group. Had we taken a bit more time to work on our Spanish before leaving, the experience would have been all the richer. That was before we discovered the language and culture resources available on the Internet.

The Internet offers an astonishing and somewhat intimidating number of resources: foreign language newspapers and magazines, maps, videos and virtual tours, not to mention online language courses (some free), chat rooms, and USENET sites. You can even develop listening and speaking skills on interactive web sites.

Travelers using the resources below can not only get a jump on learning at least some essential words in the language, the informational web sites to which many of these sites provide links include extensive information on the culture of the target countries as well as practical travel information. New sites are coming on and old ones are expanding daily.

World Newspapers and Magazines on the WWW. Media Links, [http://emedia1.mediainfo.com/emedia/]. Browse by geographic location and category.

World Radio Stations on the WWW. The MIT List, [http://wmbr.mit.edu/stations/list.html]. Choose any country or any state in U.S.

World Video Sites on the WWW. Tommy's List of Live Cams Worldwide, [http://chili.rt66.com/ozone/countries.htm].

Foreign Languages and Culture Page [www.speakeasy.org/~dbrick/Hot/foreign.html]. Offers easy access to hundreds of language and culture related sites.

World Society and Culture Directory [http://dir.yahoo.com/society_and_culture/cultures_and_groups/cultures/]. An alphabetical list of countries, each with links to sites relating to its culture. Create your own online connections abroad with chat, message boards, email.

Foreign Language Test and Exercises Page [http://Goethe-verlag.com/tests/]. Offers exercises and vocabulary tests in German, French, Italian, Dutch, Czech, Hungarian, Indonesian, Portuguese, and English.

Foreign Language for Travelers [www.traveling.com/languages/]. Offers basic lessons in 74 languages.

Language Resources on the Web [http://depts.washington.edu/llc/main/links/world.html]. This is a good place to begin a web search for language and culture related sites.

NRCSA [www.nrcsa.com/]. Preregisters language learners of all ages in a choice of language schools in 30 countries. 823 N. 2nd St., P.O. Box 1393, Milwaukee, WI 53021; 414-278-0631, fax 414-271-8884.

Human-Languages Page [www.june29. com/HLP/]. A comprehensive catalog of language-related Internet resources. Its links are among the best on the web for finding online language lessons, translation services, language schools, etc.

Languages-on-the-Web [www.languages-on-the-web.com]. A team of educators provides 30,000 language related links and courses and translation services in many languages. New feature: Look up audio or video courses in all languages from Abkhaz to Zulu.

Foreign Language Resources [www.middletownK12.com/forlang.html]. Extensive list of foreign language resources.

Yahoo Language Links [http://dir.yahoo. com/Social_Science/Linguistics_and_Human_Languages/Languages/]. Links to 1,400 separate language sites.

Foreign Language Resources on the Web [www.itp.Berkeley.edu/~HumanResources.html]. A good starting point for mining the WWW for foreign language and culture resources. A self-styled "quality-only" index.

Worldwide Classroom Library of International Programs [www.worldwide.edu/]. Amongst the largest international consortium of schools, with information on 10,000 schools in 109 countries listed alphabetically by category (including languages institutes) and country. Publishes the *International Study Telecom Directory*. Worldwide Classroom, Box 1166, Milwaukee, WI 53201-1166; fax 414-224-3466.

available through U.S. accredited university. Excursions to explore this beautiful peaceful country, excellent homestays with 2 meals, all ages with special separate teen programs and children's classes, beach campus option, all levels, airport pickups included, insurance included, additional cultural classes including dance. Small classes (4-6) or private classes very suitable for professionals. Easy enrollment through our U.S. office, now in its 14th year of excellent service.

Dates: Start any Monday, year round. **Costs:** Starting at $315 per week, tuition and homestay. **Contact:** Kay G. Rafool, Language Link, P.O. Box 3006, Peoria, IL 61612; 800-552-2051, fax 309-692-2926; info@langlink.com, [www.langlink.com].

Costa Rican Language Academy (C.R.L.A.). Costa Rican owned and operated language school offers first-rate Spanish instruction in a warm and friendly environment. Teachers with university degrees. Small groups or private classes. Volunteer opportunities. Included free in the programs are airport transportation, coffee and natural refreshments, Internet, excursions, Latin dance, Costa Rican cooking, and conversation classes to provide students with complete cultural immersion.

Dates: Year round (start anytime). **Costs:** $155 per week or $235 per week for program with homestay. All other activities and services included at no additional cost. **Contact:** Costa Rican Language Academy, P.O. Box 1966-2050, San José, Costa Rica; fax 011-506-233-5065. In the U.S.: 800-854-6057; crlang@sol.racsa.co.cr, [www.learn-spanish.com].

Enjoy Learning Spanish Faster. Techniques developed from our ongoing research enable students to learn more, faster, in a comfortable environment. Classes of 2-4 students plus group learning activities; conversations with middle-class homestay families (1 student or couple per family). Homestays are in a small town near the capital, San José.

Dates: Year round. Classes begin every Monday at all levels (except Mar 25-29, Dec 14-Jan 5). **Costs:** $345 per week for 26 hours of classes and group activities including Costa Rican dance and cooking classes. Includes tuition, 3 meals per day, 7 days per week, homestay, weekly 3-hour cultural tour, laundry, all materials, and airport transportation. $25 one-time registration fee. **Contact:** Susan Shores, Registrar, Latin American Language Center, PMB 123, Suite 710, 7485 Rush River Dr., Sacramento, CA 95831-5260; 916-447-0938, 916-428-9542; lalc@madre.com, [www.madre.com/~lalc].

Immerse Yourself in Spanish. La Escuela De Idiomas D'Amore offers intensive immersion programs and homestay to students from over 30 countries. Founded in 1992, we are the original beach school and campus in Costa Rica. While our experience sets us apart from the rest, your experience is most important to us. New! Come and visit our beautiful on-campus Butterfly Farm.

Dates: Year round. **Costs:** $845-$1,540. **Contact:** La Escuela De Idiomas D'Amore, P.O. Box 67, Quepos, Costa Rica; 011-506-777-1143. In U.S. 323-912-0600, 262-389-8598; damore@sol.racsa.co.cr, [www.escueladamore.com].

Intensive Spanish and Homestay. Intercultura Costa Rica offers intensive university accredited Spanish courses. Homestays available. Volunteer programs, beach and city campuses, emphasis on individual attention. Caring, multilingual staff. Located in university town close to the capital. Daily Latin dance classes, weekly cooking, music, indigenous culture, and other classes.

Dates: Year round. **Costs:** $1,095 per month includes classes, homestay and activities (shorter stays available). **Contact:** Melvin Montero, Intercultura Costa Rica, Language Center, P.O. Box 1952-3000, Heredia, Costa Rica; 011-506-260-8480, Tel./fax 011-506-260-9243; intercul@racsa.co.cr, [www.spanish-intercultura.com].

Intensive Spanish with Social Justice Focus. The Institute for Central American Development Studies (ICADS) offers 4-week progressive programs in intensive Spanish language—4 1/2 hours daily, 5 days a week. Small classes (4 or fewer students). Activities and optional afternoon internships or group community service activities that emphasize environmental issues, women's issues, education, healthcare, social justice issues. Supportive learning environment. Homestays, lectures, and field trips. Great alternative for the socially conscious.

Dates: Programs begin first Monday of each month. **Costs:** $1,500 includes airport pick-up, classes, books, homestay, meals, laundry, lectures, activities, field trips, and internship placements. **Contact:** ICADS, Dept. 826, P.O. Box 025216, Miami, FL 33102-5216; icads@netbox.com, [www.icadscr.com].

Learn Spanish While Volunteering. Assist with the training of Costa Rican public school teachers in ESL and computers. Assist local health clinic, social service agencies, and environmental projects. Enjoy learning Spanish in the morning, volunteer work in the afternoon/evening. Spanish classes of 2-4 students plus group learning activities; conversations with middle class homestay families (1 student or couple per family). Homestays and most volunteer projects are in a small town near the capital, San José. **Dates:** Year round, all levels. Classes begin every Monday (except Mar 25-29 and Dec 14-Jan 5), volunteer program is continuous. **Costs:** $345 per week for 26 hours of classes and group activities including Costa Rican dance and cooking classes. $25 one-time registration fee. **Contact:** Susan Shores, Registrar, Latin American Language Center, PMB 123, 7485 Rush River Dr., Suite 710, Sacramento, CA 95831-5260; 916-447-0938, fax 916-428-9542; lalc@madre.com, [www.madre.com/~lalc].

Spanish and Latin American Studies in Puntarenas. Puntarenas offers intensive language studies which fulfills up to 2-year university Spanish requirements in a semester. Additional courses offered in political science, history, biology, teacher ed., business, literature, etc. Program organized week-long and weekend field trips, homestays, and many local university activities. **Dates:** Fall semester: Aug-Dec; spring semester: Jan-May. **Costs:** One semester $4,980; both semesters $7,980. **Contact:** University Studies Abroad Consortium (USAC), Univ. of Nevada, USAC 323, Reno, NV 89557; 775-784-6569, fax 775-784-6010; usac@unr.edu, [http://usac.unr.edu].

Spanish, Ecology and Latin American Studies in Heredia. Heredia offers intensive language studies which fulfills up to 2-year university Spanish requirements in a semester or 1 year in the 8-week summer program. Additional courses offered in political science, history, biology, teacher ed., business, literature, etc. Program organized week-long and weekend field trips, homestays, and many local university activities. **Dates:** Fall semester: Aug-Dec, spring semester: Jan-May, summer sessions: Jun, Jul, and Aug. **Costs:** One semester $4,980; both semesters $7,980; Jun or Jul $2,040; Aug $1,660; Jun and Jul $3,790; Jun/Jul, and Aug $3,280; Jun, Jul, and Aug $4,820. **Contact:** University Studies Abroad Consortium (USAC), Univ. of Nevada, USAC 323, Reno, NV 89557-0093; 775-784-6569, fax 775-784-6010; usac@unr.edu, [http://usac.unr.edu].

Univ. Nacional Autónoma. Costa Rica is exceptional for its political stability and environmental sensitivity. Our undergraduate program at Universidad Nacional Autónoma allows participants to enroll in both program classes and regular university courses while living with local host families. Many extracurricular activities are available through the University. All coursework is in Spanish. **Dates:** Spring semester: Jan-May, fall semester: Aug-Dec. **Costs:** Call for details. **Contact:** Cooperating Programs in the Americas, Institute for Study Abroad, 1100 W. 42nd St., Suite 305, Indianapolis, IN 46208-3345; 888-344-9299, fax 317-940-9704; COPA@butler.edu, [www.isabutler.org].

Czech Republic

Cambridge RSA/CELTA. The Cambridge/RSA Certificate in English Language Teaching to Adults is the most widely-recognized qualification for teaching English as a foreign language. This practical, intensive course is essential as a basis for a career in teaching, combining methodology, teaching practice, and general principles of teaching and learning. **Dates:** Mar 5-30; May 14-Jun 8; Jul 9-Aug 3; Nov 5-30. **Costs:** 43,800 Korunas. **Contact:** Vicky Gemmill, International Language Centres Prague (ILC), Opletalova 39/1525, 110 00 Prague 1, Czech Republic; 011-420 2 2100 4333, fax 011-420 2 2100 4640; celta@ilcprague.cz, [www.ilcgroup.com].

East/Central European Studies: Prague. This program is ideal for students, teachers, and others who wish to combine academic coursework with the experience of living in an extraordinary medieval city. Students will appreciate the beautiful architecture of the city, its walls, castles, and frescoes. Intensive Czech language courses available. **Dates:** Fall semester Aug-Dec; spring semester Jan-May; summer May-Jul. **Costs:** One semester $3,980; summer $2,480; both semesters $6,650. **Contact:** University Studies Abroad Consortium (USAC), Univ. of Nevada, USAC 323, Reno, NV 89557; 775-784-6569, fax 775-784-6010; usac@unr.edu, [http://usac.unr.edu].

Denmark

Danish as a Foreign Language. Danish folk high school offers courses in Danish for people from all over the world. Danish and foreign students live together. **Dates:** Starts Sep, 19 weeks. **Costs:** Approx. DRK20,000. **Contact:** The Kalo School of Languages, Skovridervej 1, DK 8410 Ronde, Denmark; adm@kalo-adm.dk, [www.kalo.dk].

Intensive Danish Language Courses. Danish study at 11 levels, 9 hours per week. **Dates:** Year round. **Costs:** Residents free; visitors $10 per hour. **Contact:** K.I.S.S. Danish Language School, Norrebrogade 32, DK-2200

Copenhagen N, Denmark; 011-45-35362555; info@kiss.dk, [www.kiss.dk].

Ecuador

Academia Latinoamericana. Proud to be the friendliest Spanish school you have ever known. Family owned and operated. The program offers language study at 9 levels, for complete beginners through advanced. Experienced staff, native Ecuadorians. Carefully selected host families within walking distance of school. Exclusive "Cloud Forest and Galápagos" extension program, volunteer program. U.S. college credit available. **Dates:** Year round. **Costs:** $255 per week. Includes 20 hours of lessons, 7 days with host family, 2 meals per day, transfer, services at the school, and teaching material. **Contact:** Suzanne S. Bell, Admissions Director, USA/International, 640 East 3990 South, Suite E, Salt Lake City, UT, 84107; 801-268-4608, fax 801-265-9156; ecuador@access.net.ec, [www.latinoschools.com].

Green Life Spanish Center. Intensive one-to-one Spanish immersion programs for students at all levels. Homestay with Ecuadorian families available, as well as, environmentally and culturally educational excursions to complement study program. Exciting Study in the Jungle and Study on the Coast programs available. A portion of profits support local conservation and community development projects. **Dates:** Year round. **Costs:** Contact organization for details. **Contact:** Green Life Spanish Center, Attn: Rosa Proano or Jeremy Davis, 18 de Septiembre E-4, 135 y Av. Amazonas, P.O. Box 17-03-600, Quito, Ecuador; 011-593-2-237709, fax 011-593-2-237709; info@vidaverde.com, [www.vidaverde.com].

Spanish in the Middle of the World. Affiliated with Benedict International, Quito S.I. Spanish Institute, with 4 schools in town and 37 years language teaching experience, offers intensive and immersion one-to-one and group courses to fit all needs, levels, and ages. Accommodations in selected families or hostels. Social and cultural activities, trips, and adventures. Spanish for specific purposes. **Dates:** Classes start any day of the week (except holidays). **Costs:** $198 (plus tax) per week includes 20 hours of language lessons, registration, 7 days homestay, full board and laundry, airport transfer, cultural activities, completion diploma. **Contact:** Benedict Schools of Languages, Edmundo Chiriboga, N47-133y Jorge Paez, Quito, Ecuador; 011-593-2-

2432729, 011-593-2-2462972, fax 011-593-2-2272263; benedict@accessinter.net, [www.quitospanish.com].

Egypt

SUNY Cortland in Cairo. AUC's academic offerings include the Humanities and Social Sciences; Sciences and Engineering; and Business, Economics and Communication. AUC is also renowned for its Arabic language, literature, and culture courses as well as its Egyptology, Islamic Studies, and Middle Eastern Studies programs. Classes taught in English except for Arabic language and literature classes. Housing in dormitories and apartments. Excellent student support services. Wide range of student organizations and activities. **Dates:** Fall: late Aug-late Dec; spring: mid-Jan.-end of May; summer: early Jun.-end of Jul. **Costs:** Fall and spring estimate $7,000; summer estimate $3,300. SUNY tuition not included. **Contact:** Office of International Programs, Box 2000, SUNY Cortland, Cortland, NY 13045; 607-753-2209, fax 607-753-5989; studyabroad@cortland.edu, [www.studyabroad.com/suny/cortland].

The American Univ. in Cairo. Intensive Arabic study of modern standard and Egyptian colloquial for a year, semester, and summer. All levels from elementary to advanced are given in this intensive, full-time program. Course-related travel is included. **Dates:** Sep-Dec; Jan-May; Jun-Jul. **Costs:** Year $11,710, semester $5,805, summer $2,920. Approx. tuition and fees only. **Contact:** Matrans Davidson, The American Univ. in Cairo, 420 5th Ave., 3rd Fl., New York, NY 10018-2729; aucegypt@aucnyo.edu, [www.aucegypt.edu].

El Salvador

Melida Anaya Montes School. The MAM Spanish School offers intensive courses at all levels, utilizing popular education techniques and participatory methodology. An integral part of the program includes participation in afternoon meetings with popular organizations, excursions to developing communities and other places of interest, and housing with Salvadoran families with diverse interests. Volunteer opportunities also available. **Dates:** Classes begin every Monday, except on national holidays (Easter week, May 1, Jun 22, 1st week of Aug, Sep 15, Nov 2, and Christmas and New Year's week). **Costs:** Weekly costs: Spanish classes $100, administrative fee $12.50, political-cultural program $25, room and board $60, application fee $25. **Contact:** CIS MAM

Language School, Boulevard Universitario, Casa #4, San Salvador, El Salvador, Centro America; Tel./fax 011-503-226-2623; cis@netcomsa.com, [www.cis-elsalvador.org].

Europe

¿?don Quijote Spanish Schools. Offers Spanish language courses in our 6 schools in Spain and 5 partner schools in Latinoamerica. Our courses (standard, intensive, business, D.E.L.E., tourism, flight attendants and refresher for teachers) are year round, from 2 weeks on. Students can combine different cities and schools. Academic credit is available. **Dates:** Year round—fall, spring, winter, and summer, 2 weeks to a full year of study. **Costs:** Email or check web site for details. **Contact:** ¿?don Quijote In-Country Spanish Language Schools, calle/Placentinos n°2, Salamanca 37008, Spain; 011-34-923-268860, fax 011-34-923-268815; amusa@donquijote.org, [www.donquijote.org].

Language, Arts, and Sports. Active learning vacations: French, Spanish, Italian, Portuguese; cooking, painting, drawing, photography workshops. Combine eduVacational interests: French and sailing or skiing; Spanish and golf; bicycle tours—more countries, more ideas. We match individual needs and interests with programs and options: family stay, apartment, hotel; intensive to total immersion; small groups or study in and live in your teacher's home. **Dates:** Programs run from 1 week to months. **Costs:** Includes room and board, tuition. **Contact:** Mary Ann Puglisi, eduVacations®, 1431 21st St. NW, Suite 302, Washington, DC 20036; 202-857-8384, fax 202-463-8091; eduvacate@aol.com, [www.eduvacations.com].

Learn German in Salzburg (Austria). Small intensive groups (3-8 participants) on all levels offered year round. Lessons taught exclusively by native speakers trained constantly. Follow-up courses available at 280 inlingua schools worldwide. Accommodations, transfer, special free time activities (festival of music, rafting, skisafari, etc.). Tailor-made packages for agencies, schools, companies, etc. on request. **Dates:** Beginners: Jan 15, Feb 5, Mar 5, Apr 2, May 28, Jul 7, 30, Aug 8, 27, Oct 1, Nov 5, Dec 3. With knowledge (assessment test before start): every Monday year round. **Costs:** Costs in EURO (1EURO = approx. 97 cents): 2 weeks: 420, 3 weeks: 580, 4 weeks: 715, 1 additional week 170. Includes 20 lessons (45 min. each) per week plus 3 hours free time activities per week, inlingua book, registration fees, assessment test, exempt from VAT. **Contact:** inlingua Salzburg, Linzer Gasse 17/t, A-5020, Salzburg, Austria; 011-43-662-87-11-01, fax 011-43-662-87-11-01-85; inlinguiasbg@fc.alpin.or.at.

France

BLS - French Language Courses. B.L.S offers intensive French language courses for adults in Bordeaux and a teenage summer programme in Biarritz. The school is recognized by the Rectorate of Bordeaux and a member of SOUFFLE (Quality Control Organization for French Language Schools and Universities in France). **Dates:** 2001. For beginners: Jan 7, Feb 4, Mar 4, Apr 2, May 13, Jun 10, Jul 8, Aug 5, Sep 2, Sep 30, Oct 28, Nov 25. Long-stay courses (3, 6, 9, 12 months), start on the same dates as the beginners. **Costs:** Administration fee EURO 62 (must be applied to all courses except the Biarritz program); 22 lessons standard course per week for 2 weeks EURO490. **Contact:** BLS, 42 rue Lafaurie de Monbadon 33000 Bordeaux, France; 011-33-556-51-00-76, fax 011-33-556-51-76-15; info@bls-frenchcourses.com, [www.bls-frenchcourses.com].

Français General et de Specialité. Courses for adults who need to express themselves with the greatest possible fluency, whether for leisure or professional purposes. General French, commercial and business French, language and culture courses are available. One to 13 weeks, 4 lessons or more per day in small groups. Extracurricular activities: cooking, wine tasting, painting, golf, tennis, excursions. Senior courses. **Dates:** Every second Monday year round. **Costs:** From FF3,500 for 2 weeks. **Contact:** Anna Berg, IS, Aix-en-Provence, 9 Cours des Arts et Mètiers, Aix-en-Provence 13100, France; 011-33-4-42-93-47-90, fax 011-33-4-42-26-31-80; info@is-aix.com, [www.is-aix.com].

French Courses. Inlingua Rouen can offer you the French language program that you need. From business and specific language courses to French and cookery and holiday courses. Groups and individual bookings. **Dates:** Year round. **Costs:** From FF1,300 per week (2001). **Contact:** Mrs. Eleri Maitland, Inlingua Rouen, BP 156, 76144 Le Petit Quevilly, Cedex, France; rouen@inlingua.fr, [www.inlingua.fr/rouen].

French in the Mediterranean. Standard course, intensive course, DELF exam preparation, business French, one-to-one tuition. Small classes of 3-10 students. All levels from beginner to advanced. Carefully chosen accommodations options (host families, student residences, apartments, hotels). Cultural activities. Beautiful

Resources for Teachers and Students
Web Sites Dedicated to Language Teaching and Learning

By Clay Hubbs

Organizations

American Council on the Teaching of Foreign Languages (ACTFL), 6 Executive Plaza, Yonkers, NY 10701; 914-963-8830, fax 914-963-1275; actflhq@aol.com, [www.actfl.org]. A national organization dedicated to the improvement and expansion of teaching and learning of languages at all levels. Its extensive web site includes a listing of language learning resources and publishers.

ERIC Clearinghouse on Languages and Linguistics, 4646 40th St., NW, Washington, DC 20016-1859; 202-362-0700; eric@cal.org, [www.accesseric.org/]. The Educational Resources Information Center (ERIC) is a vast national information system providing access to an extensive body of education-related literature including language learning and teaching (including ESL).

Center for Applied Linguistics, 4646 40th St., NW, Washington, DC 20016-1859; 202-362-0700, 202-362-3740; info@cal.org, [www.cal.org/public/about.htm]. Private, nonprofit organization of scholars and educators that carries out a wide range of language-related activities including serving as a resource for information about language and culture.

Web Sites

Academic Info: Foreign Language Studies [www.academicinfo.net/lang.html]. Compiled by Mike Madin (lang@academicinfo.net). Provides indexes and links to a substantial list of language learning resources for teachers and students.

WWW Resources for Language Teachers is a section of Foreign LanguageTeaching Forum (FL Teach) [www.Cortland.edu/www-root/flteach]. Extensive links to material on foreign language teaching around the world, by language.

Foreign Language and Culture [www. speakeasy.org/~dbrick/Hot/foreign.html]. Extensive.

Foreign Language Study Abroad for Teachers [www.csun.edu/~hcedu013/LanguageAbroad.html]. Hosted by a retired professor of secondary education, includes directories of language schools and foreign language resources for teachers.

www.net-language.com. Comprehensive site for language learners and teachers who use the Internet.

Study Abroad Resources/List by Language School (IIE) [www.iie.org/SVCS/sar/sartype2.htm]. Alphabetized list of links to language schools worldwide plus links to major study abroad resources maintained by a lending organization in international education.

Foreign Language Teaching Forum [www.Cortland.edu/flteach/]. An integrated service for FL teachers which also includes an email LISTSERV academic discussion list and the FLTEACH gopher at the state Univ. of New York College at Cortland. Web page carries a list of Web resources for language teachers.

Teaching with the Web [http://polyglot.lss. wisc.edu/lss/lang/teach/teachlink.html]. A compilation of ideas for using www resources as a language teaching tool. Links to sites with pedagogical information for a wide range of languages, including ESL. Also includes a list of language learning centers and associations and their resources.

location in 18th century private mansion in historic center.

Dates: Year round. Start every Monday. **Costs:** From EURO210 per week. **Contact:** Institut Linguistique Adenet (I.L.A.), 33, Grand Rue Jean Moulin, 34000 Montpellier, France; 011-33-4-67-60-67-83, fax 011-33-4-67-60-67-81; ila.france@mnet.fr, [www.ila-france.com].

French Language Learning Vacations. Learn French while discovering the chateaux of the Loire Valley, the secrets of Provence, or the sandy beaches of the Mediterranean. Our programs are designed for independent travelers sharing a passion for the French culture and lifestyle. We offer a choice of locations in Tours, Aix-en-Provence, Montpellier, Paris, or Nice.

Dates: Two or more weeks year round. **Costs:** Two-week packages range from $825-$1,265. Includes classes, housing and fees. **Contact:** Jim Pondolfino, French-American Exchange, 3213 Duke Street, #620, Alexandria, VA 22314; 800-995-5087, fax 703-823-4447; faetours@erols.com, [www.faetours.com].

French Riviera Homestays. Intensive French course with homestays in teacher's home. Full board, one student at a time, 60 hours of complete immersion per week in French culture and French language. Year round: 15-20-25 hours of private tuition. Prices on demand.

Dates: Year round. One to 4 weeks. **Costs:** 15 hours per week with full board $820, 20 hours $980. **Contact:** Roger Cucchi, French Riviera Homestays, 31 Avenue des Baumettes, 06000 Nice, France; Tel./fax 011-33-4-93-44-12-46; cucchio@hotmail.com, [www.french-intensive-course-homestays.com].

French Studies: Pau and Bayonne. Pau offers intensive language studies—up to 4 semesters of university language courses in 1 semester, 1 year in the 8-week summer program—in addition to art, political science, history, literature, second language teaching methods, etc. Week-long field trips to Paris, homestay or student residence, and many activities at the French university.

Dates: Summer terms: Jun, Jul, and Aug (taught in Bayonne); fall semester: Sep-Dec; spring semester: Jan-Apr. **Costs:** One semester $4,590; both semesters $7,690; Jun $2,040; Jul $2,040; Aug $1,660; Jun and Jul $3,790; Jun and Aug $3,280; Jul and Aug $3,280; Jun, Jul, and Aug $4,820. **Contact:** University Studies Abroad Consortium (USAC), Univ. of Nevada, USAC 323, Reno, NV 89557; 775-784-6569, fax 775-784-6010; usac@unr.edu, [http://usac.unr.edu].

Immersion Course in French. Intensive 2-4 week course for professional adults in

Villefranche (next to Nice) overlooking the French Riviera's most beautiful bay; 8 hours a day with 2 meals. Audiovisual classes, language lab, practice sessions, discussion-lunch. Evening film showings, evening outings with teachers, excursions to cultural landmarks. Accommodations in comfortable private apartments.

Dates: Courses start Jan, Feb, Mar, May, Jun, Aug, Sep, Oct, Nov, Dec. **Costs:** Tuition fees: Dec-Apr EURO 200/4 weeks; May-Nov EURO 2,650/4 weeks. Accommodations: Dec-Apr EURO300-EURO800/4 week; May-Nov EURO350-EURO900/4 weeks. **Contact:** Frédéric Latty, Institut de Francais, 23, avenue General Leclerc, 06230 Villefranche Sur Mer, France; 011-33-493-01-88-44, fax 011-33-493-76-92-17; instfran@aol.com, [www.institutdefrancais.com].

Language and Culture in Burgundy. In an international environment students (ages 12-17) live together with many other nationalities (French included) to pursue an active approach to French in small groups and fun during the cultural and sports activities.

Dates: Jul-Aug. **Costs:** $560. **Contact:** S.L.C.B., rue Général Leclerc, 21320 Pouilly-en-Auxois, France [http://pro.wanadoo.fr/slcb].

Live and Learn French. Live with a carefully selected, welcoming French family in the Paris region. Learn from a family member/teacher who has a university degree and will tailor a private course to suit your needs. Share in a cultural and learning experience that will develop both your understanding of the language and the people who speak it. Minimum of 1 week stay. We also offer touristic stays in English or French.

Dates: Year round. **Costs:** Fifteen hours of study per week $1,150; 20 hours of study per week $1,310. Two people $1,675 per week. Prices include room, 3 meals a day, and instruction. **Contact:** Sara S. Monick, Live & Learn, 4215 Poplar Dr., Minneapolis, MN 55422; 763-374-2444, fax 612-333-3554; monick4215@aol.com.

Sejours Linguistiques en France. Intensive French course on the Univ. campus of Montpellier-Mediterranean (literature, civilization, grammar, conversation, drama) plus activities with French natives (beach excursions, guided tours, wine tasting, conferences).

Dates: Jul-Aug. **Costs:** $333 per week inclusive (classes, activities, room and board). **Contact:** A.P.R.E.-Institut Cultural Francais, BP 5032, 34032 Montpellier, France; 011-33-4-6772-2277, fax 011-33-4-6779-1528; etudesfr@aol.com, [www.institutefrancaismontpellier.com].

Welcome in Burgundy. The CIEF, founded in Dijon in 1902, offers 16-20 hours of tuition a week throughout the year at the Univ. of Burgundy by specialists in the teaching of French as a foreign language. Further recreational possibilities: winetasting sessions, cooking classes, drama or French song workshops, concerts, cinema, outings, and guided tours. Accommodations provided.
Dates: Year round. **Costs:** FF2,250-FF6,300. **Contact:** Centre International d'Études Françaises, Maison de L'Université, Esplanade Érasme, BP 87874, 21078 Dijon Cedex, France; 011-33-80-39-35-60, fax 011-33-80-39-35-61; cief@u-bourgogne.fr, [www.u-bourgogne.fr/CIEF].

Germany

Collegium Palatinum Heidelberg. A language school located in downtown Heidelberg, offering German courses at all levels from beginner to advanced. Forty years of language teaching experience, 2-, 4-, 8-week courses year round. Intensive courses, exam preparation courses, combination courses, one-on-one tuition and customized courses for groups. Leisure and cultural program. Accommodations available in residential, guest-family, private arrangement or hotel.
Dates: Year round (except Public Holidays). **Costs:** DM370 for 24 class hours, DM115 accommodations (double room in student residence without meals), DM325 for half-board with guest family. More prices upon request. **Contact:** Mrs. Martine Berthet, Collegium Palatinum Heidelberg, Friedrich-Ebert-Anlage 4, 69117, Heidelberg, Germany; 011-49-6221-436289, fax 011-49-6221-182023; palmbr@aol.com, [www.cp-languages.com].

Europa-Kolleg Kassel. Language, culture, life in the heart of Germany. Study with efficient, experienced, dynamic teachers. Stay with a carefully selected, friendly family. Participate in our varied and extensive extracurricular program. Enjoy the city of Kassel: Large enough to be fun, small enough to be safe—where people speak standard German.
Dates: Summer courses: Jun-Sep. Also year round. **Costs:** $390 per week includes tuition and materials, extracurricular program, room and partial board (30 meals per week). Inquire about fees for college credit. **Contact:** Prof. K.E. Kuhn-Osius, 238 W. 106 St., Apt. 4A, New York, NY 10025; Tel./fax 212-865-7332; ekuhnos@hunter.cuny.edu.

German Language and Culture. German languge courses at low intermediate, intermediate, and advanced level (24 hours per week), including 8 hours cultural studies. Field trips to Berlin, Hamburg, Celle, Goslav, etc. Wide variety of social and cultural activities.
Dates: Jul-Aug. **Costs:** DM2,190 includes tuition, excursions, accommodations, books. (2000). **Contact:** Sprachenzentrum TU Braunschwieg, Pockelsstr. 4, Braunschwieg, D-38106, Germany; c.neidert@tu-bs.de, [www.sz.tu-bs.de/english/Soku].

German Studies: Lüneburg. Intensive language study—up to 2 years of university language requirements in 1 semester. Additional courses in history, political science, culture, literature, etc. Program-organized field trips and housing. Beautiful city only 30 minutes from Hamburg.
Dates: Summer terms: Jun and Jul; fall semester: Aug-Dec; spring semester: Jan-May. **Costs:** One semester $3,980; both semesters $6,650; summer term $2,040 per session, $3,790 both sessions. **Contact:** University Studies Abroad Consortium (USAC), Univ. of Nevada, USAC 323, Reno, NV 89557; 775-784-6569, fax 775-784-6010; usac@unr.edu, [http://usac.unr.edu].

International Univ. at Heidelberg. Schiller Univ. is an American-style university with all courses except language classes taught in English. Schiller's particular strengths are in international business and international relations but it offers courses in the humanities and social sciences as well. Students may take German at Schiller or intensive German at the Collegium Palatinum, a specialized language division. One semester college German or equivalent is recommended. Housing in residence halls, with families, or in student apartments.
Dates: Fall: late Aug-mid-Dec; spring: mid-Jan-mid-May. **Costs:** Fall or spring estimate: $6,000 per semester (prices somewhat higher for Collegium students staying in homes). Includes overseas instructional costs, pre- and post-departure orientation, room and food allowance, health and accident insurance, German Residence Permit, administrative fees. SUNY tuition, airfare, incidental expenses not included. **Contact:** Dr. John Ogden, Director, Office of International Programs, Box 2000, SUNY Cortland, Cortland, NY 13045; 607-753-2209, fax 607-753-5989; studyabroad@cortland.edu, [www.studyabroad.com/suny/cortland].

Learn German and Discover Berlin. GLS, one of the leading institutions teaching German as a foreign language in Germany, offers various levels of German all year round (age 16 and up), preparation for all language certificates, business German, German for bankers and lawyers.

Special feature: internships in German companies. GLS has accreditation with some U.S. universities. **Dates:** Year round. **Costs:** Price example: $1,080 standard 4-week course and apartment share. **Contact:** GLS Sprachenzentrum, Barbara Jaeschke, Managing Director, Kolonnenstrasse 26, 10829 Berlin, Germany; 011-49-30-780-08-90; fax 011-49-30-787-41-92; germancourses@gls-berlin.com, [www.german-courses.com].

Semesters in Munich or Magdeburg. Fall semester in the heart of the Bavarian capital. Germans teach humanities and social science classes in English. Extended tour of Germany, Austria, and the Czech Republic. Language intensive. Spring term at the Universität in Magdeburg. Participants must come with equivalent of four college-level German classes. Housing in dorms. Classes offered Deutsch als Fremdsprache. Tour to Berlin, Eisenach, the Harz, etc. **Dates:** Sep 1-Dec 15 for Munich; Feb 15-Jun 1 for Magdeburg. **Costs:** Approx. $4,900-$5,650 (for Wisconsin residents; tuition surcharge for out-of-staters), room and board, group travel, airfare, etc. **Contact:** International Programs, Univ. of Wisconsin-Stevens Point, 2100 Main St., Stevens Point, WI 54481; 715-346-2717, fax 715-346-3591; intlprog@uwsp.edu, [www.uwsp.edu/studyabroad].

Greece

Greek Language. Program of Greek language and culture courses. Ten or 20 hours per week. **Dates:** Year round. **Costs:** DR190,000. **Contact:** Aristoteleio, Univ. of Thessaloniki, School of Modern Greek Language, GR 54006, Thessaloniki, Greece; 011-3031-997571/997572, fax 011-3031-997573; thkaldi@auth.gr.

Modern Greek Language. The modern Greek language program is a comprehensive, integrated approach to learning modern Greek. Courses are year round, and include beginning through advanced proficiency levels. The syllabus has been created to teach the language to adults of all nationalities, using textbooks developed at the Center. Classes are small, with an average of 8-12 participants in each course. Three-week summer courses in July on the island of Spetses. **Dates:** Year round, new courses begin every month. **Costs:** $500 per 60-hour course. **Contact:** Rosemary Donnelly, Program Director, 48 Archimidous St., Athens 116 36, Greece; 011-301-701-5242, fax 011-301-701-8603; athenscr@compulink.gr; [athenscr@compulink.gr].

Guatemala

Antigua, Proyecto Linguistico, Francisco Marroquin. Private Spanish instruction in the most prestigious school in beautiful Antigua. A nonprofit foundation which helps preserve Mayan languages. Seven hours daily of one-on-one classes. Family stays and excursions. Airport pickups can be arranged. Academic credit available. **Dates:** Start any Monday, year round. **Costs:** $200 per week, tuition and family stay. **Contact:** Kay G. Rafool, U.S. Office for P.L.F.M., Language Link, P.O. Box 3006, Peoria, IL 61612; 800-552-2051, fax 309-692-2926; info@langlink.com, [www.plfm-antigua.org].

Spanish Immersion Program. Probigua is dedicated to two goals: 1) providing the beginning, intermediate, and advanced Spanish student with an intensive, total immersion experience with one-on-one instruction, trips, daily group activities and homestays; 2) helping the children of Guatemala by donating the school's profits to establish and maintain libraries in many rural villages. **Dates:** Year round. **Costs:** Homestay $60 per week; 4 hours of daily classes $90 per week; 5 hours $105 per week; 6 hours $120 per week; 7 hours $130 per week. (Prices subject to change without notice in 2002.) **Contact:** Rigoberto Zamora Charuc, General Manager, Academia de Español Probigua, 6a. Avenida Norte #41-B, La Antigua 03001, Guatemala; Tel./fax 011-502-8320-860, alternative fax 011-502-8320-082; probigua@conexion.com.gt, [http://probigua.conexion.com]; aegnow@guate.net, [http://probigua.conexion.com].

Universidad Rural de Guatemala. Spanish and Quiché language instruction, internships, voluntary work, and educational and cultural tours. Academic semester in Quetzaltenango, Guatemala (starting in 2001) with courses in Spanish, Latin America literature, history, political sciences, development, women's issues, anthropology, business, human rights, internship, etc. Homestay, daily activities, excursions, reforestation/community projects, and lectures on women, development, cultural issues. **Dates:** Year round. Spanish classes start any Monday year round. Academic semester January, summer, and August. **Costs:** For information about tuition, please visit web site. **Contact:** Julio E. Batres, Director General, Casa Xelajú, 3034 47th Ave. S, Minneapolis, MN 55406; 888-796-CASA, 612-729-9253, fax 612-729-9264. In Guatemala: Casa Xelajú, Callejon 15, Diagonal 13-02, Zona 1, Quetzaltenango,

Guatemala; 011-502-761-5954, fax 011-502-761-5953; info@casaxelaju.com, office@casaxelaju.com, [www.casaxelaju.com].

Italy

International Business, Art and Architecture, Italian Studies: Turin. Turin offers a diversified curriculum in business, economics, art, and architecture plus intensive courses in Italian language and culture, literature, etc., at the foot of the majestic Alps. Program-organized housing and field trips and many Italian university activities.
Dates: Summer term: May-Jul and Jun-Aug; fall semester: Sep-Dec; spring semester: Jan-May. **Costs:** Summer term $2,040 per session $3,790 both sessions; 1semester $4,590; both semesters $7,690. **Contact:** University Studies Abroad Consortium (USAC), Univ. of Nevada, USAC 323, Reno, NV 89557; 775-784-6569, fax 775-784-6010; usac@unr.edu, [http://usac.unr.edu].

Italiaidea in Rome. All levels and formats of Italian language study from intensive short-term "survival Italian" to advanced, semester-long courses, business Italian, conversation, and flexible scheduling. For nearly 20 years we have been offering college credit courses at U.S. college and university programs in Italy; we now offer academic assistance and travel and study assistance to client institutions. Housing including homestays or shared apartments possible.
Dates: Year round. **Costs:** Sixty-hour group course EURO 423.49, 25-hour one-on-one program EURO 692.05, 24-hour business Italian EURO 258.22; registration fee EURO 20.65. **Contact:** Carolina Ciampaglia or Dana Prescott, Piazza della Cancelleria 85, 00186 Roma, Italy; 011-390-0668307620, fax 011-390-066892997; italiaidea@italiaidea.com, [www.italiaidea.com].

Italian for Foreigners. The Bergamo Univ. organizes the following courses: non-intensive course (4 hours per week) in fall and spring; writing courses (2 hours per week) in fall and spring; business Italian courses (2 hours per week); summer intensive course (5 hours per day) with cultural trips; History of Italian Cinema (1 week, 15 hours); Italian Contemporary Literature and Linguistics.
Dates: Vary. **Costs:** Vary. **Contact:** Universita di Bergamo, Segreteria dei Corsi di Italiano per Stranieri, Via Salvecchio 19, Bergamo 24129, Italy; Tel./fax 011-39-035-220557; citastra@ibgu.uni.it, [www.unibg.it].

Italian Language and Art. Institute Galilei specializes in personalized full immersion courses in Italian language especially designed for excutives, business people, professionals, and students. Courses are held in Florence, in the near countryside (Chianti), and at the seaside. Training in specific vocabulary (economics, law, commercial, art history). Courses at 10 levels.
Dates: One-to-one courses start and finish on any day requested. Small group courses start every 2 weeks from the first week of Jan. **Costs:** Starting from $365 per week. **Contact:** Ms. Alexandra Schmitz, Institute Galilei, Via degli Alfani 68, 50121 Florence, Italy; 011-39-055-294680, fax 011-39-055-283481; info@galilei.it, [www.galilei.it].

Italian Language Course by the Sea. The courses: conversation course (2 hours a day); main mini-groups (4 hours a day); intensive (main course plus 6 private lessons); individual tuition. Special courses: tourist industry, commercial Italian for import/export; small groups (max. 6 students). Sports (sailing, catamaran, surfing). Excursions (Calabria, Sicily). Accommodations in apartments.
Dates: Mar 5-Nov 23. **Costs:** Two-week course includes single room $423. **Contact:** Caffè Italiano Club, Largo A. Pandullo 5, 89861 Tropea (VV), Italy; 011-390-963-60-32-84, fax 011-390-963-61786; caffeitaliano@tin.it, [www.caffeitalianoclub.com].

Italian Language Courses. International courses in Italian language and culture for students with a good grasp of Italian and teachers of Italian as a foreign language. Scholarships are offered.
Dates: Jul and Aug. **Costs:** LIT1,600,000 for 4 weeks (accommodations, food, school). **Contact:** Donatella Zema; 011-390-258352812, fax 011-390-58302778; gargnano@mailserver.unimi.it, [http://studenti.unimi.it/foreign/gargnano.htm].

Italian Language Courses in Perugia. Italian language courses all year round. School founded in 1986. Member of ASILS, association of Italian teaching institutes, with strict puslidy criteria. Location in the old city center. Friendly environment. Small groups. Highly qualified teachers. Cultural activities. Accommodations. Beginners courses every month.
Dates: Year round. **Costs:** Standard (4 weeks) LIT800,000; Intensive (4 weeks) LIT1,200,000; Enrollment fee LIT100,000. **Contact:** Durante Sabatino, Comitato Linguistico, XIV Settembre, 57, n. 13, 06122 Perugia, Italy; 011-390-755-721471, 011-390-755-734258; ctlingua@edisons.it, [www.edisons.it/homepages/ctlingua].

WHERE STUDY SPANISH?

INEXPENSIVE GUATEMALA TOPS YOUR LIST

By Diane Slawych

There is no shortage of places to go to study the Spanish language. But if you're looking for inexpensive courses and a beautiful locale—combined with plenty of cultural activities and vivid community life—Guatemala should be at the top of your list.

Four hours of private instruction per day can be had for as little as $125 a week—and that includes room and board with a local family!

Choosing a School: Many schools offer accredited courses endorsed by the Ministry of Education and the Institute of Tourism. But the best way to find out if a particular school is right for you is to consider your preferences and goals and ask to speak to some of the students.

Information on specific schools can be found before you leave through study abroad offices at most universities as well as on the Internet (try entering "Guatemala language schools" under your favorite search engine).

Where to Study: Dozens of language schools in Guatemala offer Spanish courses to foreigners. The city of Antigua provides the most choices, and its popularity is easy to understand. It is arguably the most beautiful city in Central America. Set amidst three volcanoes, it has cobblestone streets, many fine colonial buildings, and amazing Indian handcrafts. The influx of foreigners over the years has resulted in the establishment of a number of good restaurants, bars with satellite television, bookstores, and even places to view foreign films.

Despite all its positive aspects, however, studying in Antigua does have one major disadvantage. The presence of a large number of English-speaking foreigners makes it easy to neglect opportunities to practice Spanish. You're less likely to encounter this dilemma in more remote places such as Quetzaltenango, Huehuetenango, and the El Petén region—all of which also offer Spanish language schools. In El Petén, two schools emphasize an ecological curriculum in the teaching of Spanish.

Where to Stay: You can live with a local family in a homestay arranged by the schools, or you may find your own accommodations.

A homestay is best in terms of cost and opportunities to practice Spanish. For a very reasonable fee, often as little as $50 per week, you receive a private room and three meals a day. If you choose a home-stay, ask the school if you may change families if for some reason it doesn't work out.

Some schools offer informative lectures about Guatemalan history and culture and a number of them donate a portion of your tuition fees to community projects such as saving depleting rainforests in northern Guatemala.

The money you save by studying in Guatemala can be spent on visiting other parts of this beautiful country before returning home.

Italian Language for Foreigners. Courses of Italian language from absolute beginners up to perfecting in small groups (max 8 students).

Dates: Every 2 weeks year round. **Costs:** Standard course: 1 month, LIT770,000. **Contact:** Alberto Del Melia, Scuola Toscana, Via del Benci 23, 50122 Florence, Italy; Tel./fax 011-390-55-24-4583; scuola.toscana@ firenze.net, [www.inter-med.net/scuolatoscana].

Italian Language in Tuscany. Il Sillabo is a small, intimate school in the Tuscan town of San Giovanni Valdarno, a carefully kept secret on the doorsteps of Florence, Arezzo, Siena. A wide, flexible variety of Italian language courses and quality complementary courses: Cooking, Wine Tasting, Drawing, Painting, etc. Extracurricular activities. Convenient accommodations. New: Internship program.

Dates: Every 2 weeks. **Costs:** EURO 765 for 2-week course, in a shared apartment. Call for details. **Contact:** Anna Paola Bosi, Il Sillabo, via Alberti, 31, San Giovanni Valdarno (AR), Italy 52027; 011-390-55-9123-238, fax 011-390-55-9424-39; info@sillabo.it, [www.sillabot.it].

Study Italian in Florence or Tuscan Town. Study Italian in a 16th century Renaissance palace in the center of Florence or in a classic Tuscan town just 30 minutes from the sea. Koiné Center's professional language teachers and small class sizes encourage active participation by each student. Cultural program, guided excursions, choice of accommodations including host families.

Dates: Year round; starting dates each month. **Costs:** Two-week intensive program $325; 3 weeks $395; homestay accommodations from $220 for 2 weeks. **Contact:** In North America: Talking Traveler, 800-274-6007, fax 503-274-9004. In Italy: Dr. Andrea Moradei, Koiné Center, Via Pandolfini 27, 50122 Firenze, Italy; 011-390-55-213881, [www.koinecenter.com]; homestay@teleport.com, [www.talkingtraveler.org].

Japan

Intensive Language and Culture. Japan is one of the most dynamic countries in the world, with the world's second largest economy. The Western Washington Univ., Univ. of Idaho, Lincoln Univ., and KCP offer a unique opportunity to learn more about this country and its language, people, and culture. Programs are open to all English speaking students in good class standing as well as recent college graduates. Our carefully integrated language and culture program offers the student a unique opportunity to develop Japanese language proficiency while gaining an understanding of the Japanese culture and modern society.

Dates: Jan-Mar; Apr-Jun; Jul-Sep; Jul-Aug; Oct-Dec. **Costs:** $5,150 for dorm option and $5,500 for homestay option. Includes registration fee's at sponsor university, tuition, textbooks, local transportation in Tokyo, numerous excursions in and around Tokyo, homestay or private dormitory. Summer short-term is $3,950 and includes all above. **Contact:** Mike Anderson, KCP International, P.O. Box 28028-0028, Bellingham, WA 98228-0028; 888-KCP-7020 or 360-647-0072, fax 360-647-0736; kcp@kcp-usa.com, [www.kcp-usa.com].

Mexico

Always Your Best Link, Language Link, Cuernavaca, Oaxaca, Cancun. Quality complete immersion Spanish language programs in 3 different locations in Mexico. Academic credit available through U.S. accredited university. Excursions to archaeology sites, colonial cities, and cultural Mexico, excellent homestays with meals, all ages with special separate teen programs, executive programs, all levels, airport pickups available, insurance included. Small classes (5) or private. Easy enrollment through our U.S. office, now in its 14th year of excellent service.

Dates: Year round, begin any Monday. **Costs:** Starting at $175 per week, tuition and homestay. **Contact:** Kay G. Rafool, Language Link, P.O. Box 3006, Peoria, IL 61612; 800-552-2051, fax 309-692-2926; info@langlink.com, [www.langlink.com].

Baja California Language College. This Spanish immersion program offered in Ensenada has been the site of Spanish language education for thousands of students from throughout the world. Contemporary new campus 1 mile from the Pacific and 1 hour south of the U.S. border. Homestay program. Groups and children welcome. Well-appointed cafeteria offers free coffee, soda, teas, beer, and purified water.

Dates: Classes begin every Monday all year. Orientation each Sunday at 2 p.m. Weekend sessions are also available. **Costs:** No registration fees. Weekly rates: small group immersion program (5 or fewer per instructor) $240 M-F classes, 20 percent discount for 5 pre-paid weeks, 25 percent discount for 10 pre-paid weeks; weekend rate $140 Sat and Sun; private immersion program $425 per week, $85 per day. Executive immersion program $690 per week (2-week minimum). Homestay is $25 per night, 3 meals included. **Contact:** Keith Rolle, Baja

California Language College, P.O. Box 7556, San Diego, CA 92167; 877-444-2252 (toll free from U.S.); college@bajacal.com, [www.bajacal.com].

Bicultural Programs IMAC. Learn Spanish in Guadalajara, a modern metropolis with a colonial attitude. Group sizes of 1 to 5. Competitive tuition rates, and free Internet access. Only 1 student per host family, hotel discounts also available. A few hours drive from Puerto Vallarta.

Dates: Year round. Group classes start every Monday. Individual tutoring may begin any day. Easter vacation Apr 8-22. Christmas vacation Dec 16, 2001-Jan 7, 2002. **Costs:** Contact organizations for details. **Contact:** Luis Tamayo, Instituto Mèxico Americano de Cultura, Donato Guerra 180, Guadalajara, Jalisco, 44100 Mèxico; 011-52-3-613-1080, fax 011-52-3-613-4621; spanish-imac@imac-ac.edu.mx, [www.spanish-school.com.mx].

Cancun Language Institute. Spanish classes at all levels, in small group or private lessons. New classes start weekly. Located in the heart of downtown Cancun. Air conditioned classrooms. Academic credit available. Social and cultural excursions. Housing assistance.

Dates: Clases start every Monday, year round. **Costs:** From $130 per week for up to 20 hours of instruction. **Contact:** Francisco Romero, Cancun Spanish Language Institute, 44 Avenida Nader, SM 2-A, Cancun, Quintana Roo 77500, Mexico; U.S. office: 763-566-6840, fax 309-412-4332; info@studyspanish.mexico.com, [www.studyspanish-mexico.com].

Center for Bilingual Multicultural Studies. Intensive semester or intensive Spanish language programs for executives, bilingual teachers, healthcare professionals, seniors, nurses, high school students. Group-5 system, 40 class hours per week include Spanish class, Latin American courses and lectures, housing with Mexican host family or guest residence; excursions to historical and archaeological sites. Students enrolled may attend the university courses at no additional cost.

Dates: Year round starting every Monday. **Costs:** Registration fee $100; tuition $200 per week; lodging $168 per week, Plan A. **Contact:** Javier Espinosa, President, San Jeronimo #304, Col. Tlaltenango, Cuernavaca, Mor. 62179, Mexico; 011-527-317-10-87, fax 011-527-3-17-05-33; U.S. 800-932-20-68; admission@bilingual-center.com.mx, [www.bilingual-center.com].

Chac-Mool Cuernavaca. The ultimate Spanish language and cultural program. You can study from 1 to 16 weeks in a pleasant, relaxed setting. Our program offers free individual instruction to all registered students, allowing you to focus on areas where you are weak, or have a specific interest. Extracurricular activities and excursions.

Dates: Year round. Group classes begin every Monday. **Costs:** Weekly tuition begins at $160 with discounts for extended stays. Join a Mexican family, $16-$22 includes 3 meals per day. **Contact:** Sherry Howell, Chac-Mool, 1303 Candelero Ct., Placerville, CA 95667; 888-397-8363 (toll-free U.S./Canada) or 530-622-4262, fax 530-626-4272; spanish@chac-mool.com, [www.chac-mool.com].

Encuentros in Cuernavaca. Spanish immersion program in Cuernavaca, Morelos that focuses on students who need the language for professional purposes or other specific reasons such as travel in Spanish-speaking countries. Fun and effective communicative approach.

Dates: Year round. **Costs:** $75 registration fee. Regular program $150 per week, private tutorials $15 per hour. Homestays $15 per night shared room, $25 per night single room including meals. **Contact:** Jeannie K. Andersen, Encuentros, Calle Morelos 36, Colonia Acapantzingo, CP 62440 Cuernavaca, Morelos, Mexico; 011-52-73-12-50-88, messages 011-52-73-12-98-00; encuent@infosel.net.mx, [www.learnspanishinmexico.com].

Have Fun While You Learn Spanish!. O.L.E. offers intensive Spanish language courses. Choose from any of our 10 practical and dynamic programs opened for all levels and ages. We offer a wide variety of cultural events, extracurricular activities, city tours, and field trips. Accommodations with Mexican families.

Dates: Year round. Courses start every Monday. Group programs arranged at reduced fees. **Costs:** Programs start at $115 per week; homestay $130 per week, meals included. **Contact:** Dulce Wirz and Karina Ayala, O.L.E., Organización Lingüística de Español, Av. Universidad Pte. #1-D, Querétaro 76000, México; 011-52-4-224-1628; info@ole.edu.mx, [www.ole.edu.mx].

Instituto Cultural Oaxaca. All levels of Spanish and literature. Seven hours daily of grammar, conversation, and cultural workshops.

Dates: Begin on any Monday. **Costs:** Contact organization for details. **Contact:** Lic Lucero Topete, Director, Instituto Cultural Oaxaca, Apartado Postal #340, Oaxaca, Oaxaca, C.P. 68000, Mexico; 011-52-951-53404, fax 011-52-951-51323, fax 011-52-951-53728; inscuoax@prodigy.net.mx, [www.instculturaloax.com.mx].

Intensive Spanish in Cuernavaca.
Cuauhnahuac, founded in 1972, offers a variety
of intensive and flexible programs geared to
individual needs. Six hours of classes daily with
no more than 4 students to a class. Housing
with Mexican families who really care about you.
Cultural conferences, excursions, and special
classes for professionals. College credit available.
Dates: Year round. New classes begin every
Monday. **Costs:** $70 registration fee; $680 for 4
weeks tuition; housing $18 per night. **Contact:**
Marcia Snell, 519 Park Dr., Kenilworth, IL
60043; 800-245-9335, fax 847-256-9475;
mexmarcia@hotmail.com,
[www.cuauhnahuac.edu.mx].

Intensive Spanish in Yucatan. Centro de
Idiomas del Sureste, A.C. (CIS), founded in
1974, offers 3-5 hours per day of intensive
conversational Spanish classes with native-
speaking, university-trained professors.
Maximum 6 students per group, average 3.
Program includes beginner courses to very
advanced with related field trips and recommended optional homestay. Also special classes
in business, legal, medical vocabulary, or Mayan
studies.
Dates: Year round. Starts any Monday, except
last 2 weeks in Dec. **Costs:** Tuition (3 hours per
day program: $370 first 2 weeks, $135 each
additional week); tuition 5 hours per day
programs $570 first 2 weeks, $235 each
additional week. **Contact:** Chloe C. Pacheco,
Director, Centro de Idiomas del Sureste, A.C.,
Calle 14 #106 X25, col. Mexico, CP 97128,
Mérida, Yucatán, Mexico; 011-52-99-26-11-55
or 011-52-99-26-94-94, fax 011-52-99-26-90-
20; cisnorte@prodigy.net.mx,
[www.cisyucatan.com.mx].

Intensive Spanish: San Miguel. The Academia
Hispano Americana, the oldest full-time
specialized Spanish language program in Mexico,
offers students 35 hours per week of activities in
the Spanish language. Courses are held year
round and start almost every 4 weeks. San
Miguel is a pleasant mountain community with
clear air and many cultural opportunities.
Dates: Jan 7-Feb 1, Feb 4-Mar 1 (no classes
Feb 5), Mar 4-29 (no classes Mar 21), Apr 8-
May 3 (no classes May 1), May 6-31, Jun 3-28,
July 1-26. **Costs:** Tuition $300 for 2 weeks, $450
per session, $800 for 2 sessions, $1,100 for 3
sessions. Room and board from $17 per day.
Contact: Gary De Mirjyn, Director, Academia
Hispano Americana, Mesones 4, San Miguel de
Allende, Gto., Mexico; 011-52-415-2-0349 or 2-
4349, fax 011-52-415-2-2333;
academia@unisono.net.mx,
[www.unisono.net.mx/academia,
www.mexonline.com/academia].

Interactive Spanish. Spanish from A to Z in 40
hours. Groups of 3 maximum.
Dates: Open **Costs:** $320 for 40 hours in
group of 3. **Contact:** Spanish4U, 20 de Enero
Sur 42, Colonia San Antonio, San Miguel
Allende, Guanajuato, Mexico; 011-52-415-2-41-
15, [www.spanish4u.com].

**Mar de Jade Ocean-front Center, Chacala,
Nayarit.** Celebrating our 20th year as a center
for responsible tourism, we are located in the
fishing village of Chacala on its beautiful beach
north of Puerto Vallarta. For 15-years, our
volunteer/study program has been offering
opportunities to guests to learn Spanish and put
it to use in rural community volunteer projects,
including a medical clinic, an after school
program for children, a community kitchen and
garden project, ESL classes, and house construction. Guests gain insight into local culture
through volunteering. Surrounded by lush jungle
with the warm, clear Pacific at our door, they
enjoy swimming, surfing, hiking, horseback
riding, snorkeling, kayaking, whale-watching,
and other excursions. Our calendar of retreats
include yoga, meditation among others as well as
our teen summer camp.
Dates: Year round. **Costs:** All rates are per
person per night and include accommodations
and 3 meals daily. Rates start at $60 per person
per night for shared accommodations (up to 4 in
a room), or $1,200 for 21 day/20 night optional
volunteer program. Doubles, singles, suites,
master suites, and apartments available. Add 15
percent tax to all rates.Reduced 3-week rates
available in May, June, September, October.
Children welcome. Optional Spanish classes:
$80 per week with minimum of 6-night stay.
Group rates available. **Contact:** In Mexico, Tel./
fax 011-52-322-21171; Tel. 011-52-322-23524.
U.S. mailing address: PMB 078-344, 705
Martens Ct., Laredo, TX 78041-6010;
info@mardejade.com, [www.mardejade.com].

Spanish Language and Mexican Culture. Five
6-week programs each year (introductory course
and 5 levels of Spanish), Mexican and Latin
American culture courses offered in Spanish (art
history, history, literature, and Chicano studies).
Intensive and semester courses.
Dates: Spring: Jan-May; summer: Jun-Aug;
fall: Aug-Dec. **Costs:** Vary. **Contact:** Lic. Marta
Basave, Head, Information Dept., fax 011-525-
616-26-72; marta@servidor.unam.mx,
[www.cepe.unam.mx].

Winter Session in Cuernavaca. Spend winter session studying Spanish Language and Culture with SUNY Cortland's program at SLI, Spanish Language Institute, in Cuernavaca, Mexico, the City of the Eternal Spring. Grammar classes with no more than 5 students, homestays, excursions to Mexico City and Teotihuacán included. All levels from basic to proficient. Three undergraduate credits. Faculty director accompanies group.
Dates: Dec 28-Jan 18. **Costs:** Approx. $975 (does not include SUNY tuition, airfare, insurance or spending money) **Contact:** SUNY Cortland International Programs, P.O. Box 2000, SUNY Cortland, Cortland, NY 13045; 607-753-2209, fax 607-753-5989; studyabroad@cortland.edu, [www.studyabroad.com/suny/cortland].

Nicaragua

Casa Xalteva Language Center. Casa Xalteva offers high-quality intensive Spanish language courses at beginning, intermediate, and advanced levels with Nicaraguan teachers. Classes have a maximum of 4 students and meet 4 hours per day Monday-Friday. We also offer homestays with families, volunteer work opportunities, and cultural programs.
Dates: Classes begin each Monday year round. **Costs:** Instruction $125 per week, $425 per month; homestays $70 per week. **Contact:** Casa Xalteva, Calle Real Xalteva #103, Granada, Nicaragua; 011-505-552-2436. In U.S.: P.O. Box 4542, Albuquerque, NM 87196; 505-254-7535; casaxal@ibw.com.ni, [www.ibw.com.ni/~casaxal].

Nicaragua Spanish Schools. Learn Español in one of Latin America's most hospitable countries where you can choose to study consecutively at 2, 3, or all 4 of our diverse Nica-run Spanish schools for the same price as a single school program. Program includes 4 hours individualized instruction daily, experienced, all materials, hospitable family homestay, edu-cultural activities, volunteer opportunities, edu-excursions, and mucho más! Transferable university credit is available.
Dates: Year round. Start any day of the week. **Costs:** One week $195, 2 weeks $365, 3 weeks $535, 4 weeks or more $175 per week; tutoring $7 per hour. Subtract $60 per week for no homestay. **Contact:** Nicaragua Spanish Schools, Apartado Postal SL-145, Managua, Nicaragua; Tel./fax 011-505-244-4512. U.S.: 805-687-9941; nss-pmc@prodigy.net, [http://pages.prodigy.net/nss-pmc/].

Spain

=elemadrid=. Learn Spanish at home and in Madrid! Spanish courses in small groups or private tuition for adults, professionals, Spanish teachers, unique program of Spanish culture classes, Spanish conversation, art seminars, Spanish dances, leisure activity courses, fascinating weekend excursions. Free Spanish word of the month. Conjugate Spanish verbs online.
Dates: Courses start every other Monday year round. **Costs:** Courses $235-$1,075 per week, culture classes included; accommodations $90-$980 per week; art seminars, dancing classes, leisure activity courses, and weekend excursions vary. **Contact:** =elemadrid=, Calle Serrano 4, 28001 Madrid, Spain; Tel./fax 011-34-91-432-4540/41; hola@elemadrid.com, [www.elemadrid.com].

Always Your Best Link, Language Link, Seville, Madrid, Vejer de la Frontera. Quality complete immersion Spanish language programs in 3 different locations in Spain, 2 large cities and 1 small village on the coast. Academic credit available through accredited U.S. university. Excursions to explore this exciting country, homestays with meals, residence halls, flats, all adult ages with special separate teen program (15-17), all levels, airport pickups available, insurance included. Small classes with additional cultural classes including flamenco dance. Easy enrollment through our U.S. office, now in its 14th year of excellent service.
Dates: Start any Monday, year round. **Costs:** Starting at $250 per week, tuition and homestay. **Contact:** Kay G. Rafool, Language Link, P.O. Box 3006, Peoria, IL 61612; 800-552-2051, fax 309-692-2926; info@langlink.com, [www.langlink.com].

Aula Magna Castellana. The best place for a study abroad experience, Segovia is one of the most beautiful cities in the world. We offer a large variety of courses: Spanish Language, History, Art, Literature, Business, and Technical Language. All of them include leisure and cultural activities. We also arrange weekend excursions, conversation exchanges with Spaniards, and job opportunities.
Dates: Semester (fall, winter, spring) plus summer programs beginning in Jul and Aug. **Costs:** Start at $1,470 all inclusive (meeting and transportation, housing and full room and board for 4 weeks, 40 hours of class, and 32 hours of activities). **Contact:** Aula Magna Castellana, Santo Tomás 1, 3° D, 40002 Segovia, Spain; 011-34-921-412155, 011-34-649-560511 (English contact), fax 011-34-921-412521;

amagnac@arrakis.es,
[www.aulamagnacastellana.com].

CP Language Institute Madrid. Located in the town center of Madrid. Two- to 8-week standard and intensive courses, 4 hours per day. One-on-one instruction, customized courses for groups and combination courses. All levels available. Classes are small and thus offer a great deal of attention to the student. Cultural and leisure activities are an integral part of the program. Accommodations with selected guest families.
Dates: Year round (except Aug). **Costs:** PTS25,000 per week, 20 hours tuition; PTS28,000 full-board accommodations with guest family. **Contact:** Mrs. Maria Dolores Romero, CP Language Institute, c/o Schiller International Univ., Calle San Bernardo 97/99, 28015 Madrid, Spain; 011-34-91-448-2488, fax 011-34-91-445-2110; cp@schillermadrid.edu, [www.cp-languages.com].

ENFOREX Language School. ENFOREX Spanish School was 6 schools in Spain (Madrid, Barcelona, Salamanca, Marbella, Granada, and Almuñecar) open all year round and 1in Quito (Ecuador), Cuzco (Peru), Sucre (Bolivia). Small groups and more than 15 different intensive programs.
Dates: Start every Monday. **Costs:** One month $800 includes accommodations and tuition. **Contact:** ENFOREX, Calle Alberto Aguilera 26, 28015 Madrid, Spain; fax 011-34-91-5945-159; spanish@enforex.es, [www.enforex.es].

Escuela Montalbán. Founded in 1986, is located in Granada, one of the most beautiful cities in southern Spain. Year-round intensive Spanish language courses, business Spanish with exam preparation, Spanish for specific purposes, exam courses D.E.L.E., teacher training and cultural courses. Courses are complemented by a daily cultural program, trips to other parts of Anadulsia during weekends and linguistic exchanges with local students. All accommodations offered to students is carefully selected by the school. A member of TANDEM International and belongs to Asociación de Escueles de Español de Andalucia (AEEA).
Dates: Year round. Starts every Monday; beginners start every 2 weeks. **Costs:** Four-week standard, intensive, or superintensive courses (4-6 hours per day) with daily cultural program $418-$630. Accommodations in student residence or with host family: half board, single room, 4 weeks $440-$470. **Contact:** Margret Fortmann, Escuela Montalbán, C/Conde Cifuentes, 11, Granada, 18005 Spain; Tel./fax

011-34-958-25-68-75; info@escuela-montalban.com, [www.escuela-montalban.com].

Institute for Spanish Teachers. Two-week program designed for teachers of Spanish that offers a unique opportunity to be in contact with Spanish culture and lifestyle while practicing the language and obtaining credits for course work. Up to 6 graduate credits will be awarded. Hosted by the Insitute of Spanish Studies in Valencia, Spain.
Dates: Jul 15-29. **Costs:** $1,850. **Contact:** Dr. Lily Anne Goetz, Longwood College, International Studies Programs, 201 High St., Farmville, VA 23909; 804-395-2158; info@spanish-studies.com, [www.spanish-studies.com].

Institute of Spanish Studies. Founded in 1950, ISS offers courses in Valencia (Spain) in Spanish language, literature, art, history, geography, civilization, and culture. In collaboration with Longwood College, the Institute offers 2 summer sessions as well as fall and spring semesters with over 40 different courses of instruction from beginners to graduate level.
Dates: Fall and spring semesters, summer 1 (May-Jun, 4 weeks), summer 2 (Jul, 4 weeks). **Costs:** Semester $6,700, summer $2,700. **Contact:** Institute of Spanish Studies, 17303 SW 80 Pl., Miami, FL 33157; 888-454-6777, fax 305-971-5354; info@spanish-studies.com, [www.spanish-studies.com].

Intensive Spanish Courses, Seville. CLIC IH one of Spain's leading language schools, is located in the heart of Seville, the vibrant capital of Andalusia, and boasts a beautifully renovated Sevillian mansion as its center. Year-round intensive Spanish language courses, business Spanish, and official exam preparation are taught by highly qualified and motivated native teachers. CLIC IH combines professionalism with a friendly atmosphere. Academic credits available. Accommodations are carefully selected and we offer a varied cultural program as well as exchanges with local students.
Dates: Year round. **Costs:** Approx. $859 for a 4-week Spanish course and homestay, individual room, 2 meals per day. **Contact:** Bernhard Roters, CLIC IH Seville, C/ Albareda 19, 41001 Sevilla, Spain; 011-34-95-450-2131, fax 011-34-95-456-1696; clic@clic.es, [www.clic.org].

Intensive Spanish Language Courses. Four hours tuition per day Monday-Friday. All levels. Students can enroll for as many weeks as they like. Average 8 students per class. A social program is included in the price. Wide range of accommodations options.

FREQUENTLY ASKED QUESTIONS ABOUR SPANISH LANGUAGE SCHOOLS

By Ron Mader

Traveling to a country where you don't speak the language can be scary, but it's also a great adventure. Here's a quick review of some of the most frequently asked questions about Spanish language schools.

What are the choices?

Many schools in Latin America and Spain not only teach foreigners the Spanish language but provide an immersion experience as well. Some are run in conjunction with a university; others are less formal. Reservations can be made ahead of time or at the door. Note that some countries and cities like Quito, Ecuador, and Antigua, Guatemala, have more schools than others.

Why should I study abroad?

Cultural and language immersion is an excellent way of learning and retaining a living language while learning about the culture.

Where should I study?

There are so many choices that the decision about where to go may seem overwhelming. First, choose the country where you'd like to learn. Then choose by the city and school. How to find the best school? Ask! Get recommendations from friends, write or call the schools directly for details and a short list of former students for you to contact. Best of all, visit.

What are the characteristics of a good Spanish language school?

Personal attention. You don't want to be treated like a number. The better schools offer family stays and cultural outings. In other words, they offer immersion into the local culture as well as the language. Some of my favorite schools donate a percentage of their income to social projects and offer the students an opportunity to volunteer or link up with worthwhile projects in the host country. Another sign of a good school is original study materials for the student to use immediately as well as after returning home.

What should I expect to learn?

This depends on your commitment. If you can only afford a week, at the least you'll be a better prepared for your travels; if you can devote more time, you'll have a greater command of the language. Many language vacationers use the school as a base and venture out from there—often with their tutors alongside them.

What do I need to take with me?

If you are combining education with travel, make sure you cover the bases. Bring the appropriate clothes, travel necessities (camera, guidebooks, medicine), and a bilingual dictionary.

Where do I live?

Many schools offer homestays with local families. You can also arrange your own lodging or live in an apartment or hotel. Consult a guidebook or ask the school officials to get a good idea of what lodging typically costs.

How do I know if a school is right for me?

The best bet is to select a school on prior recommendations. A school's reputation is worth more than all of the advertising in the world. If you have any doubts, don't commit yourself to more than a week of classes. If you can, visit the school and talk with the teachers and students. The best advice is to let the director of the school and your teacher know what you'd like to accomplish—is it survival Spanish or do you have more specific goals. They will be happy to accommodate your needs if you let them know what your needs are.

Can I get university credit for classes taken abroad?

Many schools offer credit transfers. Ask your college first.

What are the pros and cons of using an agency instead of arranging schooling with an individual school?

On the plus side, an agency can handle international payments—many accept credit cards—and it offers an international point of contact. On the downside, many agencies require you to prepay before starting a program and some charge a registration fee.

How long are typical language courses?

Courses can last from one day to several months. Most schools encourage students to take at least one week of classes and preferably two or three weeks for maximum benefit. As always, it depends upon your abilities and needs.

Editor's Note: Planeta.com's Directory of Spanish Language Schools can be found online, part of its Education Resources Collection, at [www.planeta.com].

Dates: Year round, starting every 2 weeks. **Costs:** EURO560 for a 2-week course (accommodations included). **Contact:** Carmen Sanchez, International House Barcelona, Trafalgar, 14, 08010 Barcelona, Spain; 011-34-93-268-4511, fax 011-34-93-268-0239; spanish@bcn.ihes.com, [www.ihes.com/bcn].

International Program-Seville. Semester, academic year. Classes for foreign students at the Univ. of Pablo de Olavide include Spanish language classes at three levels, science and Spanish civilization classes in English and many classes in Spanish ranging from political science and social work to environmental studies. Social/cultural activities included in program fee.
Dates: Sept 10-Dec 21; Jan 21-May 17. **Costs:** EURO1,142 (approx. $1,100) **Contact:** Joanna Wandycz-Mejias, Program Director Carretera de Utrera, km. 1, 41013 Sevilla, Spain; 617-733-6457; intl@upo.es, [www.upo.es/estu/intl.htm].

Madrazo Language School. Spanish language courses from 1 week to 1 year, throughout the year. Small group classes professionally taught at our school in the center of Madrid. Business Spanish and one-to-one also available. Book and audio-visual lending library. Conversation exchanges with Spanish students. Social and cultural program.
Dates: Jan 8-Dec 15. **Costs:** Vary. **Contact:** Madrazo Language School, Calle Los Madrazo, 16, 28014 Madrid, Spain; 011-34-91-369-04-73, fax 011-34-91-369-04-73; madrazo@interbook.net, [www.madrazo-school.com].

Spanish and Basque Studies: San Sebastián. San Sebastián offers intensive language (Spanish or Basque) that fulfills up to 2 years of university language requirements in 1 semester, plus courses in history, literature, political science, economics, art, teacher education, etc. Program organized field trips to Madrid and other exciting locations, housing, and many local university activities at this beautiful seaside resort.
Dates: Summer terms: Jun, Jul, Aug; fall semester: Aug-Dec, spring semester: Jan-May. **Costs:** One semester $7,470; both semesters $11,980; Jun or Jul session $2,340; Aug session $1,990; Jun and Jul sessions $4,290; Jun and Aug sessions $3,920; Jul and Aug sessions $3,920; Jun, Jul and Aug sessions $5,660. **Contact:** University Studies Abroad Consortium (USAC), Univ. of Nevada, USAC 323, Reno, NV 89557; 775-784-6569, fax 775-784-6010; usac@unr.edu, [http://usac.unr.edu].

Spanish Courses. In a 19th century palace, meters away from the Retiro Park, close to Prado Museum, we offer intensive Spanish courses, Business Spanish and DELE preparation courses focusing in immersion in our way of life and culture. Come with us and discover the secrets of our country while learning our language.
Dates: Every Monday. **Costs:** 24,750 ESP per week. **Contact:** FORMULA ¡SÍ! Escuela de español, Director, Jaiver Lopez de Ceballos, calle Velazquez, 3, 28001 Madrid, Spain; 011-34-91-576-74-53, fax 011-34-91-577-36-55; info@formula-si.com, [info@formula-si.com].

Spanish for Seniors. Widely recognized to be one of Spain's leading language schools, Malaca Instituto has a special program designed for seniors who want to improve their Spanish to enjoy holidays in Spanish-speaking countries. Lessons in Spanish of everyday situations combined with cooking lessons, gallery and museum visits, small excursions, dance classes, etc.
Dates: Sep 24; Oct 8, 22; Nov 5; starting Feb 11, 25; Mar 11, 25; Apr 8, 22; May 6, 20; Jun 3, 2002. **Costs:** PTS69,000 for 2-week course and activities. **Contact:** Bob Burger, Malaca Instituto, c/Cortada 6, 29018 Malaga, Spain; 011-34-95-229-3242, fax 011-34-95-229-6316; espanol@malacainst-ch.es, [www.malacainst-ch.es].

Spanish in Spain and Latin America. Spanish in Spain (Madrid, Barcelona, Marbella, Granada, Almunecar, Salamanca) and Latin America (Ecuador: Quito, Cuzco; Peru; Sucre, Bolivia; Cordoba, Argentina; Flamingo Beach, Costa Rica. Year round, starting every Monday, for all ages (childrens' summer camps for 6-18 years old), university students, adults, executives. Accredited by CEELE (Univ. of Alcala).
Dates: Year round, starting every Monday, for all ages. **Costs:** From $840 for 4 weeks, includes accommodations and tuition. **Contact:** Head office: ENFOREX, Alberto Aguilera 26, 28015 Madrid, Spain; 011-34-91-594-3776, fax 011-34-91-594-5159; spanish@enforex.es, [www.enforex.com].

Spanish Language and Culture. Intensive Course on Spanish language and culture with total immersion in the Spanish way of life. Program of conferences and visits every day and broad activity program to discover the secrets of our country. Individualized instruction. Accommodations with host families, apartments, and students residence.
Dates: Year round. **Costs:** $1,100. **Contact:** FORMULA ¡SÍ!, Calle Velázquez,3, 1ª 28001, Madrid, Spain, Director: Javier Ceballos, 011-34-915767453, fax 011-34-915773655; info@formula-si.com, [www.formula-si.com].

Spanish Studies: Alicante. Alicante offers intensive Spanish language studies that fulfille up to 2 years of university language requirements. Additional courses available in Spanish studies. Alicante is a seaside year round resort built around a natural habor.

Dates: Summer: Jun, Jul, and Aug. Fall: Aug-Dec. Spring semester: Jan-May. **Costs:** Jun or Jul session $2,340; Aug $1,990; Jun and Jul sessions $4,290; Jun and Aug 1 semestre $6,680, both semester $9,980. Jul and Aug $3,920; Jun, Jul, and Aug sessions $5,660. **Contact:** University Studies Abroad Consortium (USAC), Univ. of Nevada, USAC 323, Reno, NV 89557; 775-784-6569, fax 775-784-6010; usac@unr.edu, [http://usac.unr.edu].

Spanish Studies: Madrid. The Madrid program offers intensive language study—up to 2 years of university language requirements may be met in 1 semester. This program opens a window on the Spanish people, introducing you to the rich diversity of Spain and offering a truly, multicultural experience.

Dates: Fall semester: Sep-Dec; spring semester: Jan-May. Summer: Jun and Jul. **Costs:** One semester $7,180; both semesters $11,556. Summer 1 semester $2,340 or both $4,290. **Contact:** University Studies Abroad Consortium (USAC), Univ. of Nevada, USAC 323, Reno, NV 89557; 775-784-6569, fax 775-784-6010; usac@unr.edu, [http://usac.unr.edu].

Spanish, International Business and/or Basque Studies: Getxo-Bilbao. The Getxo-Bilbao area offers intensive language studies (Spanish or Basque) that fulfill up to 2 years of university language requirements in 1 semester, plus courses in history, political science, art, culture, economics, teacher education, literature, etc. Program organized field trips, housing, and many local university activities at this seaside city.

Dates: Fall semester: Aug-Dec; spring semester: Jan-May. **Costs:** One semester $4,620; both semesters $7,600. **Contact:** University Studies Abroad Consortium (USAC), Univ. of Nevada, USAC 323, Reno, NV 89557; 775-784-6569, fax 775-784-6010; usac@unr.edu, [http://usac.unr.edu].

Univ. of Salamanca. Founded in the early 13th century, the Univ. of Salamanca is one of the most distinguished centers of learning in Europe. SUNY Cortland is celebrating the 34th consecutive year in this "City of the Golden Stones." Fields of study include Spanish language (7 levels) and literature, humanities, social sciences. Specially contracted course on the Arab influence in Spain (concluding with excursion to Andalucía) is offered in the spring in addition to traditional classes. Homestays. Excursions. Resident Director.

Dates: Fall: early Sep-mid-Dec; spring-option 1: early Jan-end of Mar; option 2: early Jan-mid-May. **Costs:** Fall estimate: $3,850, spring Jan-Mar $2,200; Jan-May $4,500. Includes pre and post departure orientation programs, Spanish insurance, overseas instructional costs, room and board with a family, transportation from Madrid airport if arriving with group flight, excursions, administrative fees. SUNY tuition and airfare not included. **Contact:** Liz Kopp, Assistant Director, Office of International Programs, Box 2000, SUNY Cortland, Cortland, NY 13045; 607-753-2209, fax 607-753-5989; studyabroad@cortland.edu, [www.studyabroad.com/suny/cortland].

Sweden

Intensive Summer Courses in Sweden. Intensive summer courses in Swedish: 3 weeks, 5 lessons per day, Mon-Fri, from beginners level to advanced courses. Executive courses in Swedish, 2 weeks, 5 lessons per day, Mon-Fri, small groups, 4-6 participants. Beginners to advanced.

Dates: Jun, Jul, Aug. **Costs:** SEK6,850-SEK9,150. **Contact:** Marlene Wälivara, Folkuniversitetet, Box 386, S-75106 Uppsala, Sweden; 011-46-18-680010, fax 011-46-18-693484; marlene.walivara@folkuniversitetet.se, [www.folkuniversitetet.se/uppsala].

Switzerland

Univ. of Geneva Summer Courses. Three-week French language and civilization at all levels, beginners to advanced. All instructors have a university diploma. Excursions and visits to Geneva and its surroundings. Class of 15-20 students. Minimum age 17.

Dates: Jul, Aug, Sep. **Costs:** SFR500 for 3 weeks (tuition). **Contact:** Mr. G. Benz, Univ. of Geneva, Summer Courses, rue de Candolle 3, CH-1211 Geneva 4, Switzerland; 011-41-22-705-74-34, fax 011-41-22-705-74-39; elcfete@unige.ch, [www.unige.ch/lettres/elcf/coursete/cournet.html].

Univ. of Lausanne Summer Courses. Courses are taught in French in 4 series of 3 weeks each for elementary level to advanced. We also offer 2 courses for beginners that last at least 6 weeks. One or more series may be attended. Classes are constituted according to the students' test.

Dates: Series I: Jul 8-26; Series II: Jul 29-Aug 16; Series III: Aug 19-Sep 6; Series IV: Sep 9-27. **Costs:** CHF500 for 3 weeks; CHF1,100 for 6 weeks (2002). **Contact:** Univ. of Lausanne, Cours de Vacances, BFSH2, CH-1015 Lausanne,

SPANISH STUDY IN THE NORTH OF SPAIN
CHOOSE SALAMANCA FOR HISTORY, SANTANDER FOR GEOGRAPHY

By Steve Wilson

Because of the purity of its language, north-central Spain remains one of the top choices for Spanish language studies. Salamanca stands out for its history, Santander for its geography.

The Towns

There's no denying that the north is different from the rest of Spain. The mountains are more rugged, the weather colder, the architecture more influenced by Rome than by Islam. But, like everywhere in Spain, the pace of life is relaxed and the emphasis is on spending time with friends and family. People get up late, take a long break in the middle of the day, and on weekend nights stay out until dawn.

This partying spirit is especially strong in the student-rich city of Salamanca, the location of the medieval Universidad de Salamanca as well as a large private university and over a dozen private language schools. It is said that there are more bars per capita in Salamanca than anywhere else in the country.

With its ancient city center, narrow passageways, and the nearly-perfect Plaza Mayor—a paradise for people watchers—Salamanca is also a beautiful city. Narrow, pedestrian-only streets wind through the old town past stores and plazas and old architectural gems built of a beautiful rosy sandstone.

The university itself, a 13th-century building tucked away behind the Pontificia, is a good example of how well the Spanish have managed to modernize the interior of their old buildings while leaving the exterior untouched. Light and airy inside, the exterior maintains the dignity and strength befitting a building 700 years old. Around the corner, the city's old cathedral, built in 1160, is a wonderful example of Romanesque architecture with high arched ceilings and a fine quiet feel inside.

A few hours to the north is the more active town of Santander, a modern, planned city on the coast of Cantabria, mostly known as a summer resort for *Madrilenos*. While it may lack the structural charm of Salamanca. Santander is a great place for language students who like to surf, hike, ski, or sail.

Like San Francisco, Santander is situated on a hilly peninsula overlooking a protected bay. Across the bay is a long beach at the holiday village of Somo, rarely crowded and easily reached by boat every half hour. On weekends the bay fills with sailboats, and it's possible to join them by signing up at the sailing school located on an island just off Bikini Beach.

Beyond beach life, Santander is well-placed for trips to the Picos de Europa, among the most rugged mountains in Europe. Most of the small villages in the Picos have an *aubergue* or a *fonda,* basic hostels that allow you to hike all day and not have to lug around camping gear. Many of the schools organize weekend trips to the mountains, but if you stay long enough a Spanish friend is sure to take you there.

The Schools

Most of the schools in these towns are professionally-run, taught by qualified teachers, and offer excellent value for the money. Prices average $400-$500 a month for intensive classes of 20 to 25 hours a week.

In Salamanca in particular the competition among schools is strong, and many try to offer small extras in order to lure students in their direction.

While some of the large private schools have their own student residences, the most common options will be a room with a family or in a shared apartment. To live with a family, including three meals a day, you can expect to pay around $500 a month. For about $200 a month you can rent a room in an apartment shared with other students and do your own cooking. If you prefer eating out, Spain is still a European bargain. A typical menu of the day, featuring two entrees, bread, glass of wine, salad and dessert costs about $7.50; a glass of the house wine less than $1.

To really get to know the area, the food, and the culture, the best thing one can do is find an intercambio—a Spanish conversation exchange partner. Most schools will help you arrange this; if not, put up a sign at an English language school. Meeting and befriending a local Spaniard will not only give you a chance to put what you've learned into practice, it is a sure way to get beyond the surface of the country and into its soul.

Switzerland; 011-41-21-692-30-90, fax 011-41-21-692-30-85; CoursDeVacances@cvac.unil.ch, [www.unil.ch/cvac].

United Kingdom and Ireland

IELTS General English Course. Full-time course in IELTS (International English Language Testing System) course. Students can enroll for courses beginning every Monday and can study for as long as they feel it necessary.
Dates: From Jul 2. **Costs:** Please inquire. **Contact:** Edith Larsen, Finchley House Art and Language Centre, 707 High Rd., London N12 0BT, England; 011-44-208-446-3807, fax 011-44-208-446-3865; artandlanguage@yahoo.co.uk, [www.art-and-language.com].

United States

Intensive English Program. Intensive English Program has over 20 years of experience providing English instruction to students. Students progress toward their academic, professional, or personal language goals using our up-to-date computer/language lab. We organize activities for international students, including trips, volleyball, rafting, skiing, and dinners. We provide homestays, and conversation partners.
Dates: Aug, Oct, Jan, Mar, May, Jul. **Costs:** Call or email for details. **Contact:** Anita Hobbes, Administrative Assistant, Intensive English Program, 101 Co-Op Units Building, Colorado State Univ., Ft. Collins, CO 80523-1788; 970-491-6616, fax 970-491-5399; iep@vines.colorado.edu, [www.colostate.edu/Depts/IEP].

Masters for International and Intercultural Management and Study Abroad. The School for International Training (SIT) offers academic curriculum integrated with field-based practice, reflection, and application including professional practice. SIT offers master's degrees in Teaching (ESOL, French, Spanish), Intercultural Relations, International Education. Sustainable Development, Organizational Management, Conflict Transformation, and a self-design option. SIT also offers 5 undergraduate study abroad programs in over 45 countries.
Dates: Call for details. **Costs:** Call for details. **Contact:** Admissions, School for International Learning, P.O. Box 676, Kipling Rd., Brattleboro, VT 05302; 800-336-1616, fax 802-258-3500; admissions@sit.edu, [www.sit.edu].

TEFL Programs in Boston. The Boston Language Institute offers full-time and part-time teaching training programs: no previous teaching experience required; practical classroom experience before you leave; career guidance; certificate recognized internationally.
Dates: Every month. **Costs:** $2,495. **Contact:** Yeny Kim, Program Coordinator, TEFL, The Boston Language Institute, 648 Beacon St., Boston, MA 02215; 617-262-3500 ext 228, fax 617-262-3595; tefl@boslang, [www.teflcertificate.com].

Venezuela

SUNY Cortland at the VEN-USA Institute. Students enroll at the VEN-USA Institute of International Studies and Modern Languages in Mérida, located in the heart of the Venezuelan Andes. Sessions include 10-week semester, 15-week semester, 2 6-week summer sessions or academic year. All levels of Spanish proficiency can be accommodated. Homestays. Latin American Studies; Venezuelan history, culture, and folklore. Most classes taught in Spanish with a limited number in English. Human services internships available to qualified students who are fluent in Spanish.
Dates: Fall: 10-week semester late Sep-mid-Dec, 15-week semester late Aug-mid-Dec; spring: 10 week semester mid-Feb-end of Apr, 15-week semester early Jan-end of Apr; summer: session 1 late May-early Jul, session 2 early Jul-mid-Aug. **Costs:** Fall and spring 10-week semester $3,500, 15-week semester $4,400; summer $2,500 per 6-week session. Teacher's Institute $1,984 (includes tuition), SUNY tuition, insurance, airfare or spending money not included. **Contact:** Office of International Programs, Box 2000, SUNY Cortland, Cortland, NY 13045; 607-753-2209, fax 607-753-5989; koppl@cortland.edu, [www.studyabroad.com/suny/cortland].

Vietnam

Vietnamese Language Centre. Vietnamese language programs from beginner to advanced levels. Vietnamese for specific purposes: diplomats, business, social science, etc. Vietnamese culture and study tour: from 4-6 weeks program, visiting major historical sites in north and south Vietnam.
Dates: Year round, summer courses. **Costs:** Vietnamese language study: $350 per month. **Contact:** Nguyen Ngoc Hung, Vice Director, Vietnamese Language Centre, Hanoi; 011-84-4-8542453, fax 011-84-4-8262468; esp@vietnam.org.vn.

Worldwide

Language Link. Quality complete immersion Spanish language programs in Ecuado, Peru, Guatemala, Costa Rica, Mexico, and Spain.

Academic credit available through U.S. accredited university. Excursions with included trips to Machu Picchu, Amazon jungle programs, beach programs, homestays, all ages, all levels, easy enrollment through our U.S. office, now in its 14th year of excellent service.
Dates: Start any Monday, year around. **Costs:** Starting at $175 per week, tuition and homestay. **Contact:** Kay Rafool, Director, Language Link, P.O. Box 3006, Peoria, IL 61612; 800-552-2051 or 309-692-2961, fax 309-692-2926; info@langlink.com, [www.langlink.com].

Dutch Language Study. Dutch language instruction (one-to-one or group lessons) to people of all ages interested in language and culture of Holland. Students stay with carefully chosen host families.
Dates: Year round. **Costs:** Homestay DFL385 per week. Group lessons DFL20 per day, private lessons DFL35 per hour. **Contact:** ISOK, Mr.J.F.H. de Zeeuw, Principal, Jan-Tooropstraat 4, 2225 XT, Katwijk Zh, Holland; 011-31-71-40-13533.

EF Flexible Language Immersion Programs. Live and learn a foreign language with students from all over the world! Intensive foreign language training offered in Spain, France, Italy, Germany, Ecuador, Russia, and China for students aged 16 and older, including adults. Eight proficiency levels are available and are suitable for beginners as well as those with advanced linguistic skills. All courses include accommodations and meals. Extracurricular activities available. College credit is offered through an American University.
Dates: Short-term ourses begin every other Monday year round. Year and semester programs commence in Sep and Jan. **Costs:** Varies with program, begins at $690 for 2-week course. **Contact:** Megan De Lisi, Director of, Admissions, EF International Language Schools, EF Center, 1 Education St., Cambridge, MA 02141; 800-992-1892, fax 617-619-1071; ils@ef.com, [www.ef.com/US/ls/ils/virtualtour].

Language School Programs. Language School Programs emphasize language study in small classes and the opportunity to participate in planned cultural activities while sharing in the daily life of a host family. Programs available for teens and adults in Spain, France, Italy, Germany, Mexico, and Ecuador.
Dates: Year round, some summer only. Available for 3, 4, or 6 weeks. Longer stays available. **Costs:** Approx. $1,990 for 3 weeks, $2,200 for 4 weeks. **Contact:** Outbound Department, Center for Cultural Interchange,

17 N. 2nd Ave., St. Charles, IL 60174; 888-ABROAD1, fax 630-377-2307; karen@cci-exchange.com, [www.cci-exchange.com].

Live the Language. Live the language by learning where it's spoken. Carefully selected host families complement the cultural immersion experience. Programs are available to all levels and range from weekend and week-long courses in Ensenada to 2 weeks and longer in Guadalajara, Madrid, Salamanca, Paris, and Florence. UCSD Extension credit available.
Dates: Flexible start dates each month. **Costs:** Vary. Call organization for details. **Contact:** University of California, San Diego, Extension, Travel Study Program, 9500 Gilman Dr., 0176-Z, La Jolla, CA 92093-0176; 858-822-2747, fax 858-534-7385; travelstudy@ucsd.edu, [www.extension.ucsd.edu/travelstudy].

Spanish and Portuguese Immersion Programs. Study with small groups or private tutor. Live with local host families or in hotels. One-week to 6 months. All ages and levels. Various settings: beaches, mountains, small towns, large cities, etc. Country options: Costa Rica, Guatemala, Honduras, Panamá, Argentina, Chile, Ecuador, Peru, Uruguay, Venezuela, Puerto Rico, Dominican Republic, Bolivia, Spain, and Brazil.
Dates: Rolling admission. Programs start every week or every month. **Costs:** Depends on location. Prices start at $210 per week and include classes, homestay, travel insurance, most meals, some cultural activities. **Contact:** AmeriSpan Unlimited, P.O. Box 40007, Philadelphia, PA 19106; 800-879-6640, fax 215-751-1100; info@amerispan.com, [www.amerispan.com].

SUNY Brockport Study Abroad. Semester, year, and summer study programs in Costa Rica, Mexico, France, and Vietnam. SUNY Brockport's language programs offer the opportunity to study abroad while fully immersing oneself into the language and culture of the country. Programs provide enrollment and immersion opportunities at foreign universities, with transcripts provided by a U.S. accredited 4-year academic institution.
Dates: Vary by program: call or visit web site. **Costs:** Vary by program: call or visit web site. **Contact:** Office of International Education, SUNY College at Brockport, 350 New Campus Dr., Brockport, NY 14420; 800-298-7869, fax 716-637-3218; overseas@brockport.edu, [www.brockport.edu/studyabroad].

*T*HIRTEEN

TEEN STUDY & TRAVEL
BEST RESOURCES AND PROGRAMS

No longer limited to traditional academic year or summer exchange programs, teens are taking short trips with their language classes or musical groups, spending a "gap year" working overseas before attending college, or living with a host family for a summer while studying a language. The choices are virtually limitless. Have a look, then make plans to go! Program listings start on page 228.

Teen Study and Travel Organizations

Alliance for International Educational and Cultural Exchange, 1776 Massachusetts Ave., Suite 620, Washington, DC 20036; 202-293-6141, fax 202-293-6144; info@alliance-exchange.org, [www.alliance-exchange.org]. Publishes the *International Exchange Locator: A Resource Directory of Educational and Cultural Exchange.* Annual. $19.95 plus $6 s/h.

Council on Standards for International Education Travel (CSIET), 212 S Henry St., Alexandria, VA 22314; 703-739-9050, fax 703-739-9035; mailbox@csiet.org, [www.csiet.org]. CSIET is a nonprofit organization committed to quality international educational travel and exchange. It establishes standards for organizations operating international educational travel and exchange programs at the high school level and monitors compliance with those standards by annually reviewing those programs that submit themselves for evaluation. It also disseminates information on international educational travel organizations. *Advisory List of International Educational Travel & Exchange Programs,* published annually ($15 postpaid, $20 overseas), lists programs for highschool students which adhere to CSIET's standards.

Department of State, Exchange Visitor Program Service, 301 4th St., SW, (FEMA Rm. 200), Washington, DC 20547; 202-401-9810. Evaluates not-for-profit organizations to determine whether they meet criteria for Teenage Visitor Programs.

FFA, 1410 King St., Suite 400, Alexandria, VA 22314; 800-772-0939, fax 703-838-5888; global@ffa.org, [www.ffa.org]. Organizes homestays, work-study programs, and seminars overseas for students interested in agriculture.

Institute of International Education (IIE). IIE Books, Institute of International Education, P.O. Box 371, Annapolis Junction, MD 20701-0371; 800-445-0443, fax 301-206-9789; info@iie.org, [www.iie.org]. Free catalog. Publisher of authoritative directories for study abroad and financial aid. IIE publications of interest to secondary schools students include *Basic Facts on Study Abroad* (free), *Vacation Study Abroad,* and *Academic Year Abroad.*

Intercultural Press, Box 700, Yarmouth, ME 04096; 800-370-2665, 207-846-5168, fax 207-846-5181; books@interculturalpress.com, [www.interculturalpress.com]. Publishes numerous books on international living, travel, study, and cross-cultural experiences. Titles include: *Survival Kit for Overseas Living.*

LEAPNow: Lifelong Education Alternatives and Programs, P.O. Box 1817, Sebastopol, CA 95473; 707-829-1142, fax 707-829-1132; info@leapnow.org, [www.leapnow.org]. Consulting service aimed primarily at preuniversity and university students looking to tailor experiences in the U.S. and abroad. 20,000 plus options—college and high school credit. Experiential semester programs in Latin America and Asia.

Mobility International USA (MIUSA), P.O. Box 10767, Eugene, OR 97440; 541-343-1284, fax 541-343-6812; info@miusa.org, [www.miusa.org]. A national, nonprofit organization dedicated to expanding equal opportunities for people with disabilities in international exchange, leadership development, disability rights training, and community service. The **National Clearinghouse on Disability and Exchange (NCDE),** a joint venture by MIUSA and the Bureau of Educational and Cultural Affairs of the U.S. Department of State, strives to increase the participation of people with disabilities in international exchange opportunities by providing free information and referrals to individuals, disability organizations and exchange.

NAFSA: Association of International Educators, 1875 Connecticut Ave., NW, Suite 1000, Washington, DC 20009-5728; 202-462-4811, fax 202-667-3419; [www.nafsa.org]. NAFSA provides training, information, and other educational services to professionals in international educational exchange. For inquiries concerning NAFSA publications: P.O. Box 1020, Seawickley, PA 15143; 800-836-4994.

Teen Study and Travel Programs

Information on programs marked with an asterisk (*) was summarized by the editors from the Advisory List of International Educational Travel and Exchange Programs, published by the Council on Standards for International Educational Travel, below.

Americas

Educational Homestays. Foreign students or visitors live with host families and may also have optional ESL teaching and/or excursions. Short- or long-term homestays provided for high school or college students in universities, at language schools, or just visiting America or Canada.
Dates: Any time of year. **Costs:** Depends on program and city. Programs includes room, meals, airport or bus transfers, plus use of all household amenities, and local area supervision.
Contact: Connections, John Shephard, 17324

185th Ave. NE, Woodinville, WA 98072; 425-788-9803, fax 425-788-2785 [www.connections-inc.com].

Asia

Youth For Understanding (YFU). The YFU International Exchange program, established in 1951, offers high school students and recent graduates the opportunity to gain the global skills, insights and knowledge needed to succeed in a multicultural, interconnected world. YFU offers year, semester, and summer homestay student exchange opportunities to 35 countries (including China, Japan, South Korea, and Thailand). Thanks to the generous support of governments, global-minded corporations and foundations, numerous scholarship opportunities and financial aid are available.
Dates: Year: Jan-Dec and Aug-Jun, Semester: Jan-Jul and Jul-Dec, summer: 3-8 weeks. **Costs:** Contact sponsor. **Contact:** See details at [www.YouthForUnderstanding.org] or call 1-800-TEENAGE for a free viewbook of programs and scholarships. Email to Admissions@us.yfu.org or write to: Program Information, Youth For Understanding International Exchange 3501 Newark St., NW, Washington, DC 20016-3199.; admissions@us.yfu.org, [www.youthforunderstanding.org].

Australia/New Zealand

BUNAC's Work Australia and Work New Zealand Programs. Work and travel down under for up to a year (Australia 4 months, New Zealand 12 months). Full support services, job listings, meet and greet, etc. provided in Australia and New Zealand by BUNAC subsidiary, IEP. For U.S. students and young people 18-30 years old.
Dates: Year round. Call for details. **Costs:** $450/$475 includes visa, admin, arrival package, and on-the-spot support. **Contact:** BUNAC USA, P.O. Box 430, Southbury, CT 06488; 800-GO-BUNAC; info@bunacusa.org, [www.bunac.org].

Youth For Understanding (YFU). The YFU International Exchange program, established in 1951, offers high school students and recent graduates the opportunity to gain the global skills, insights, and knowledge needed to succeed in a multicultural, interconnected world. YFU offers year, semester, and summer homestay student exchange opportunities to 35 countries (including China, Japan, South Korea, and Thailand). Thanks to the generous support of

CAN MY CHILD TRAVEL SOLO?

A CHECKLIST TO MEASURE YOUR CHILD'S READINESS

By Carol Dalton Sebilia

When I address the eager and excited audience of potential junior ambassadors I see their parents nervously sitting next to them trying to stifle the question: "Can my child manage international travel without me?" My job is to select students for international educational tours on criteria that include maturity, positive attitudes, health issues, possible homesickness, and learning capacity. Parents can use these same criteria to measure their child's readiness for a trip abroad.

- **Is my child mature enough?** The key question is can the child handle new situations safely and effectively? If separated from the group, could he or she develop a plan of action? Would he know to find the proper authority and request assistance? Would he panic? Would he be able to keep himself safe?
- **Does my child require medicines or eyeglasses?** If so, pack the primary set of medications in a carry-on bag and a duplicate set of medications and a copy of prescriptions, including eyeglass prescriptions, in different pieces of luggage. Educate travel companions about the symptoms of serious conditions. Include your insurance company's coverage information and form.
- **Does my child have a positive attitude?** Travel is uncomfortable. I remind my students that you will begin your adventure jet lagged and exhausted; you will not sleep in your own bed. On a tour you will go wherever the bus takes you and your mother will not be around to make sure things work smoothly.
- **What about pre-existing health issues?** Is a rigorous schedule with limited sleep damaging to your child's condition? Would your child be better served traveling with a group that includes medically trained staff?
- **What if my child gets homesick?** Most children miss their parents, but severe homesickness can immobilize a child. Occasional homesickness can be managed by substituting fax or email for phone contacts. The sound of Mom's voice is often the trigger for an inconsolable flood of tears. Rooming with a nurturing friend or comforting sibling who will give occasional hugs is another way to manage the sadness that hits hardest at bedtime. One mother explained how she carefully instructed her son to take Tylenol for headaches, Ibuprofen for muscle aches, and Imodium for diarrhea. "What do I take for homesickness?" he asked innocently. "That is why I packed the M and Ms, she responded. Eat a package and know that I love you."
- **Is my child old enough to appreciate it?** Appreciation builds in direct proportion to enthusiastic preparation. Encouraging research in advance of the trip enhances a traveler's understanding immeasurably.
- **Am I pushing my child before he is ready?** Occasionally, parents are more enthusiastic about the child's trip than the child is. As I interviewed a young man for a trip to Australia and explained the itinerary, the mother could not contain her excitement. Her son weakly smiled in return. In the planning meetings he acted silly, behaviorally begging me to reject him from the trip. I did.

Parents commonly express amazement at their son's or daughter's increased maturity level following a trip. The kids knew they could do it all along.

governments, global-minded corporations, and foundations, numerous scholarship opportunities and financial aid are available.

Dates: Year: Mar-Dec, semester: Mar-Aug and Aug-Dec, summer: 3-8 weeks. **Costs:** Contact sponsor. **Contact:** See details at [www.YouthForUnderstanding.org] or call 1-800-TEENAGE for a free viewbook of programs and scholarships. Email to Admissions@us.yfu.org or write to: Program Information, Youth For Understanding International Exchange 3501 Newark St., NW, Washington, DC 20016-3199; admissions@us.yfu.org, [www.youthforunderstanding.org].

Canada

Canadian Adventure Camp. Beautiful island camp offering 4 main programs for boys and girls 6-16. Camping, gymnastics, trampoline, or water skiing. Daily choice of over 30 activities: swimming, sailing, climbing wall, canoeing, kayaking, theater, music, arts and crafts, giant water slides, and more. L.I.T. program for 17-18-year-olds. Easy transportation available. Color brochure and video available.

Dates: Jun-Sep. **Costs:** Contact organization for details. **Contact:** Canadian Adventure Camp, 15 Idleswift Dr., Thornhill, ON, Canada L4J 1K9; 905-886-1406, fax 905-889-8983; info@canadianadventurecamp.com, [www.canadianadventurecamp.com].

Study/Work Abroad, Tours, etc. CANPAC offers variety of ESL and cultural courses in Vancouver. Choose from 8 levels of ESL: Intensive to Business English programs, TEFL and TESL for teachers, Study/Canada Culture tours or private lessons. Homestays, 3 meals per day. Work placement assistance for working holiday visa candidates.

Dates: Year round. **Costs:** CAN$1,950, 1 month includes ESL and Homestay plus city tour. **Contact:** Michele Mikkelsen, CANPAC - Study Abroad, 15286-111A Ave., Surrey, BC, Canada V3R 6G7; 604-951-9512, fax 604-582-7555; canpacific@home.com.

Summer Camp. Wilvaken is a bilingual summer camp situated in the Eastern Townships of Quebec. We have children from many parts of the world coming to enjoy our traditional camp setting as well as learning or improving their second language (English/French).

Dates: Two-, 4-, 6-, 8-week from Jun-Aug. **Costs:** CAN$1,090 for 2 weeks, CAN$4,090 for 8 weeks (2001). **Contact:** Camp Wilvaken (Sep 1-Jun 15), Maya and Dave Willis, P.O. Box 141, Hudson Heights, QC, J0P 1J0, Canada; 450-458-5051, fax 450-458-2581; wilvaken@wilvaken.com, [www.wilvaken.com]. Summer address: 241 ch. Willis, Magog, QC, J1X 3W2, Canada; 819-843-5353, fax 819-843-3024.

Central Europe

Youth For Understanding (YFU). The YFU International Exchange program, established in 1951, offers high school students and recent graduates the opportunity to gain the global skills, insights and knowledge needed to succeed in a multicultural, interconnected world. YFU offers year, semester, and summer homestay student exchange opportunities to 34 countries (including Czech/Slovak Republics, Estonia, Hungary, Latvia, Poland, Russia, and Ukraine). Thanks to the generous support of governments, global-minded corporations, and foundations, numerous scholarship opportunities and financial aid are available.

Dates: Year: Aug-Jun, semester: Aug-Jan, summer: 4, 6, 8 weeks (Jun, Jul, Aug). **Costs:** Contact sponsor. **Contact:** See details at [www.YouthForUnderstanding.org] or call 1-800-TEENAGE for a free viewbook of programs and scholarships. Email to Admissions@us.yfu.org or write to: Program Information, Youth For Understanding International Exchange 3501 Newark St., NW, Washington, DC 20016-3199.; pio@yfu.org, [www.youthforunderstanding.org].

Costa Rica

Enjoy Learning Spanish Faster. Techniques developed from our ongoing research enable students to learn more, faster, in a comfortable environment. Classes of 2-4 students plus group learning activities; conversations with middle-class homestay families (1 student or couple per family). Homestays are in a small town near the capital, San José.

Dates: Year round. Classes begin every Monday at all levels (except Mar 25-29, Dec 14-Jan 5). **Costs:** $345 per week for 26 hours of classes and group activities including Costa Rican dance and cooking classes. Includes tuition, 3 meals per day, 7 days per week, homestay, weekly 3-hour cultural tour, laundry, all materials, and airport transportation. $25 one-time registration fee. **Contact:** Susan Shores, Registrar, Latin American Language Center, PMB 123, Suite 710, 7485 Rush River Dr., Sacramento, CA 95831-5260; 916-447-0938, 916-428-9542; lalc@madre.com, [www.madre.com/~lalc].

CREATING SCHOOL-TO-SCHOOL EXCHANGES

INTERNATIONAL SCHOOL EXCHANGES NEED NOT BE EXPENSIVE

By Pamela S. Turner

International school exchanges don't have to involve expensive tour packages, only a little goodwill between communities and individuals.

Once you know you have the full support of local school and community leaders, you need to identify an appropriate community in another country. Look for a town that is similar to yours in some respect. Does your town already have a sister city relationship? Does someone in your community have personal contacts that might lead to an exchange arrangement? In our case, a young woman from our town, Orinda, California, was teaching English in Asuke, Japan. Her Japanese principal asked if her hometown would agree to host Asuke middle school students for a 1-week exchange.

The two schools then need to work out the basic outlines of the exchange. Orinda and Asuke students spend approximately a week in the host country, with five days devoted to a homestay and a few days for visiting nearby cultural and historical sites.

Student participants can be chosen by lottery, by academic achievement, by teacher recommendation, or by some combination of the above. However, because students will likely miss some schoolwork, it is wise to consider both academic standing as well as how well they will represent their country when choosing participants. (In Orinda, 40 students applied for the exchange with Asuke. The final 10 students were selected after writing an essay and personal interviews with the principal and several teachers. The selection committee looked for students with strong academic and citizenship skills and outgoing, adaptable personalities.)

Local government, parent-teacher organizations, local businesses, foundations, parents, and students can all be part of the fundraising mix. Host schools can keep the cost of an exchange down not only by arranging for stays with host families, but by soliciting volunteer tour guides and private transportation and finding low-cost travel alternatives. Orinda's funds come from parent contributions, business donations, and student fundraising efforts.

A series of classes or informal meetings can help prepare students to live with a family in another country or to host a student. Foreign language teachers, parents, and community members can all be tapped to answer questions about local customs, food, language, history, and culture. Students should be encouraged to get to know their host families in advance through letters or email.

Europe

Pre-College Summer Abroad. For 37 years, the American Institute For Foreign Study (AIFS) has been a leader in the field of international education. Each year AIFS organizes cultural exchange programs throughout the world for more than 50,000 students. Programs are offered on college campuses throughout Europe to students who have completed their sophomore or junior year of high school. All students are issued transcripts from the host institution. **Dates:** Jun-Jul, varying by location. **Costs:** $3,700-$4,700 includes tuition (students are issued a college transcript upon successful completion of the program), housing and meals, social and cultural activities, services of a program director and airfare. **Contact:** 800-727-2437 ext. 5163; precollege.info@aifs.com.

Rassias Programs. Rassias Programs offers French and Spanish study and homestay programs for high school students. Tours and Arles, France; Gijón and Segovia, Spain. Instruction uses the famed Rassias Method(r) developed by Prof. John Rassias of Dartmouth College. **Dates:** Jun 23-Jul 28; Jun 28-Jul 28; Jun 25-Jul 25; Jul 1-31. **Costs:** $5,500-$6,200 includes airfare. **Contact:** Bill Miles, Rassias Programs, P.O. Box 5456, Hanover, NH 03755; 603-643-3007, fax 603-643-4249; rassias@sover.net, [www.sover.net/~rassias].

Youth For Understanding (YFU). The YFU International Exchange program, established in 1951, offers high school students and recent graduates the opportunity to gain the global skills, insights, and knowledge needed to succeed in a multicultural, interconnected world. YFU offers year, semester, and summer homestay student exchange opportunities to 35 countries (including Belgium, France, Germany, Greece, Ireland, Italy, Netherlands, Spain, and Switzerland). Thanks to the generous support of governments, global-minded corporations and foundations, numerous scholarship opportunities and financial aid are available. **Dates:** Year: Aug-Jun and Jan-Dec, semester: Aug-Jan and Jan-Jul, summer: 3-weeks. **Costs:** Contact sponsor. **Contact:** See details at [www.YouthForUnderstanding.org] or call 1-800-TEENAGE for a free viewbook of programs and scholarships. Email to Admissions@us.yfu.org or write to: Program Information, Youth For Understanding International Exchange 3501 Newark St., NW, Washington, DC 20016-3199.; admissions@us.yfu.org, [www.youthforunderstanding.org].

France

Academic Year Program. For students 16-18 years of age, full academic program follows the French national curriculum, including French as a foreign language courses and some courses in English. Residential, full board accommodations. Family at the weekends, tutoring, support. Also summer courses open to all. **Dates:** Sep-Jun. **Costs:** $10,970. **Contact:** Ph. Minereau, Saint-Denis European School, BP 146, 37600 Loches, France; 011-33-267-94-0450; euroschool@saint-denis.net.

Youth For Understanding (YFU). French culture, food, fashion, and industry will fascinate you and provide many opportunities to perfect your conversational French. Day tours to many historical highlights are included with the 6-week homestay program. **Dates:** Vary. **Costs:** Contact sponsor. **Contact:** See details on this and 100 more programs at [www.YouthForUnderstanding.org] or call 1-800-TEENAGE for a free viewbook of programs and scholarships. Email to Admissions@us.yfu.org or write to: Program Information, Youth For Understanding International Exchange 3501 Newark Street N. W. Washington, DC 20016-3199.

Germany

Youth For Understanding (YFU). Experience and learn about the excitingly diverse and stimulating culture of Germany by living with a family in the heart of Europe. Thanks to the generous support of the German and U.S. governments and several foundations, numerous scholarship opportunities and financial aid are available. The YFU International Exchange program, established in 1951, offers high school students and recent graduates the opportunity to gain the global skills, insights, and knowledge needed to succeed in a multicultural, interconnected world. Year, semester, and summer exchange and scholarship opportunities in 34 countries. **Dates:** Vary. **Costs:** Contact sponsor. **Contact:** See details on this and 100 more programs at [www.YouthForUnderstanding.org] or call 1-800-TEENAGE for a free viewbook of programs and scholarships. Email to Admissions@us.yfu.org or write to: Program Information, Youth For Understanding International Exchange 3501 Newark St., NW,

Washington, DC 20016-3199.;
admissions@us.yfu.org,
[www.youthforunderstanding.org].

Italy

Language Courses by the Sea. The courses: conversation course (2 hours a day); main minigroups (4 hours a day); intensive (main course plus 6 private lessons); individual tuition. Special courses: tourist industry, commercial Italian for import/export; small group (max. 6 students). Sports (sailing, catamaran, surfing); excursions (Calabria, Sicily). Accommodations in apartments.
Dates: Mar 6-Nov 24. **Costs:** Two-week course includes single room LIT1,010,000. **Contact:** Caffè Italiano Club, Largo A. Pandullo 5, 89861 Tropea (VV), Italy; 011-390-0963-60-32-84, 011-390-0963-61786; caffeitaliano@tin.it, [www.paginegialle.it/caffeital].

Japan

Youth For Understanding (YFU). Experience Japan like no tourist ever can. YFU offers year, semester, and summer student exchange and scholarship opportunities to 34 countries. The YFU International Exchange program, established in 1951, offers high school students and recent graduates the opportunity to gain the global skills, insights and knowledge needed to succeed in a multicultural, interconnected world.
Dates: Vary. **Costs:** Contact sponsor. **Contact:** See details on this and 100 more programs at [www.YouthForUnderstanding.org] or call 1-800-TEENAGE for a free Viewbook of programs and scholarships. Email to Admissions@us.yfu.org or write to: Program Information, Youth For Understanding International Exchange 3501 Newark St., NW, Washington, DC 20016-3199.; admissions@us.yfu.org, [www.youthforunderstanding.org].

Latin America

Amigos de las Americas (AMIGOS).* Amigos de las Américas is a private international volunteer organization which provides youth volunteers with leadership development opportunities during training and while serving in community development projects in Latin America. More than 18,000 AMIGOS volunteers have lived and worked in 15 Latin American and Caribbean countries.
Dates: Students at least 16 years of age, who meet the AMIGOS language and training requirements, spend 6-8 weeks living in rural

and semi-urban communities and provide community development services in Latin American countries. **Costs:** $3,000 includes international transportation. Fundraising materials are provided and some scholarships are available. **Contact:** Amigos de las Americas, 5618 Star Lane, Houston, TX 77057-7112; 800-231-7796, fax 713-782-9267; info@amigoslink.org, [www.amigoslink.org].

Youth for Understanding (YFU). The YFU International Exchange program, established in 1951, offers high school students and recent graduates the opportunity to gain the global skills, insights, and knowledge needed to succeed in a multicultural, interconnected world. YFU offers year, semester, and summer homestay student exchange opportunities to 34 countries (including Argentina, Brazil, Chile, Ecuador, Mexico, Uruguay, and Venezuela). Thanks to the generous support of governments, global-minded corporations and foundations, numerous scholarship opportunities and financial aid are available.
Dates: Year: Aug-Jun and Jan-Dec, semester: Aug-Jan, Jan-Jul, summer: 4, 6, 8 weeks (Jun, Jul, Aug). **Costs:** Contact sponsor. **Contact:** See details at [www.YouthForUnderstanding.org] or call 1-800-TEENAGE for a free Viewbook of programs and scholarships. Email to Admissions@us.yfu.org or write to: Program Information, Youth For Understanding International Exchange 3501 Newark St., NW, Washington, DC 20016-3199.; admissions@us.yfu.org, [www.youthforunderstanding.org].

Mexico

Center for Bilingual Multicultural Studies. Intensive semester or intensive Spanish language programs for executives, bilingual teachers, healthcare professionals, seniors, nurses, high school students. Group-5 system, 40 class hours per week include Spanish class, Latin American courses and lectures, housing with Mexican host family or guest residence; excursions to historical and archaeological sites. Students enrolled may attend the university courses at no additional cost.
Dates: Year round starting every Monday. **Costs:** Registration fee $100; tuition $200 per week; lodging $168 per week, Plan A. **Contact:** Javier Espinosa, President, San Jeronimo #304, Col. Tlaltenango, Cuernavaca, Mor. 62179, Mexico; 011-527-317-10-87, fax 011-527-3-17-05-33; U.S. 800-932-20-68.; admission@bilingual-center.com.mx, [www.bilingual-center.com].

NIS

ACTR/ACCELS. The American Councils is a professional and educational association and exchange organization devoted to improving education, professional training, and research within and about the countries of the former Soviet Union. Supervision and monitoring are provided by 45 American Councils offices throughout the NIS and its headquarters in Washington, DC.
Dates: Contact organization for details.
Costs: $550-$1,800 includes transportation, insurance, and visa fees. **Contact:** ACTR, 1776 Massachusetts Ave., NW, Suite 700, Department CS, Washington, DC 20036-1904; 202-833-7522, fax 202-833-7523; hardman@actr.org, [www.actr.org].

Scandinavia

Youth For Understanding (YFU). The YFU International Exchange program, established in 1951, offers high school students and recent graduates the opportunity to gain the global skills, insights, and knowledge needed to succeed in a multicultural, interconnected world. YFU offers year, semester, and summer homestay student exchange opportunities to 34 countries (including Denmark, Finland, Norway, and Sweden). Thanks to the generous support of governments, global-minded corporations, and foundations, numerous scholarship opportunities and financial aid are available.
Dates: Year: Aug-Jun, Jan-Dec, semester: Aug-Jan, Jan-Jul, summer: 4, 6, 8 weeks (Jun, Jul, Aug). **Costs:** Contact sponsor. **Contact:** See details at [www.YouthForUnderstanding.org] or call 1-800-TEENAGE for a free viewbook of programs and scholarships. Email to Admissions@us.yfu.org or write to: Program Information, Youth For Understanding International Exchange 3501 Newark St., NW, Washington, DC 20016-3199.; admissions@us.yfu.org, [www.youthforunderstanding.org].

Spain

Courses for Teenagers. It is a course focused on students between 15-17 years old, with a varied social program 4 afternoons a week including sports, cultural visits, parties, films, and days at the beach. Accommodations are full board with a specially selected Spanish family.
Dates: Jul 2 (beginners to advanced); Jul 16 (elementary to advanced). Last day of program Jul 27. **Costs:** Approx. $771 for 2-weeks, $1,094 for 3 weeks, $1,282 for 4 weeks. **Contact:**

Spanish Dept., CLIC IH Seville, C/ Albareda 19, 41001 Sevilla, Spain; 011-34-954-502131, fax 011-34-954-561696; clic@clic.es, [www.clic.es].

Thailand

GlobalQuest. GlobalQuest offers 12-week fall and spring semester study programs in Thailand for high school seniors, students deferring college for a semester or a year, and for college students. Each cluster is for 12 students and 3 teachers. Study takes place throughout Thailand and includes an individual research project, Thai language, natural history and environmental issues, culture, a homestay, and service.
Dates: Mid-Feb-mid-May; mid-Sep-mid-Dec.
Costs: $12,000. **Contact:** Tim Ellis, Executive Director, GlobalQuest, 195 Montsweag Rd., Woolwich, ME 04579; 207-443-5451, fax 207-443-2551; tellis@wiscasset.net, [www.gquest.org].

United Kingdom and Ireland

BUNAC's Work in Britain Program. Allows full-time U.S. university or college students and recent graduates to work for up to 6 months, in any job, any time of year in England, Scotland, Wales, or Northern Ireland. Job and accommodations listings and general support from BUNAC in London and Edinburgh offices.
Dates: Year round. **Costs:** $250 work permit, admin., U.K. support. **Contact:** BUNAC USA, P.O. Box 430, Southbury, CT 06488; 800-GO-BUNAC; 203-264-0901; info@bunacusa.org, [www.bunac.org].

Worldwide

4-H. 4-H is one of the largest youth-serving organizations in the U.S., reaching over 5 million youth each year through the involvement of over 650,000 youth and adult volunteers. It offers high school study and homestay programs in the U.S. and abroad for students ages 15-18 1/2. Summer Programs: 1-month summer homestay programs in the U.S. and abroad for teens ages 12-18.
Costs: High School Programs: $5,000 including insurance. Summer Programs: $2,365 includes transportation and insurance. **Contact:** 4-H (Cooperative Extension 4-H Youth Dev.), 4-H Exchange Central Office, 1015 Pacific Avenue, Suite A, Tacoma, WA 98402; 800-407-3314, fax 253-396-9639; 4h-exchange@worldwise.org.

Academic and Cultural Exchange. The purpose of Academic and Cultural Exchange is to enhance the relationship between the U.S. and

CHILE UP CLOSE
A ONE-YEAR EXCHANGE STUDENT'S REPORT

By Heidi Schmaltz

Last year I lived in Chile for half a year as an exchange student with the American Field Service. Compared to most visitors, I didn't travel much. I lived with a Chilean family and had the responsibilities of any Chilean teenager. I went to school every day, in uniform. I had good days and bad days and days that I didn't understand.

Chuquicamata, my host community, is a mining camp high in the Atacama desert. Tourists come to see the mine, but no one stays longer than a day. There is no discotheque, no shopping center, no anthropological museum or beach. Driveways must be watered daily to keep the dust down.

When I arrived in "Chuqui," I was scared. It was so different from the temperate, urban middle-class America I was accustomed to. There were stray dogs on the streets, and a constant cloud of brick-colored dust came from the mine. There was no downtown, few smoothly paved streets, and little to do for entertainment. The people worked extremely hard. Students were worried about escaping to college in Antofagasta, Santiago, or some wetter place down south. Rain was a rare phenomenon; earthquakes and windstorms were frequent.

I had studied Spanish 2 1/2 years and was always one of the best students in my class. But in my first week in Chile I was barely able to communicate and desperate for one person to whom I could explain my shock. I couldn't speak the thoughts in my head—and there were so many.

Most exchange students experience this. Culture shock reveals itself in everything from increased aggression toward the people to lack of appetite or weight gain and depression. Being an exchange student requires suspending all judgments. At the same time, it is part of the learning process to become aware of what one does assume. Being an exchange student is not easy.

As time passed, everything changed. I began to forget words in English and to dream in Spanish and crave Chilean food. I got used to not depending on costly things for fun. Fun in Chuquicamata was being with people. The stray dogs didn't seem so strange anymore. The American sitcoms that came in on cable really did seem strange.

I began to identify myself less and less as a *gringa*—I wasn't like the tourists that passed though the downtown, loaded with lots of special gear. I was more a member of "tercero B," my class at school, or at least a gringa who also knew a little something about being Chilean.

I took math, physics, chemistry, biology, two history classes, Spanish, art, and philosophy—for which I received a half a credit in global studies. Somehow my high school couldn't figure out a way to relate my experience to its curriculum.

But the sacrifices were nothing compared to the gain. I learned how to accept as well as to succeed in another culture. I now know the world is my community and have a much deeper understanding of both myself and others.

other countries of the world by fostering understanding through international educational homestays. Participants live the culture on a day-to-day basis.

Dates: U.S. students, age 15-19, travel abroad for 10 months, during which time they live with a host family and attend school. Call for more details. **Costs:** $4,300 includes insurance. Transportation and personal expenses not included. **Contact:** Academic and Cultural Exchange, 22827 Kinross Ln., Moreno Valley, CA 92557; 800-950-4073; acelaf@aol.com, [www.academicculturalexch.com].

Adventures in Real Communication.*
Adventures in Real Communication (ARC) was founded by language teachers to help students motivate themselves to reach proficiency and to focus foreign language instruction on day-to-day communication skills that are relevant to their lives.

Dates: U.S. students ages 11-18 and their teacher(s) stay with selected host families for 2 to 4 weeks. **Costs:** $1,500-$3,200. Includes transportation, based on host country, season, and length of stay.

American Intercultural Student Exchange.*
AISE programs stress family living as the heart of the learning experience and are designed to enable students to share in other cultures through personal involvement in homes, schools, and communities.

Dates: U.S. students ages 15-18 live with a host family and attend school for a semester in Western Europe (Jan-Jun or Aug-Jan) or Australia (Jan-Jun or Jul-Nov). **Costs:** $5,203 to Europe and $5,314 to Australia, includes transportation and insurance. **Contact:** American Intercultural Student Exchange, 7720 Herschel Ave., Dept. CS, La Jolla, CA 92037-4405; 800-742-5464, fax 858-459-5301; aiseusa@aol.com, [www.aise.com].

American Int'l. Youth Student Exchange Program (AIYSEP). Nonprofit AIYSEP offers high school exchange programs for students in Europe, Australia, New Zealand, America, and many other countries. Area counselors are located in Europe, U.S., Australia, New Zealand, South America, Peru, Canada, and Japan.

Dates: Year, semester, and summer programs. **Costs:** Year $3,995-$6,000, semester $3,495-$4,200, summer $1,900-$3,500. **Contact:** American International Youth Student Exchange, 200 Round Hill Rd., Tiburon, CA 94920; 800-347-7575 or 415-435-4049, 415-499-7669, fax 415-499-5651; AIYSEP@aol.com, [www.aiysep.org].

American Trails West. Exciting camping/hotel/ dorm trips or deluxe hotel/dorm trips. Ages 13-17, grouped by age, 3-6 weeks. Action-oriented with responsible supervision. Accredited by Student Youth Travel Association.

Dates: Jun-Aug. **Costs:** $3,695-$6,795 (2000). **Contact:** Director, American Trails West, 92 Middle Neck Rd., Great Neck, NY 11021; 800-645-6260, 516-487-2855, fax 516-487-2855; atwtours@aol.com, [www.americantrailswest.com].

ASSE Int'l. Student Exchange Programs.*
Founded by the Swedish government as American Scandinavian Student Exchange to facilitate student exchanges between the U.S. and the Scandinavian countries, ASSE has expanded to include exchanges between the U.S. and Australia, Canada, South Africa, Mexico, Brazil, New Zealand, Japan, Thailand, Hong Kong, Mongolia, China, Taiwan, and 15 European countries, as well as NIS (former Soviet Union).

Costs: Academic year abroad $3,250-$7,500; summer homestay in Europe and Japan, $2,800, includes transportation and comprehensive insurance; summer language study/homestay program in France, Germany, or Spain, $2,550-$3,150, includes transportation, comprehensive insurance, instruction, activities, and excursions. **Contact:** ASSE, 228 North Coast Highway, Dept. CS, Laguna Beach, CA 92651; 949-494-4100, fax 949-497-8704 [www.asse.com].

ASSIST.* American Secondary Schools for International Students and Teachers is an educational and cultural exchange organization that provides cross-cultural experiences for young people age 15-18 from around the world to spend 1 year as a student ambassador in a U.S. independent school.

Dates: Sophomores and juniors from U.S. ASSIST member schools travel to Europe as a group for a 2-week traveling seminar entitled "21st Century Europe." **Costs:** $1,250 plus personal expenses, some land transportation, and some meals. Airfare and some program costs covered by donations. **Contact:** ASSIST, 40 General Miller Rd., Peterborough, NH 03458-1215; 603-924-9659, fax 603-924-3767.

Broadreach Summer Adventures. International scuba, sailing, marine biology, and wilderness programs for teenagers ages 13-19. Locations include the Caribbean, Australia, Costa Rica, Honduras, Ecuador, the Galapagos Islands, Egypt, Fiji, and the Solomon Islands. Activities include whitewater rafting, sea kayaking, waterskiing, rainforest trekking, community service, and leadership training. No experience required.

Dates: Programs of 17-31 days in Jun, Jul, and Aug. Most trips are 3 weeks long. **Costs:** $3,400-$4,900. Airfare not included. **Contact:** Carlton Goldthwaite, Broadreach, P.O. Box 27076, Raleigh, NC 27611; 888-833-1907, 919-833-1907, fax 919-833-2129; info@ gobroadreach.com, [www.gobroadreach.com].

CHI Travel/Study for All Ages. CHI was established in 1980 as a nonprofit organization to encourage people to reach out and explore the world. Call us or visit our web site. We have worldwide highschool academic programs, cultural and/or language immersions with homestays; group tours personalized for schools or for the general public. Internships, au pair and teaching positions also available.
Dates: Vary. **Costs:** Vary according to destination and length of program. **Contact:** Cultural Homestay International, 2455 Bennett Valley Rd., #B210, Santa Rosa, CA 95404; 800-395-2726, fax 707-523-3704; chimaryd@msn.com, [www.chinet.org/outbound.html].

Children's International Summer Villages (CISV). CISV in the U.S. is one of 60 National Associations around the world administered by the parent organization in England. Interchange: Students, ages 12-15, participate in a bilateral family-oriented exchange program consisting of reciprocal 1-month stays, generally in 2 summers. Seminar Camp: Students, ages 17 and 18, participate in a 3-week camp stressing educational and cultural exchange. Junior Counselor: Ages 16-17, are selected through local chapters to serve as assistants during a 4-week International Summer Village camp for 11-year-old children from 10-12 nations. Summer Camp: Students, ages 13-15, attend a 3-week residential camp program. Delegations consist of 4 to 6 boys and girls with 1 adult leader from 6 to 9 countries.
Costs: Interchange cost is approx. $400 including insurance. Seminar Camp is approx. $500 including insurance. Junior Counselor is approx. $400 including insurance. Summer Camp is approx. $600 including insurance. **Contact:** Children's International Summer Villages (CISV), 1375 Kemper Meadow Dr., Suite 9H, Cincinnati, OH 45240; 888-247-8872, fax 888-686-2478; CISVUSA@aol.com.

Council for Educational Travel, USA.* CETUSA is a nonprofit, educational and cultural exchange organization dedicated to provide youth from around the world the opportunity to exchange ideas, arts, philosophies, and ways of life with host families in the U.S. and abroad. U.S. Academic Year/Semester Program: Foreign students, age 15-18 live with an American host for a school year or semester while attending a U.S. public or private high school. Academic Year/Semester Abroad Program: Students age 15-19, travel to Germany, Spain, France, U.K., Brazil, Mexico, Australia, China, or Japan for a school year or semester. Live with a host family. Cultural Homestay Program: Students age 12-21, travel in groups or as individuals to various communities throughout the U.S.
Costs: U.S. Academic Year/Semester Abroad Program: approx. $2,800-$6,000, depending on country of origin and program inclusions. Academic Year/Semester Abroad Program: $2,725 does not include transportation, insurance or personal spending money. Cultural Homestay Program: $500-$1,950, depending on program length and options selected. Transportation, insurance, and personal spending money not included. **Contact:** Council for Educational Travel, USA, 1403 View Ave., Centralia, WA 98531; 360-736-6472, fax 360-736-6525; terry@cetusa.org.

Cultural Academic Student Exchange, Inc.* Cultural Academic Student Exchange, Inc. is an educational organization that promotes understanding, respect and goodwill among people of all nations through international student exchange. Academic Semester/Year Abroad: U.S. students, ages 16-18, travel to Belgium, Mexico, or Costa Rica for 1 semester, 1 school year or a summer program.
Costs: $1,200-$6,500 not including transportation and insurance. **Contact:** Cultural Academic Student Exchange, Dept. CS, 19 Charmer Ct., Middletown, NJ 07748-1506; 732-671-6448, fax 732-615-9183; casenj@home.com, [www.exchangestudents.org].

ERDT/SHARE! Exchange Program. ERDT/ SHARE! provides American students, ages 16 to 18, opportunities for summer, semester, or academic year homestays/study abroad. Language proficiency, academic standing, maturity are criteria for selection. Students live with host families and, depending upon program selected, attend local school or language school. ERDT/ SHARE! Also provides opportunities for American families to host international high school exchange students.
Dates: Vary with type of program selected and academic year dates. Student and host family applications are accepted year round. **Costs:** $1,500-$7,000 (depending on program), excluding transportation and personal expenses.

Contact: Roger Riske, President, 475 Washington Blvd., Suite 220, Marina del Rey, CA 90292; 800-321-3738, 310-821-9977, fax 310-821-9282; info@erdtshare.org, [www.erdtshare.org].

Foreign Study League.* FSL is an international educational and cultural exchange organization with an emphasis on placement of international students in nonpublic U.S. secondary schools for 10- or 5-month academic programs.

Costs: Summer program: $1,300 includes insurance. Transportation not included. **Contact:** Foreign Study League (FSL), 1903 Old Swede Rd., Douglassville, PA 19518; 610-689-4401, fax 610-689-4477; info@fsleducation.com.

The Foundation for Worldwide Int'l. Student Exchange.* WISE is a nonprofit organization dedicated to promoting world peace and understanding through cultural, academic, and recreational programs with an emphasis on participation in family stays.

Costs: Cultural Homestay Programs Abroad: $1,500-$2,500 includes airfare, insurance, and planned activities. **Contact:** The Foundation for Worldwide International Exchange (WISE), P.O. Box 1332, Dyersburg, TN 38025; 800-264-0948, 901-287-9949; davedahl@wisefoundation.com, [www.wisefoundation.com].

International Cultural Exchange Services.* ICES is a U.S.-based organization that promotes a more peaceful world by advancing international awareness and cultural understanding.

Costs: Academic Year Abroad: $6,000 includes insurance. Transportation not included. Academic Semester Abroad: $5,000 includes insurance. Transportation not included. **Contact:** International Cultural Exchange Services, 2888 Sacramento St., San Francisco, CA 94115; 800-344-3566, fax 415-440-7695; ehoggard@ices-services.org, [ehoggard@ices-services.org].

NorthWest Student Exchange.* NWSE works to improve international understanding by creating affordable opportunities for high school students to participate in reciprocal and 1-way exchanges abroad. Students in the 9th, 10th, and 11th grades should begin the application process by December of the school year prior to the exchange.

Costs: $3,050 for 1 semester and $3,600 for an academic year. Includes health and accident insurance, and roundtrip transportation. **Contact:** Northwest Student Exchange, 1314 56th St., NE, Suite 100, Seattle, WA 98105-4400; 206-527-0917, fax 206-527-0338; nwse@nwse.com, [www.nwse.com].

Spanish Programs Abroad. For teens traveling alone, with family, or school group. Various supervision levels available. Homestay or dorm. Cultural activities. Summer camp options. Spain, the Caribbean, Mexico, Central and South America. Beaches, mountains, small towns, large cities. One week to 6 months.

Dates: Programs start every week or month. **Costs:** Depends on location. Prices begin at $200 per week and include classes, homestay, travel insurance, most meals, some cultural activities. **Contact:** AmeriSpan Unlimited, P.O. Box 40007, Philadelphia, PA 19106; 800-879-6640, fax 215-751-1100; info@amerispan.com, [www.amerispan.com].

Summer Discovery (Musiker).* Summer Discovery offers pre-college enrichment programs for high school students (ages 14-18) at the college campuses of Univ. of California-Los Angeles (UCLA), Cambridge, Univ., England.

Dates: Summer Discovery: Jul 1-29. **Costs:** $5,299. **Contact:** Summer Discovery Educational Programs, 1326 Old Northern Blvd., Roslyn, NY 11576-2127; 888-878-6637, fax 516-625-3438; discovery@summerfun.com, [www.summerfun.com].

SuperCamp. SuperCamp, held on prominent college campuses worldwide, is a fun 8-10 day residential program that balances an academic environment with everyday life skills. A learning experience, for grades 4 through college, which raises grades, self-confidence, and motivation. Call for free brochure and CD.

Dates: Jun, Jul, Aug. **Costs:** $1,595-$2,095 (2001). **Contact:** Learning Forum, 1725 South Coast Hwy., Oceanside, CA 92054; 800-285-3276, fax 760-722-3507; info@supercamp.com, [www.supercamp.com].

Terra Lingua USA.* Terra Lingua is a not-for-profit, educational organization dedicated to promoting language education and international understanding by providing family homestay immersion experiences. Short-Term Homestay Program: U.S. students, ages 13-18, live with a family in France, Germany, Mexico, or Spain for 2 weeks anytime during the school year, or 4 to 7 weeks during the summer. Language Study Abroad: U.S. participants (students of all ages and language levels, businessmen and women, travelers), study French, German, or Spanish through an intensive 2-, 3-, or 4-week language study/homestay program. Teacher's Home Program Abroad: U.S. participants of all ages participate in a one-to-one program in which the participant lives with a host family and studies German. Cultural Study/Homestay in England or Ireland: Students, ages 14-18, live with a host family while participating in daily classes, excursions, and history. Semester Abroad: U.S. students, ages 15-18, attend school abroad for 4 to 6 months during which time they live with host families. Academic Year Abroad: U.S. students, ages 15-18, attend school abroad for 9 to 10 months during which time they live with host families.

Costs: Short-Term Homestay Program: $2,010. Language Study Abroad: $2,620 includes all domestic and international airfare, ground transportation, and insurance (if needed). Teacher's Home Program Abroad: $2,480. Cultural Study/Homestay in England or Ireland: $2,540. Semester Abroad: $3,780. Academic Year Abroad: $4,775. **Contact:** Terra Lingua USA, 1351 Timberbrook Dr., St. Louis, MO 63122-6720; Tel./fax 314-966-8808; terralinguaus@aol.com, [www.terralingua.com].

Ventures International Association.* VIA is a not-for-profit organization which strongly advocates international cross-cultural understanding and the development of foreign language proficiency.

Dates: Barbara Hyland Summer Scholarship Program: Students age 15-18 1/2 for 4 weeks in the summer, students live with a host family in France, Germany, Spain, or Mexico. **Contact:** Ventures International Association (VIA), P.O. Box 500, Oley, PA 19547; 610-689-8141, fax 610-689-4374; ventures@fast.net.

World Heritage Int'l. Student Exchange.* World Heritage Int'l. Student Exchange, formerly known as Spanish Heritage, was founded in 1980 to promote the Spanish language and culture in the U.S. and English language and culture in Spanish-speaking countries. Academic Year Abroad: Students, ages 15-18 spend an academic year living with a host family. Summer Program Abroad: U.S. students, ages 15-18, spend 6 weeks during the summer living with a host family. Summer Language Adventure: U.S. students, ages 15-18, travel abroad for 28 days, living with a host family and attending classes.

Costs: Academic Year Abroad: $3,250-$7,500 includes insurance and transportation. Summer Program Abroad: $2,800 includes insurance and transportation. Summer Language Adventure: $2,550-$3,150 include international transportation. **Contact:** World Heritage Int'l. Student Exchange, 210 North Lee St., Alexandria, VA 22314; 703-518-5035, fax 703-518-5033 [www.world-heritage.org].

Youth International. An experiential education program focusing on international travel and intercultural exchange, adventure, community service, and homestays. Teams of 14, aged 18-25, travel together for 1 semester to Asia (including the Philippines, Thailand, India, and Nepal) or Africa (including Kenya, Tanzania, Botswana, and Namibia). Assist refugees, hike the Himalayas, live with and help an African tribe, scuba dive, and much more.

Dates: Every year, early Sep-mid-Dec, and early Feb-late May. **Costs:** $7,500 including airfare. **Contact:** Brad Gillings, Youth International, 1121 Downing St., #2, Denver, CO 80218; 303-839-5877, fax 303-839-5887; director@youthinternational.org, [www.youthinternational.org].

Living Abroad

FOURTEEN

Living abroad is more than a logistical problem. It's also a rich experience for our minds and our senses. So many impressions get under our skin. They move us, excite us, and also change us. The following resources will help with the practical aspects of the transition to living in another country—getting there, setting up, adapting to the language. But this is only the beginning.

Key Publications (All Countries)

Cupid's Wild Arrows: Intercultural Romance and Its Consequences edited by Dianne Dicks. 1993, $15.99 (Bergli Books Ltd., Eptingerstrasse 5, CH-4052 Basel, Switzerland; 011-41-61-373-2777, fax 011-41-61-373-2778; info@bergli.ch; [www.bergli.ch]).

Do's and Taboos of Body Language Around the World by Roger E. Axtell (John Wiley & Sons, Inc., 1998, $16.95). Information about gestures and body language for over 80 countries world-wide. Covers the various meanings of gestures and how they are used, as well as country-by country listing of the most important gestures. Available by same author: *Do's and Taboos Around the World: A Guide to International Behavior.* Advice for travelers on what to do and not to do in other cultures.

Hidden Immigrants: Legacies of Growing up Abroad by Linda Bell (Cross Cultural Publications, 1996, $19.95). Intercultural Marriage, Promises & Pitfalls by Dugan Romano (Intercultural Press Inc., 2nd ed., 1997, $16.95). Based on interviews of intercultural couples, this practical book gives useful advice on the challenges of intercultural marriage, covering topics from food and personal values to friendship, sex, religion and more.

The Insiders' Guide to Relocation: Expert Advice to Move Across the State, the Country or the World by Beverly Roman. $14.95. 1996 by Falcon Publishing, P.O. Box 1718, Helena, MT 59624; orders: 800-582-2665; fax (800)508-8938; e-mail: cs@falcon.com; [www.falconbooks.com].

International Living Magazine, St. Catherine's Hall, Catherine Street, Waterford, Ireland; 011-353-51-304-556, fax 011-353-51-304-561; customerservice@internationalliving.com; [ww.escapeartist.com/international/living.htm]. $89 per year. The free online edition is a short version of the printed edition.

The ISS Directory of Overseas Schools. $34.95 from International Schools Services, P.O. Box 5910, Princeton, NJ 08543-5910; 609-452-0990, fax 609-452-2690; iss@iss.edu, [www.iss.edu]. ISS is a private, non-profit organization that operates and supports international schools. The directory provides current, accurate information on nearly 600 American-style elementary and secondary schools in more than 140 countries.

Let's Move Overseas by Beverly D. Roman. 2000. $8.45 from BR Anchor Publishing, 2044 Montrose Ln., Wilmington, NC 28405; 910-256-9598, fax 910-256-9579;

broman@branchor.com, [www.branchor.com]. A book full of activities, safety advice, and positive thoughts for children moving internationally.

Love & Sex, Cross-Cultural Perspectives by Elaine Hatfield and Richard L. Rapson. 1996, $24.95 (Allyn and Bacon, 160 Gould St., Needham Heights, MA 02494; to order call 800-666-9433; www.abacon.com). This academically researched book covers love and sexuality from a number of cultural viewpoints.

Schools Abroad of Interest to Americans (9th ed., $45). Porter Sargent Publishers, Inc., 195 McGregor St., Manchester, NH 03102. To order: 800-342-7470, fax 603-647-4383; orders@portersargent.com, [www.portersargent.com]. Lists 650 elementary and secondary schools in 125 countries for young Americans.

The Directory of Overseas Schools (International Schools Services). American elementary and secondary schools overseas.

The Unknown Ambassadors by Phyllis Michaux. 1996. Traces the history of efforts to establish and improve the rights of Americans living abroad, including citizenship rights of children of dual-national couples, Social Security and Medicare benefits for Americans living or traveling overseas, equitable tax treatment and voting rights. $15.95 plus $4 s/h from Aletheia Publications.

U.S. Expatriate Handbook, Guide to Living & Working Abroad by John W. Adams (1998, $20). College of Business and Economics, West Virginia Univ., P.O. Box 6025, Morgantown, WV 26506-6025; 304- 293-7534, fax 304-293-7061; moore@be.wvu.edu, [www.be.wvu.edu]. Practical handbook gives general advice on moving overseas. The author also publishes the *Adams Report* (9 times per year), an online newsletter with useful information for expatriates [www.globalassignment.com]).

Where in the World Are You Going? by Judith M. Blohm (Intercultural Press, 1996, $11.95). An activity book for children ages 5-10 that will make their move overseas more manageable.

World's Top Retirement Havens: How to Relocate, Retire, and Increase Your Standard of Living edited by Margaret J. Goldstein (John Muir Publications, 1999, $16.95). Profiles 15 countries, with information on where to live, the culture and people, renting versus buying, medical care, taxes, etc.

Country-Specific Publications

Background Notes Series. Published irregularly throughout the year. Available from Superintendent of Documents, P.O. Box 371954, Pittsburgh, PA 15250-7954; 202-512-1800, fax 202-512-2250; [www.access.gpo.gov/su_docs]. Pamphlets about the people, land, history, foreign relations, etc. for nearly 160 countries. Subscription price: $23 a year; single copy: $1.25.

CultureGrams, 1305 N. Research Way, Bldg. K, Orem, UT 84907-6200; 800-528-6279, fax 801-705-4350; [www.culturegrams.com]. Four-page summaries of the basic features of over 175 cultures worldwide. InfoGrams are briefings on international and intercultural topics which are helpful for international travelers.

Germany, Unraveling an Enigma by Greg Nees (Intercultural Press, 2000, $19.95). Explains the cultural differences of Germans to an American readership.

Getting a Job in Australia by Nick Vandome. £9.99 plus £4 s/h from How to Books.

Into Africa—Intercultural Insights by Yale Richmond and Phyllis Gestrin (Intercultural Press, 1998, $18.95). Explores the cultures of contemporary sub-Saharan Africa and includes a general introduction to the African community. Indispensable for anyone traveling, working, or living in Africa.

Live Well Series (Avalon Travel Publishing). Relocation, retirement, employment, and information. Titles include *Ireland* and *Mexico*.

Living and Working Abroad (Survival Books [www.survivalbooks.net], $21.95). Practical information about everyday life in a foreign country. Available for Australia, Canada, France, Germany, Great Britain, Ireland, London, New Zealand, Italy, Spain, and Switzerland. Also *Buying a Home Abroad* and similar titles for Britain, France, Greece and Cyprus, Ireland, Italy, Portugal, Spain.

Living and Working Abroad Series (How to Books Ltd., 3 Newtec Pl., Magdalen Rd., OxfordOX4 1RE, U.K.; fax 011-44-1-865-248780; info@howtobooks.co.uk, [www.howtobooks.co.uk]). Over 40 books offering country-specific information on immigration formalities, education, housing, health, law, economy, and leisure. Titles include Australia, Britain, France, Germany, Greece, Italy, New Zealand, Portugal, Saudi Arabia, Spain, The Netherlands.

Overseas Move Checklist
Take Time for Careful Preparation and Research

By Karin Gallagher

Leave your old car at home and buy locally. You'll save money and time for three reasons: First, importing your car may require you to make some adjustments. Second, shipping the car costs a minimum of $600 each way and takes six or more weeks. Third, if your car is not a common make or model, parts will be expensive or unavailable. If you're overseas longer than a year, consider selling your car instead of storing it.

Store most things, buy the rest. To start with, shipping is expensive. UPS charges $90 for a small box to Europe. A 40-foot container— enough to ship a medium-sized household— costs a minimum of $3,000, not including moving costs to and from the ship. A storage locker, on the other hand, costs from $600 per year. So, pack only what you know you'll need regularly and immediately. It may be cheaper to rent a furnished apartment than to ship your furniture back and forth.

Bring your computer but not electrical appliances. The U.S. is one of the cheapest places in the world to buy computer equipment, so you'll want to bring a laptop with you. Include a modem, printer, software, and backup disks, as well as accessories to adapt everything for overseas use.

Find a property manager experienced with hard-to-reach clients to manage your house. Most property managers charge 7 percent to 10 percent of the monthly rental income.

Keep phone numbers, addresses, and paperwork handy. Write down every phone number, address, and email address of every business and government organization you've dealt with in the last two years—including auto, health, and home insurance, computer technical support, doctors, magazine subscriptions, and the IRS. Include account numbers for mutual funds, bank accounts, frequent flyer miles, business license numbers, and serial numbers for any equipment you bring, such as computers, cameras, and bicycle locks. You never know when you are going to need the numbers. For example, you may need to transfer money from your U.S. account to your foreign one, or you may lose the only key to your Kryptonite lock.

Make copies of important paperwork such as birth certificates, marriage certificates, divorce decrees, school transcripts, and old tax returns. To buy auto insurance at a reduced rate in Germany, for example, you must get letters from the insurance companies you've used in the previous seven years. As part of the work permit process, you must show a copy of your college and high school diplomas, no matter how long ago you graduated.

Get your bills paid automatically. Instead of paying bills such as mortgage and credit card payments by mail every month, set up an automatic payment plan with your checking account. For credit card companies that don't have an automatic payment plan, you can prepay. Keep track of irregular bills, such as quarterly estimated taxes to the IRS and storage fees. Because mail to the U.S. takes up to two weeks, pay one month in advance.

Get a callback service and email. Calling from the U.S. is cheap. From other countries, calling anywhere else usually costs $1 or more per minute. Find a reliable callback service, which costs between 15 and 35 cents per minute, any time. With a callback service, you dial a toll-free number that connects you to a computer in the U.S. The computer then calls you back and you dial your destination number. You are essentially making a phone call from the U.S. to your location. Some callback services also offer a calling card. A good source for finding a callback service is the *International Herald Tribune.*

If you don't already have one, set up an email account to contact friends, families, and take care of personal business. You can sign up with a local Internet service provider or use your existing service provider if it has international servers, such as AOL. AOL charges a minimum of $6 per hour extra to use the account from overseas. If you don't have a computer, you can go to the local Internet cafe for $6 to $12 per hour or to the library.

Forward your mail. If you already know your foreign address, change the address for your most important mail, such as credit card bills and bank statements. Cancel mail order catalogs and magazines you can do without and change the address on the ones you can't. Otherwise, find a mail service, relative, or friend who will send you your mail regularly.

Learn the language. Take time to learn at least some basic words in the new language before you get there.

Be patient. It is a big effort to move. Before you go it feels like you are spending a lot of time researching costs and arranging things. This is only the beginning. After you arrive, you'll be running from office to office, tracking down missing shipments, or arranging permits and services. You're in a new country and you have to learn to do things someone else's way. That's part of the adventure.

Choosing an Overseas School

For a Stay of Under Five Years, an International School Is Best

By Mary Emslie

The process of choosing a school for the kids when you move overseas can be confusing and difficult.

First of all, should your child attend an international school or a national school? If you plan to live in your new country for five years or more a national school may be the better choice. Despite the difficulty with language and cultural adjustment in the beginning, children will probably establish more stable friendships in the long run.

For a short stay, an international school is probably the better alternative. In choosing keep in mind that an international or English-language school may be that in name only: many have a high percentage of native students who naturally speak their national language during recess and between classes. While there is certainly nothing wrong with children speaking their native language at school, your child can feel isolated at a time of adjustment when he or she needs friends.

Overseas Schools and Home-Country Schools: Most overseas schools are private. At our children's school in Santiago regular meetings are not open to all parents. Instead, the school administration meets with a committee that represents the parents. Check to see how much input parents can have in school policy and ask about the organization of the administration. Is there a board of directors or does a single individual with unlimited powers run the school? It's better to know ahead of time if you want to have a say in how your children are educated and what recourse you may have in the case of potential grievances.

Extracurricular Activities: Take a good look at the curriculum and find out if art, music, and computer courses are offered or if they are offered as extracurricular activities at an additional expense. Some schools have very limited sports programs, leaving the planning up to parents through private clubs or organizations.

Planning Your Budget: Ask the school administration for a projection of extra expenses. Field trips, extracurricular activities, sports clothing and equipment, school events, and school bus costs can add up. See if your employer provides an allowance for these extra expenses.

Violence and Harassment: Many countries have virtually no laws protecting children's rights. Does the administration have an effective program in place to prevent harassment and violence at school?

Admission Procedures: There will undoubtedly be an admission test; ask if you can take a look at it. If your child is not used to taking tests, you can conduct a practice test at home to familiarize them with the process as well as with questions that may be asked by school counselors.

The Curriculum: Ask for a written summary of the curriculum or at least a copy of last year's curriculum for your child's grade level. Will there be a seamless transition from what your child is learning now? Don't forget to ask what languages are required subjects. You might consider buying language materials to familiarize your child with the new language or languages they will be learning.

Learning Materials: We discovered that the English bookstores in Santiago, Chile have a limited, rather outdated, and extremely expensive selection. Find out what's available and stock up on needed books before you leave home.

Special Needs: It's essential to find a school that is prepared to give your child the support he or she needs. You may want to consult with their former teachers. Parents don't always see the needs and abilities of their own children as objectively as educators can.

My Family's Experience: After three weeks of searching, we were relieved when our children were finally accepted into a small British school in the foothills of the Andes. But would three new languages, a new school, and a new culture be an overwhelming adjustment for them? My fears were put to rest when my kids showed a surprising new sense of enthusiasm for learning. In their first semester they studied subjects ranging from Mozart to traditional Chilean dance to ancient Mayan cultures and showed a real thirst for knowledge. It's not only the new and unusual subjects they are learning. Their everyday experiences in school are an invaluable chance to expand their already multicultural horizons even further.

Editor's Note: For a complete worldwide directory of overseas schools, go to the International Schools Services' web site at [www.iss.edu].

Living Overseas Costa Rica by Robert Johnston (7th. ed., 2000, $16.95). Living Overseas Books, P.O. Box 9481, Naples, FL 34101, Tel./fax (941) 514-1418; robert@livingoverseas.com, [www.livingoverseas.com]. Practical information and advice on living in and moving to Costa Rica. By the same author: *Living Overseas Mexico* (2nd ed., 1999, ($16.95) and *Living Overseas—What You Need to Know* (2000, $16.95). Includes profiles of 10 recommended countries and reprints of consular information sheets worldwide.

The New Golden Door to Retirement and Living in Costa Rica by Christopher Howard (10th ed., $24.95). (Costa Rica Books, Suite 1 SJO 981, P.O. Box 025216, Miami, FL 33102-5216; 619-461-6131; crbooks@racsa.co.cr, [www.costaricabooks.com)].

The Traveler's Guide to Asian Customs and Manners by Elizabeth Devine and Nancy L. Braganti (St. Martin's Press, 1998, $16.95). Country-by-country information. In the same series: *Europe* (1992), *Africa* (1995), *Latin America* (2000), and *Middle East* and *North Africa* (1991).

Key Publishers

Aletheia Publications, Inc., 46 Bell Hollow Rd., Putnam Valley, NY 10579; 845-526-2873, fax 845-526-2905; alethpub@aol.com, [www.members.aol.com/alethpub]. Publishes a number of useful books on cross-cultural adjustment, living abroad, and reentry including: *The Accidental Diplomat: Dilemmas of a Trailing Spouse, Managing Cross-Cultural Transition.*

BR Anchor Publishing, 2044 Montrose Ln., Wilmington, NC 28405-6208; 800-727-7691 or 910-256-9598, fax 910-256-9579; customerservice@branchor.com, [www.branchor.com]. Publishes books with basic information for international relocation. Publications include *Home Away from Home, Turning Your International Relocation Into A Lifetime Enhancement* (1999, $14.95), and *Footsteps Around The World,* (1999, $13.95). Ask DBickel@branchor.com about "Relocation Today," a free monthly newsletter.

CultureShock! Country Guides by Times Media Private Ltd. [www.timesone.com.sg/te]. $13.95 each. Practical introductions to foreign customs, etiquette, and ways of life for 54 countries. Order from Graphic Arts Center Publishing Company, 3019 NW Yeon, Portland, OR 97210; 800-452-3032; fax 800-355-9685; sales@gacpc.com, [www.gacpc.com].

Global Business Publishers, 2907 Shelter Island Drive, Suite 105-272, San Diego, CA 92106; 888-446-4685, fax 877-846-4685; info@contact CGA.com or order@contact CGA.com, [www.contactCGA.com]. *So You're Going Overseas, A Handbook for Personal and Professional Success* by J. Stewart Black and Hal B. Gregersen (1998, $17.95) covers all the basics of moving abroad. *So You're Coming Home* by J. Stewart Black and Hal B. Gregersen (1999, $17.95) provides comprehensive advice on the problems and pitfalls of returning home.

Intercultural Press, P.O. Box 700, Yarmouth, ME 04096; 207-846-5168, fax 207-846-5181; books@interculturalpress.com, [www.interculturalpress.com]. Publishes numerous books on international living, travel, study, and cross-cultural experiences. Titles include: *Survival Kit for Overseas Living, Moving Your Family Overseas, Cross-Cultural Adaptability Inventory, Transcultural Odysseys, Women's Guide to Living Overseas, The Third Culture Kid Experience: Growing up Among Worlds, Figuring Foreigners Out,* and *The Art of Coming Home, The Art of Crossing Cultures.* InterAct Series: 15 titles providing intercultural insights about countries worldwide: *Encountering the Chinese, From Nyet to Da: Understanding the Russians, Understanding Arabs, Understanding Cultural Differences: Germans, French, and Americans, Germany: Unraveling an Enigma* and others.

John Wiley & Sons, 1 Wiley Dr., Somerset, NJ 08875; 908-469-440; [www.wiley.com]. Publications on careers.

Live and Work in . . . (Vacation Work). A series of guides written with the British reader in mind covering Europe and beyond. Most of the practical information also applies to North Americans considering work or retirement abroad. Order from Seven Hills Book Distributors, 1531 Tremont St., Cincinnati, OH 45214; 800- 545-2005, fax 888-777-7799; customerservice@sevenhillsbooks.com or direct from [www.vacationwork.co.uk].

Living Abroad Publishing Inc., 32 Nassau St., Princeton, New Jersey 08542; 609-924-9302, fax 609-924-7844; info@livingabroad.com, [www.livingabroad.com]. Provides a wide variety of services and info. The Country Profiles for 81 countries are excellent sources of information for businesses, expatriates, or anyone going overseas. $42 per Country Profile.

Porter Sargent Publishers, 11 Beacon St., Suite 1400, Boston, MA 02108-3099; 800-342-7470, fax 603-669-7945; orders@portersargent.com, [www.portersargent.com].

Put Your Best Foot Forward by Mary Murray Bosrack. International Education Systems, 26 E. Exchange St., Suite 313, St. Paul, MN 55101; 651-227-2052, fax 651-223-8383; info@internationaleducation.net, [www.internationaleducation.net]. Basic guides to behavior and communication designed for business people. Available for South America (1997, $22.95), Asia (1997, $22.95), Russia (1995, $11.95), Mexico/Canada (1995, $14.95), and Europe (1994, $22.95).

Key Expat Web Sites

Classic 164 Currency Converter [www.oanda.com/converter/classic] provides current exchange rates for 164 different currencies.

Embassy World [www.embassyworld.com] on embassy/consulate locations for most countries.

Escape Artist [www.escapeartist.com] is an extensive expatriate web site providing resources, links, a bulletin board, and information about immigration, overseas careers, investing, retirement, worldwide moving companies, embassies and consulates, taxpayer info, and more. Publishes the free monthly Escape From America E-Magazine.

Expat Access [www.expataccess.com] provides useful advice, information, news and links for "do-it-yourself" expatriate Americans moving to or living in Belgium, France, Germany, Netherlands, Spain, and U.K.

Expat Forum [www.expatforum.com] is hosted by HR International, a consulting firm that develops and manages expatriate programs for businesses and employees who relocate around the world. Offers cost-of-living info, web links, Internet search tools, country-specific chat areas, bookstore, language translator, and other useful links. HR International, 3715 Stearns Hill Rd., Waltham, MA 02451; 781-891-0878; hrintl@expatforum.com].

Global Nomads.com [www.globalnomads.com] Job listings, expat mail, expat links, and articles.

Live Radio on the Internet [www.live-radio.net/radio.shtml], while not an expat site, links to live Internet feeds of more than 2,000 radio stations around the world, and it's a dream for anyone pining for the language and music of another place. You can plug into a station, local or far-flung, and listen while you surf to other sites.

Media Link—Online Media Directory [http://emedia1.mediainfo.com/emedia] is an online database with links to newspapers, magazines, television and radio stations worldwide.

Mexico Connect [www.mexconnect.com] is a monthly Internet publication providing a plethora of information on all aspects of living in Mexico. Newsdirectory.com [www.newsdirectory.com] provides links to English online editions of newspapers and magazines worldwide.

Overseas Teacher's Digest [http://overseasdigest.com] is a monthly newsletter with information and resources for American teachers abroad. Includes discussion forum and bookstore.

Tales from a Small Planet [www.talesmag.com]. Webzine with news, stories, links, message boards and other resources for travelers and expatriates. P.O. Box 166, Vienna, VA 22183; fax 240-536-2168.

Travlang [www.travlang.com]. Provides language-related services to travelers and hosts 15,000 word translating dictionaries in a variety of languages for online search or download for Windows. Also provides online phrase book in over 70 languages with basic words, numbers, shopping/dining, travel, directions, places, time and dates and attached sound files for correct pronunciation.

WWTeach—International Education, Schools & Living [http://members.aol.com/wwteach/Teach.htm] provides links, information, and resources for teachers, students and parents.

www.liveabroad.com: A magazine about specific countries plus links to many helpful web sites and classified ads.

www.expatsite.com: Expat information arranged by channels including news, finance, education, migration, careers, sports, and more.

www.outpostexpat.nl: Detailed information for expats arranged by geographical regions.

Live Radio on the Internet [www.live-radio.net/radio.shtml], while not an expat site, links to live Internet feeds of more than 2,000 radio stations around the world, and it's a dream for anyone pining for the language and music of another place. You can plug into a station local or far-flung, and listen while you surf to other sites.

Americans Abroad Organizations

The American Church in Paris, 65 quai d'Orsay, 75007 Paris; 011-33-1-40620500, fax 011-33-1-40620511; [www.americanchurchparis.org/woac.htm]. Organizes Bloom Where You're Planted an annual orientation program for newcomers to Paris held in October, and *Bloom While You Work*, a bi-annual seminar for newcomers who work in France. Publishes the annually updated Bloom Where You're Planted, handbook with lots of practical information on living in Paris. Contact Meri-Kathryn Peed (president) at MK0816@aol.com.

American Citizens Abroad, 1051 N. George Mason Dr., Arlington, VA 22205; fax 703-527-3269; jacabr@aol.com, [www.aca.ch]. Assists Americans abroad with information, advice, useful links, country contacts, and more.

The Assn. of American Residents Overseas (AARO), 34, avenue de New York, Paris 75016 France; 011-33-1-47 20 24 15, fax 011-33-1-47 20 24 16; aaromail@aaro-intl.org, [http://aaro-intl.org]. Works to secure, protect, and improve basic American rights for U.S. citizens overseas. Offers a group medical insurance plan.

Democrats Abroad, P.O. Box 6430, Alexandria, VA 22306-0430; demsabrd@bellatlantic.net, [www.democratsabroad.org]. The official Democratic party organization for Americans living abroad.

Employee Relocation Council, 1717 Pennsylvania Ave., NW, 8th Floor, Washington, DC 20006; 202-857-0857, fax 202-659-8631; info@erc.org, [www.erc.org]. Professional membership organization addressing corporate relocation, and legal issues, professional development and networking. Publishes the monthly Mobility magazine ($48 per year).

Federation of American Women's Clubs Overseas webwoman@fawco.org, [www.fawco.org]. FAWCO is an international network to support American women living abroad. Addresses concerns about education, environmental protection, and women's and children's rights.

Global Nomad Virtual Village (GNVV) a nonprofit organization dedicated to the support and understanding of Third Culture Kids (TCKs), provides information and resources for global nomads. GNVV, 6174 Otter Run Ct., Cliftonton, VA 20124; info@gnvv.org, [www.gnvv.org].

Global Nomads International (GNI) assists internationally mobile families and publishes the journal Global Nomad Perspectives. Conferences and workshops focus on the transition and mobility issues faced by its members. Global Nomads International, P.O. Box 9584, Washington, DC 20016; 202-466-2244, fax 757-499-7320; gni@igc.org, [http://globalnomads.association.com].

Interaction International, Inc. provides resources and information for Third Culture Kids, their parents, and institutions. P.O. Box 158, Houghton, NY 14744; 716-567-8774, fax 716-567-4598; [www.tckinteract.net].

Network for Living Abroad provides resources, links, and info for expatriates and publishes an informative newsletter for its members 10 times a year ($39; email membership: $20 worldwide) on residency, living costs, healthcare, resources, and more. Includes a networking database for members. To join call 800-925-6652 or 505-438-7772, or write: Network for Living Abroad, 2442 Cerillos Rd., #171, Santa Fe, NM 87505; info@liveabroad.com, [www.liveabroad.com].

Republicans Abroad, 310 1st St., SE, Washington, DC 20003; 202-608-1423; republicansai@mindspring.com, [www.republicansabroad.org]. The official Republican party organization for Americans living abroad.

Society for Intercultural Education, Training, and Research (SIETAR). SIETAR USA: Peggy Pusch, 573 Bayview St.,Yarmouth, ME 04096; 207-846-9598, fax 207-846-0763; Sietarusa@aol.com, [www.sietarusa.org]. An international professional association providing a wide range of perspectives on the challenges and opportunities of intercultural interaction.

Terra Cognita, Inc., 300 W. 49 St., Suite 314, New, NY 10019; 888-262-2099, 212-262-4529, fax 212-262-5789; info@terracognita.com, order@terracognita.com, [www.terracognita.com]. Provides cross-cultural training for expatriates and international business people through seminars and training programs. Publishes the *Live Abroad! Workbook*, 1997, $15.95) and video.

Transition Dynamics, 2448 NW 63rd St., Seattle WA 98107; 206-789-3290, fax 206-781-2439; bfschaetti@transition-dynamics.com, [www.transition-dynamics.com]. A consulting firm that assists international expatriate families with the challenges of cross-cultural adjustment and moving overseas. Web site contains useful articles, info.

Health and Safety

Health Information for International Travel. "The Yellow Book" from the Centers for Disease Control provides health information on specific destinations about outbreaks, diseases, vaccinations, water safety, and links to other related sites. Annual. $25 each or free download of last year's edition. Order from: Public Health Foundation, Publication Sales, P.O. Box 753, Waldorf, MD 20604; 877-252-1200; info@phf.org, [www.phf.org], [www.cdc.gov/travel].

TRAILING PARTNERS
WAYS AND MEANS TO PREVENT PREMATURE REPATRIATION

By Keri Kubokawa

The experience abroad can be significantly different for the expatriate worker and the trailing partner. Not being able to find a job for the accompanying partner, difficulty with a foreign language, and not being able to establish a local group of friends are just a few of the causes of stress which can eventually lead to a premature repatriation. You can take a number of actions before you leave home to prevent that from happening.

First of all, clarify your individual and collective goals. Are your objectives to explore the region? Gain lifetime friendships? Enhance your resume? Expose your children to a different culture?

Socializing is key to enjoying your time abroad. It takes one solid friendship in the country to make the difference between a good memory and an unforgettable one. Trailing partners have greater opportunities to meet people, either locals or other expatriates, explore the area, learn new skills specific to the country such as language, arts, and sports. Pinpoint what you would like to do, pursue the interest immediately after arrival, and maintain an unflinching focus on it.

For More Info

Information sharing and online discussion groups: [www.expatspouse.com]; wide range of resources: [www.expat-moms.com]; expert advice from relocation specialist, Robin Pascoe: [www.expatexpert.com]; foreign language and cross-cultural training, including relocation consultation: [www.berlitz.com/cross_cultural/cross_cultural_relocation.html].

IAMAT, The International Association for Medical Assistance to Travelers, is an international nonprofit organization that provides travelers with info about health risks, immunization requirements for all countries, and medical care. Also provides names of English-speaking doctors in foreign countries. USA headquarters: IAMAT, 417 Center St., Lewiston, NY 14092; 716-754-4883; [www.iamat.org].

MEDexpat, 1HC, 2nd Fl., London EC4Y 1ET, U.K.; 011-44-207-353-4099, fax 011-44-207-353-4089; [www.medexpat.com]. MEDexpat is a 1-stop shop for personal and international medical insurance needs. Specialist advice and services for expatriates of any nationality.

Staying Healthy in Asia, Africa, and Latin America by Dirk Schroeder. $11.95 plus $2.16 s/h from VIA Press, P.O. Box 20266, Stanford, CA 94309; 650-723-3228, fax 650-725-1805; [www.viaprograms.org]. Sections on prevention of illness as well as guidelines in case of illness.

U.S. State Department [www.state.gov]. **Travel Publications** [http://travel.state.gov/travel_pubs.html] provide information about visa requirements, health, safety, U.S. embassies and consulates, and specific country information worldwide. **American Citizens Abroad** [http://travel.state.gov/acs.html] lists information about services for Americans living in foreign countries. *Office of Overseas Schools* [www.state.gov/www/about_state/schools] lists 180 elementary and secondary schools in 129 countries that are sponsored by the Department of State. *World Factbook* [www.odci.gov/cia/publications/factbook] compiled by the CIA, contains country profiles with basic information.

Where There Is No Doctor: A Village Health Care Handbook by David Werner (1998, $17) from Hesperian Foundation, 1919 Addison St., Suite 304, Berkeley, CA 94704; 510-845-4507, fax 510-845-0539; bookorders@hesperian.org, [www.hesperian.org]. Comprehensive health manual useful for those working or living in remote locations. Other Hesperian books include *Where Women Have No Doctor* ($20) and *A Book for Midwives* ($22).

Cross-Cultural Adjustment

The Adventures of Working Abroad by Joyce Sautters Osland. Author draws from 14 years of living abroad to help current and potential expatriates adjust. $25 from Jossey-Bass (a Wiley Company); [www.josseybass.com].

Figuring Foreigners Out by Craig Storti (Intercultural Press, $19.95, 1998). This user-friendly workbook provides helpful guidelines for dealing with cultural differences and increasing cross-cultural awareness. A useful training manual for anyone in contact with foreigners, at home or abroad. Other titles by Craig Storti at Intercultural Press: *The Art of Coming Home, Cross Cultural Dialogues, The Art of Crossing Cultures.*

Transcultural Study Guide Volunteers in Asia (VIA). 1987. $7.95 plus $1.70 postage from VIA Press, P.O. Box 20266, Stanford, CA 93409; 650-723-3228; [www.viaprograms.org]. Hundreds of questions that lead a traveler toward an understanding of a new culture.

Travel That Can Change Your Life: How to Create a Transformative Experience by Jeffrey A. Kottler from Jossey-Bass (a Wiley Company); 800-956-7739, [www.josseybass.com]. $22. Practical tips for life-changing travel.

Language Learning Software

Audio-Forum, 96 Broad St., Guilford, CT 06437; 800-243-1234, 203-453-9794; fax 888-453-4329, 203-453-9774; ta@audioforum.com, [www.audioforum.com]. One of the world's largest selections of self-instructional language courses: 285 courses in 103 languages. Publishes and distributes travel guides and adult and children's dictionaries.

Auralog Inc., 2720 S Hardy Dr., Suite #3, Tempe, AZ 85282; 480-829-1984, fax 480-829-9649; [www.auraloginc.com; www.auralog.com]. Auralog specializes in interactive languages learning software with sophisticated speech recognition and pronunciation features. Current titles: Tell Me More, available in three levels in French, German, Italian, Spanish, English, and Mandarin Chinese (2 levels); Tell Me More Kids (Spanish). CD-ROM, Windows only.

Barron's Educational Series Inc., 250 Wireless Blvd., Hauppauge, NY 11788; 800-645-3476, fax 631-434-3723; info@barronseduc.com; [www.barronseduc.com]. Barron's Educational Series publishes a large selection of language learning programs suited for all levels and needs; based on audiocassetes, phrasebooks or textbooks. Among the various series are *Express Track, Now You're Talking, Learn the Fast and Fun Way, 501 Verbs,* and *TravelWise.* Available in over a dozen languages.

Berlitz Publishing Co., Inc., 400 Alexander Park, Princeton, NJ 08540; to order: 800-526-8047 Dept. 7127 (U.S. only) or 609-514-3423, fax 800-452-0466 or 609-514-3413, Attn: Dept. 7127; publishing@berlitz.com; [www.berlitz.com]. Berlitz publishes a wide

COMING HOME
THIS COULD BE THE HARDEST MOVE OF ALL

By Joanna Parfitt

After 10 years in Dubai, Oman, and Norway, I thought coming home would be easy. I was wrong. After 20 months back home I hit rock bottom.

We were poised to move into our own home and at last begin to put down our roots. If we had been abroad we'd have been prepared to move on by now, but here we were contemplating settling in.

While we were away I had forged a career as a journalist, a computer trainer, maker of chutney, and creator of Christmas tree decorations out of local produce—all this with a language barrier and a handful of work permit problems. Fitting in back home should have been a piece of cake.

But when I offered my services at a local training company, placed ads in the local newspaper, sent out resumes, and made monthly trips to the city, nothing came of it but a lot of raised eyebrows at my unusual attitude.

I joined the PTA, helped out (for free) with the village newsletter, ran a video library in the school, published and self-marketed two books. But still the work refused to roll in.

The day I hit rock bottom was the day I started my ascent. All that hard work paid off.

Going home can be the hardest move of all. Relationships take much longer to establish, both professional and personal. Instead of being an exotic fish in a small pond, you are a minnow in an ocean. Add that to the fact that you are completely taken over by purchases and payments. You could turn to the bottle or a therapist, but if you can absorb the fact that going home takes time and that re-entry shock can be bigger than culture shock, you can make it!

Today, 23 months into our return, I can hear the larks singing over my garden. I can walk to the village school to collect my boys, or ask Granny to do it for me if I'm busy. Tonight the Women in Business Society meets at my house—the house with our furniture and the paint, curtains, and crockery that we chose. And, just for an hour or two, I'm that big fish again. At last it feels like home and nothing will make me want to leave—not for awhile anyway.

variety of teach-yourself language programs from simple phrase books to in-depth language courses. All titles are based on listen and speak methodology, with audiocassetes or CDs. Among them are Berlitz Basic, Berlitz Today, Cassette Pack with Phrase Book, and Think and Talk. Berlitz also offers language study abroad and language classes at Berlitz centers across the U.S. For more info call 800-457-7958 (U.S. only) or 609-514-9650.

Champs-Elysées, Inc., 2000 Glen Echo Rd., Suite 205, Nashville, TN 37215-8067; 615-383-8534; usorders@champs-elysees.com, [www.champs-elysees.com]. Champs-Elysées publishes a lively monthly magazine on audiocassette or CD with transcript and glossary, in Spanish, French, German, and Italian. Subscriptions range from $89 (5 months) to $259 (2 years). Study supplements with exercises also available.

Educational Services Corporation, 1725 K St., N.W., Suite #408, Washington, D.C. 20006; 202-298-8424, fax 202-659-8989; [www.language30.com]. Educational Services publishes the popular Language/30 series of introductory cassette language courses with phrasebook. Available in 33 languages. $16.95.

Living Language, 280 Park Ave., New York, NY 10017; to order: 800-726-0600 or 410-848-1900; livinglanguage@randomhouse.com, [www.randomhouse.com/livinglanguage]. Living Language publishes practical self-study language programs in 16 languages. Most courses include book and cassette/CD. Among their titles are *Complete Basic Course, Fast & Easy, Fodor's Languages for Traveler, Skill Builder: Verbs, and Ultimate Course.*

Penton Overseas, Inc., 2470 Impala Dr., Carlsbad, CA 92008; 800-748-5804; 760-431-0060, fax 760-431-8110; info@pentonoverseas.com, [www.pentonoverseas.com]. Penton Overseas is an international publisher and developer of foreign language programs available in audio, video and multimedia formats. Among their titles are *Fast Track—The Global Business Language Program, Global Access, Immersion+, Learn in Your Car, TravelTalk VocabuLearn,* and *French/Spanish in a Box.* Most titles are available for Chinese, French, German, Italian, Japanese, Russian, and Spanish.

The Rosetta Stone Language Library, published by Fairfield Language Technologies, 160 S. Main St., Harrisonburg, VA 22801, 800-788-0822 or 540-432-6166, fax 540-432-0953; info@RosettaStone.com; [www.RosettaStone.com]. Offers language learning software based on the method of associating spoken words and phrases with images, which replicates a natural immersion process. Available for 25 languages. CD-ROM for Windows and Macintosh.

Transparent Language, Inc., 9 Executive Park Dr., Merrimack, NH 03054; 603-262-6300, fax 603-262-6561; to order: 800-752-1767; info@transparent.com; [www.transparent.com, www.transparentlanguage.com, www.plustranslation.com, www.freetranslation.com]. Transparent Language produces a wide range of language learning software. Among their titles are *LanguageNow!, A+ Language Lessons,* and *101 Languages of the World.* CD-ROM for Windows and Macintosh.

Whole World Guide to Language Learning by Terry Marshall, 1990. How to learn a language while abroad. $17.95 plus $3 s/h from Intercultural Press.

ED BUTTS is a Canadian writer currently teaching at the Learning Center of Sosua in the Dominican Republic. Contact him at learningcenter@sisua.net.

ISABEL BEARMAN BUCHER and her husband, Robert, completed their first house exchange in 1999. They live in Albuquerque, NM. Contact her at ibbucher@compuserve.com.

KARI BODNARCHUK is a Boston-based freelance writer and teacher of travel classes who has explored more than 30 countries over the past 10 years. She is author of *Rwanda: Country Torn Apart* and *Kurdistan: Region Under Seige*. Contact her at ekarib@yahoo.com.

SARA COOLEY is a graduate of the Univ. of Virginia. She hopes to continue her travel experiences by working for a study abroad program or the Peace Corps. Contact her at sara_cooley@yahoo.com.

JOSEPH COLLINS, STEFANO DeZEREGA, and **ZAHARA J. HECKSCHER** are the co-authors of *How to Live Your Dream of Volunteering Overseas* (Penguin Putnam, 2002) from which their article is adapted. The book includes evaluations of over 80 volunteer programs. Visit [www.volunteeroverseas.org] or email peacepeace@CompuServe.com.

CAROL DALTON SEBILIA volunteers as a teacher/leader for the People to People Junior Ambassador Program [www.juniorambassadors. org] each summer. In winter she teaches at Diablo Valley College in California. Contact her at bccseb@aol.com.

MARK DIORIO usually works biking into his overseas vacations. He lives in Gardiner, NY. Contact him at dirtboyfsr@msn.com.

MARY EMSLIE is managing editor of Parentnetsweden.com, a web site for English-speaking parents in Sweden. She lives in Santiago, Chile with her husband and two children. Contact her at mary@emsli.com.

KARIN GALLAGHER worked in Germany for two years as a technical writing instructor. Contact her at kgallag@hotmail.com.

SUSAN GRIFFITH is the co-author, with Joshua White of *Taking a Career Break* (Vacation Work, 2001). Order from Seven Hills Distributors or Amazon.com. Contact her at s.griffith@ntlworld.com.

KRISTEN HAYES helps coordinate high school environmental education programming in the National Wildlife Federation's Great Lakes office in Ann Arbor, MI. Contact her at kahay1@aol.com.

ED READICKER-HENDERSON is author of numerous guidebooks for Hunter Publishing. He lives in Scottsdale, AZ. Contact him at rhtravels@aol.com.

PAMELA HOUSTON is publicity coordinator for Mobility International USA. Contact her at pr@miusa.org.

BRIAN JOHNSON has traveled around the world. He now lives in Isle, MN. Contact him at briancameroon@yahoo.com.

ROBIN and ARLENE KARPAN are full-time travel writers from Saskatoon, Saskatchewan. Contact them at Karpan@sk.sympatico.ca.

JULIE KREMEN writes from Chicago, IL. Contact her at nomadlw@aol.com.

KERI KUBOKAWA has lived in South Korea, Japan, Germany, and Singapore as a student, at-home mother, and manager for a Fortune 15 company. She lives in Temecula, CA with her husband and son. Contact her at mailto:kubomann@yahoo.com.

JENNIFER LANGENBACH writes from Boulder, CO.

KIM LIPKER writes from Steamboat Springs, CO. Contact her atkim@springsips.com.

SIMON LYNCH is a writer and teacher based in the U.K. He is currently traveling and volunteering on an extended trip from Japan to the U.K. that involves no aircraft.

ANN McDUFFIE worked as a reporter for the *Honolulu Advertiser*. She now lives in Kuwait. Contact her at detmdrmsg@state.gov.

CHRISTOPHER MOORE as a junior at Univ. of Nevada-Reno arranged an internship at the Univ. of International Business and Economics in Beijing. Contact him at Survivorcjm@yahoo.com.

JOANNA PARFITT is the editor of *Woman Abroad* magazine. In 1997 she repatriated to England with her family. Contact her at ed@womanabroad.com.

ALIA K. SANTINI is a graduate of Brown Univ. in comparative literature and German studies. She was a peer counselor in the Office of International Programs.

HEIDI SCHMALTZ just finished her senior year of high school in Portland, OR. She plans to return to Chile. Contact her at hschmaltz@hotmail.com.

DIANE SLAWYCH is a Toronto-based freelance journalist with more than 14 years' experience writing for Canada's leading newspapers and magazines. Contact her at writer@interlog.com.

RHONDA STRICKLAND writes from Shepherdstown, WV. Contact her at rrstrick@intrepid.net.

AUTUMN TALLMAN, Coordinator of the Department of Languages and Culture at Universidad de la Sierra in Poza Rica, Veracruz, has lived in Mexico for over four years. Contact her at: aatallman@excite.com.

CATHERINE M. THOMAS is a librarian at Columbia Univ. Contact her at cmthoma@attglobalnet.com.

APRIL THOMPSON writes from San Francisco, CA. Contact her at aprilthompson@ hotmail.com.

PAMELA S. TURNER has lived and worked in South Africa, Micronesia, Haiti, the Philippines, and Japan. Contact her pstrst@pacbell.net.

STEVEN VAN YODER is a freelance travel writer who writes regularly about food, wine, culture, and international affairs from his home in San Francisco. Contact him at svy@stevenvanyoder.com.

CARLA WALDEMAR is a veteran travel writer whose work appears frequently in *Transitions Abroad*. Contact her at carla@dealer.com.

LUKE S. WHITE received his BA from the Univ. of Texas at Austin before traveling and working in Chile, Central America, Japan, and Europe. He lives in Portland, OR. Contact him at lukaas@hotmail.com.

STEVE WILSON's writing credits include *Blue, Sunset, Big World*, and regular contributions to *Transitions Abroad*. Contact him at swilson@ postmark.net.